TIM HINDS

YO-CDH-360

1983

SAE

Handbook

Index

Published by:

Society of Automotive Engineers, Inc.

400 Commonwealth Drive, Warrendale, Pa. 15096

(412)776–4841

ISBN 0–89883–851–7 (Set)

ISBN 0–89883–856–8 (Index)

ISSN 0362–8205

Library of Congress Catalog Card Number: 25–16527

Copyright © Society of Automotive Engineers, Inc. 1983

All technical reports, including standards approved and practices recommended, are advisory only. Their use by anyone engaged in industry or trade or their use by governmental agencies is entirely voluntary. There is no agreement to adhere to any SAE Standard or Recommended Practice, and no commitment to conform to or be guided by any technical report.

In formulating and approving technical reports, the Technical Board, its councils, and committees will not investigate or consider patents which may apply to the subject matter. Prospective users of the report are responsible for protecting themselves against liability for infringement of patents, trademarks, and copyrights.

—SAE Technical Board Rules and Regulations

PRINTED IN U.S.A.

1983 SAE HANDBOOK INDEX VOLUME CONTENTS

1983 SAE HANDBOOK CONTENTS 5
NUMERICAL INDEX 23
CANCELLED AND SUPERSEDED REPORTS 39
SUBJECT INDEX 43
SAE TECHNICAL REPORTS REFERENCED IN GOVERNMENT REGULATIONS 71
RELATED TECHNICAL REPORTS 75
J-REPORTS

J1271 AUG79–Technical Committee Guideposts 81
J1159 AUG79–Preparation of SAE Technical Reports—Surface Vehicles and Machines:
   Standards, Recommended Practices, Information Reports 86
J916 JUN82–Rules for SAE Use of SI (Metric) Units 89
J1115–Guidelines for Developing and Revising SAE Nomenclature and Definitions 101
J1500 JUN80–Universal Symbols for Operator Controls 102

THE SOCIETY 119
REFEREE MATERIALS 139
ENGINEERING AIDS 141
ORDERING INFORMATION 143

The 1983 SAE Handbook is comprised of four separate volumes, each available separately. The titles of the volumes are:

Volume 1–Materials
Volume 2–Parts and Components
Volume 3–Engines, Fuels, Lubricants, Emissions, and Noise
Volume 4–On-Highway Vehicles and Off-Highway Machinery

A separate Index Volume is provided with each volume or set. This index includes the Tables of Contents for the four Handbook volumes along with a Numerical Index of Standards, Recommended Practices, and Information Reports; a complete Subject Index; and Related Technical Reports not included in the Handbook volumes.

Other volumes of the 1983 SAE Handbook, or additional copies of the separate Index Volume, may be ordered by contacting Customer Service, SAE, 400 Commonwealth Drive, Warrendale, PA, 15096 (412) 776-4841.

Page numbers shown in the indexes include the volume number in bold followed by the section number and the page number within that section.

TABLE OF CONTENTS

1983 SAE HANDBOOK CONTENTS

NUMERICAL AND SUBJECT INDICES FOR SAE STANDARDS, RECOMMENDED PRACTICES, AND INFORMATION REPORTS follow the Table of Contents.

Each surface vehicle Standard, Recommended Practice, or Information Report has a designation consisting of the letter "J" combined with a number. The letter "J" is combined with a nonsignificant number to eliminate any possible confusion between the report number and the SAE numbers within the report.

Page numbers shown include the volume number in bold followed by the section number and page number within that section.

Effective with the 1981 SAE Handbook, revisions of reports are indicated by the month and year of revision, for example, J1159 AUG79. This new system will be phased in over a five year period. A lower case "a," "b," etc., appended to the report designation number indicates successive revisions of older reports.

Because the SAE Handbook is published on an annual basis, certain reports in this book may not be the latest issue of the document. Therefore, users are cautioned to contact SAE Headquarters to determine the status of specific documents.

All new and revised reports contain SI (metric) equivalents of all dimensions. The SAE Metric Advisory Committee appreciates receiving any comment and/or suggestions regarding the conversions.

The φ symbol next to a section or line of a report indicates areas where technical revisions have been made to the previous issue of the report. If the symbol is next to the report title, it indicates a complete revision of the report. The notation "ed." is used to indicate editorial changes.

VOLUME 1—MATERIALS

FERROUS METALS

1 Numbering System, Chemical Compositions

Numbering Metals and Alloys—SAE J1086 ...... **1**:1.01
Selection and Use of Steels—SAE J401 APR81 ... **1**:1.05
SAE Numbering System for Wrought or Rolled Steel—SAE J402 JUN81 ... **1**:1.07
Chemical Compositions of SAE Carbon Steels—SAE J403 SEP80 ... **1**:1.08
Chemical Compositions of SAE Alloy Steels—SAE J404 OCT80 ... **1**:1.11
Chemical Compositions of SAE Wrought Stainless Steels—SAE J405d ... **1**:1.13
Chemical Compositions of SAE Experimental Steels—SAE J1081 JUN81 ... **1**:1.14
Formerly Standard SAE Alloy Steels—SAE J778 OCT80 ... **1**:1.15
Formerly Standard SAE Carbon Steels—SAE J118a . **1**:1.16
Methods of Determining Hardenability of Steels—SAE J406c ... **1**:1.17
Hardenability Bands for Carbon and Alloy H Steels—SAE J1268 JUN81 ... **1**:1.26
Methods of Sampling Steel for Chemical Analysis—SAE J408 JUN79 ... **1**:1.71
Permissible Variations from Specified Ladle Chemical Ranges and Limits for Steels—SAE J409c ... **1**:1.72
High Strength, Low Alloy Steel—SAE J410c ... **1**:1.74
* Steel, High Strength, Hot Rolled Sheet and Strip, Cold Rolled Sheet, and Coated Sheet—SAE J1392 MAY82 ... **1**:1.76
High Strength, Quenched, and Tempered Structural Steels—SAE J368a ... **1**:1.79
Engine Poppet Valve Materials—SAE J775 JUL80 . **1**:1.80

2 General Data on Steels

Carbon and Alloy Steels—SAE J411 JUN81 ..... **1**:2.01

† High Strength Carbon and Alloy Die Drawn Steels—SAE J935 JUL81 ... **1**:2.04
General Characteristics and Heat Treatments of Steels—SAE J412h ... **1**:2.05
Mechanical Properties of Heat Treated Wrought Steels—SAE J413b ... **1**:2.13
Estimated Mechanical Properties and Machinability of Hot Rolled and Cold Drawn Carbon Steel Bars—SAE J414a ... **1**:2.15
† Glossary of Carbon Steel Sheet and Strip Terms—SAE J940 JAN82 ... **1**:2.18
Aging of Carbon Steel Sheet and Strip—SAE J763 JAN82 ... **1**:2.20
† Definitions of Heat Treating Terms—SAE J415 JUN82 **1**:2.21
Alloy Steel Machinability Ratings—SAE J770c **1**:2.24

3 Methods of Testing Steels

Tensile Test Specimens—SAE J416 JUN79 ..... **1**:3.01
Surface Hardness Testing with Files—SAE J864 JUN79 ... **1**:3.02
Hardness Tests and Hardness Number Conversions—SAE J417b ... **1**:3.03
Grain Size Determination of Steels—SAE J418a ... **1**:3.07
Methods of Measuring Decarburization—SAE J419 . **1**:3.10
† Methods of Determining Plastic Deformation in Sheet Metal Stampings—SAE J863 DEC81 ... **1**:3.14
Sheet Steel Thickness and Profile—SAE J1058 ... **1**:3.16
Properties of Low Carbon Steel Sheets and Strip and Their Relationship to Formability—SAE J877 ... **1**:3.17
Selecting and Specifying Hot and Cold Rolled Steel Sheet and Strip—SAE J126 JUN81 ... **1**:3.19
Classification of Common Imperfections in Sheet Steel—SAE J810 JUN80 ... **1**:3.24
Undervehicle Corrosion Test—SAE J1293 JAN80 . **1**:3.34
† Cleanliness Rating of Steels by the Magnetic Particle Method—SAE J421 APR82 ... **1**:3.37
Microscopic Determination of Inclusions in Steels—SAE J422 JUN79 ... **1**:3.39
Detection of Surface Imperfections in Ferrous Rods, Bars, Tubes, and Wires—SAE J349 JUN80 .... **1**:3.42

* New
† Technical revision
§ Editorial change

NOTE: Page numbers shown include the volume number in bold followed by the section number and page number within that section.

Methods of Measuring Case Depth—SAE J423a .. **1:3.43**
† Method for Determining Breakage Allowances for
Sheet Steel—SAE J424 OCT81 . . . . **1:3.45**
Nondestructive Tests—SAE J358 JAN80 . . . . . . **1:3.45**
Infrared Testing—SAE J359 JUN81 . . . . **1:3.47**
Magnetic Particle Inspection—SAE J420 MAR81 . **1:3.47**
Eddy Current Testing by Electromagnetic Methods—
SAE J425 MAR81 . . . . **1:3.48**
Leakage Testing—SAE J1267 . . . . **1:3.50**
Liquid Penetrant Test Methods—SAE J426c **1:3.52**
Penetrating Radiation Inspection—SAE J427b . . . **1:3.53**
Ultrasonic Inspection—SAE J428b **1:3.55**
Acoustic Emission Test Methods—SAE J1242 . . . **1:3.56**
Definition for Particle Size—SAE J391 JUL81 . . . **1:3.56**
Definitions for Macrostrain and Microstrain—SAE
J932 . . . . **1:3.57**
Technical Report on Fatigue Properties—SAE
J1099 . . . . **1:3.57**

4   Steel Fasteners

Mechanical and Material Requirements for Externally
Threaded Fasteners—SAE J429 JAN80 . . . . . . **1:4.01**
Mechanical and Material Requirements for Metric Ex-
ternally Threaded Steel Fasteners—SAE J1199 . . **1:4.06**
Test Methods for Metric Threaded Fasteners—SAE
J1216 . . . . **1:4.11**
Mechanical and Quality Requirements for Machine
Screws—SAE J82 JUN79 . . . . **1:4.14**
Mechanical and Material Requirements for Steel
Nuts—SAE J995 JUN79 . . . . **1:4.15**
Mechanical and Material Requirements for Wheel
Bolts—SAE J1102 . . . . **1:4.18**
Mechanical and Chemical Requirements for Non-
threaded Fasteners—SAE J430 . . . . **1:4.18**
Mechanical and Quality Requirements for Tapping
Screws—SAE J933 JUN79 . . . . **1:4.19**
Steel Self-Drilling Tapping Screws—SAE J78
JUN79 . . . . **1:4.21**
Thread Rolling Screws—SAE J81 JUN79 . . . . . . **1:4.26**
Metric Thread Rolling Screws—SAE J1237 . . . . . **1:4.29**
Surface Discontinuities on General Application Bolts,
Screws, and Studs—SAE J1061a **1:4.33**
Surface Discontinuities on Bolts, Screws, and Studs—
SAE J123c **1:4.37**
Surface Discontinuities on Nuts—SAE J122a **1:4.40**
Decarburization in Hardened and Tempered Threaded
Fasteners—SAE J121a **1:4.44**

5   Spring Wire and Springs

Oil Tempered Carbon Steel Spring Wire and Springs—
SAE J316 . . . . **1:5.01**
Oil Tempered Carbon Steel Valve Spring Quality Wire
and Springs—SAE J351 . . . . **1:5.02**
Oil Tempered Chromium-Vanadium Valve Spring Qual-
ity Wire and Springs—SAE J132 . . . . **1:5.03**
Hard Drawn Mechanical Spring Wire and Springs—
SAE J113 . . . . **1:5.04**
Special Quality High Tensile, Hard Drawn Mechanical
Spring Wire and Springs—SAE J271 . . . . **1:5.04**
Oil Tempered Chromium–Silicon Alloy Steel Wire and
Springs—SAE J157 . . . . **1:5.05**
Hard Drawn Carbon Steel Valve Spring Quality Wire
and Springs—SAE J172 . . . . **1:5.06**
Stainless Steel 17-7 PH Spring Wire and Springs—SAE
J217 . . . . **1:5.07**

Stainless Steel, SAE 30302, Spring Wire and Springs—
SAE J230 . . . . **1:5.08**
Music Steel Spring Wire and Springs—SAE J178 . . **1:5.09**

6   Ferrous Castings

Numbering System for Designating Grades of Cast Fer-
rous Materials—SAE J859 . . . . **1:6.01**
Automotive Gray Iron Castings—SAE J431 AUG79 . **1:6.01**
Automotive Malleable Iron Castings—SAE J158a . . **1:6.04**
Automotive Ductile (Nodular) Iron Castings—SAE
J434c **1:6.06**
Elevated Temperature Properties of Cast Irons—SAE
J125 . . . . **1:6.08**
Automotive Steel Castings—SAE J435c **1:6.12**

7   Tool and Die Steels

Tool and Die Steels—SAE J438b **1:7.01**
Selection and Heat Treatment of Tool and Die Steels—
SAE J437a **1:7.02**
Sintered Carbide Tools—SAE J439a **1:7.07**
Sintered Tool Materials—SAE J1072 . . . . **1:7.12**

8   Ferrous Materials

Sintered Powder Metal Parts: Ferrous—SAE J471d . **1:8.01**
Cut Steel Wire Shot—SAE J441 . . . . **1:8.05**
Test Strip, Holder and Gage for Shot Peening—SAE
J442 AUG79 . . . . **1:8.05**
Procedures for Using Standard Shot Peening Test
Strip—SAE J443 . . . . **1:8.07**
Cast Steel Shot—SAE J827 . . . . **1:8.08**
Cast Shot and Grit Size Specifications for Peening and
Cleaning—SAE J444a **1:8.09**
Metallic Shot and Grit Mechanical Testing—SAE
J445a **1:8.10**
Size Classification and Characteristics of Glass Beads
for Peening—SAE J1173 . . . . **1:8.11**

9   Ferrous and Nonferrous—General

Use of the Terms Yield Point and Yield Strength—SAE
J450 . . . . **1:9.01**
† Surface Texture Measurement of Cold Rolled Sheet
Steel—SAE J911 OCT81 . . . . **1:9.01**
Surface Texture—SAE J448a **1:9.03**
Surface Texture Control—SAE J449a **1:9.05**
Preferred Thicknesses for Uncoated Flat Metals (Thru
12 mm)—SAE J446a **1:9.07**
Welding, Brazing, and Soldering—Materials and Prac-
tices—SAE J1147 . . . . **1:9.07**

NONFERROUS METALS

10   Nonferrous Metals

Aluminum Alloys—Fundamentals—SAE J451b **1:10.01**
Alloy and Temper Designation Systems for Alumi-
num—SAE J993b **1:10.02**
General Information on SAE Aluminum Casting Al-
loys—SAE J452c **1:10.05**
Chemical Compositions and Mechanical and Physical
Properties of SAE Aluminum Casting Alloys—SAE
J453c **1:10.08**
† General Data on Wrought Aluminum Alloys—SAE
J454 JUL81 . . . . **1:10.11**
Chemical Compositions, Mechanical Property Limits,
and Dimensional Tolerances of SAE Wrought Alumi-
num Alloys—SAE J457j **1:10.26**
Anodized Aluminum Automotive Parts—SAE J399a . **1:10.27**
Bearing and Bushing Alloys (Standard)—SAE J460e . **1:10.28**
Bearing and Bushing Alloys (Information Report)—SAE
J459c **1:10.28**

NOTE: Page numbers shown include the volume number in bold followed by the section number and page number within that section.

Wrought and Cast Copper Alloys—SAE J461 SEP81   **1**:10.30
Cast Copper Alloys—SAE J462 SEP81 . . . . **1**:10.64
Wrought Copper and Copper Alloys—SAE J463
  SEP81 . . . . **1**:10.67
Magnesium Alloys—SAE J464c **1**:10.106
Magnesium Casting Alloys—SAE J465c **1**:10.106
Magnesium Wrought Alloys—SAE J466c **1**:10.111
Special Purpose Alloys ("Superalloys")—SAE J467b   **1**:10.115
Zinc Alloy Ingot and Die Casting Compositions—SAE
  J468b **1**:10.126
Zinc Die Casting Alloys—SAE J469a **1**:10.127
Wrought Nickel and Nickel-Related Alloys—SAE
  J470c **1**:10.127
Electroplating of Nickel and Chromium on Metal
  Parts—Automotive Ornamentation and Hardware—
  SAE J207 . . . . **1**:10.137
Solders—SAE J473a **1**:10.142
Electroplating and Related Finishes—SAE J474b . . **1**:10.143

NONMETALLIC MATERIALS

11 Nonmetallic Materials

Classification System for Rubber Materials for Automotive Applications—SAE J200 APR80 . . . . **1**:11.01
Recommended Guidelines for Fatigue Testing of Elastomeric Materials and Components—SAE J1183 .   **1**:11.29
Test for Dynamic Properties of Elastomeric Isolators—SAE J1085a **1**:11.34
Latex Foam Rubbers—SAE J17 OCT79 . . . . **1**:11.37
Sponge- and Expanded Cellular-Rubber Products—SAE J18 DEC79 . . . . **1**:11.40
Latex Dipped Goods and Coatings for Automotive Applications—SAE J19 NOV80 . . . . **1**:11.45
Synthetic Resin Plastic Sealers, Nondrying Type—SAE J250 . . . . **1**:11.45
Methods of Tests for Automotive-Type Sealers, Adhesives, and Deadeners—SAE J243 . . . . **1**:11.46
* Heat Insulation Materials Test Procedure—SAE J1324 DEC81 . . . . **1**:11.56
† Vibration Damping Materials and Underbody Coatings—SAE J671 APR82 . . . . **1**:11.56
Test Method for Measuring Weight of Organic Trim Materials—SAE J860 . . . . **1**:11.59
Test Method for Determining Dimensional Stability of Automotive Textile Materials—SAE J883 . . . . . . **1**:11.59
Method of Testing Resistance to Crocking of Organic Trim Materials—SAE J861 . . . . **1**:11.59
Test Method for Measuring Thickness of Automotive Textiles and Plastics—SAE J882 . . . . **1**:11.60
Test Method for Determining Cold Cracking of Flexible Plastic Materials—SAE J323 . . . . **1**:11.60
Nonmetallic Trim Materials—Test Method for Determining the Staining Resistance to Hydrogen Sulfide Gas—SAE J322 . . . . **1**:11.61
Test Method for Determining Window Fogging Resistance of Interior Trim Materials—SAE J275 . . . . **1**:11.62
Test for Chip Resistance of Surface Coatings—SAE J400 JUN80 . . . . **1**:11.64
Florida Exposure of Automotive Finishes—SAE J951 FEB80 . . . . **1**:11.67
Marking of Plastic Parts—SAE J1344 OCT80 . . . . **1**:11.68
* Automotive Plastic Parts Specification—SAE J1345 FEB82 . . . . **1**:11.71
Glossary of Fiberboard Terminology—SAE J947 JUL80 . . . . **1**:11.76
Fiberboard Test Procedure—SAE J315 SEP80 . . . . **1**:11.78
Standard Classification System for Fiberboards—SAE J1323 AUG80 . . . . **1**:11.81

Test Method for Wicking of Automotive Fabrics and Fibrous Materials—SAE J913a **1**:11.83
Method of Testing Resistance to Scuffing of Trim Materials—SAE J365a **1**:11.83
Test Method for Determining Blocking Resistance and Associated Characteristics of Automotive Trim Materials—SAE J912a **1**:11.85
† Fiberboard Crease Bending Test—SAE J119 JAN82 **1**:11.86
Definitions of Acoustical Terms—SAE J1184 . . . . . **1**:11.89
Test Method for Measuring Wet Color Transfer Characteristics—SAE J1326 AUG80 . . . . **1**:11.89
Test Method for Measuring the Relative Drapeability of Flexible Insulation Materials—SAE J1325 SEP80 . . . . **1**:11.89
Test Method for Measuring Thickness of Resilient Insulating Paddings—SAE J1355 MAR81 . . . . . . **1**:11.90
Hot Plate Method for Evaluating Heat Resistance and Thermal Insulation Properties of Materials—SAE J1361 APR81 . . . . **1**:11.91
Compression and Recovery of Insulation Paddings—SAE J1352 MAY81 . . . . **1**:11.92
* Hot Odor Test for Insulation Materials—SAE J1351 JUL81 . . . . **1**:11.92
* Corrosion Test for Insulation Materials—SAE J1389 MAY82 . . . . **1**:11.93
* Laboratory Measurement of the Airborne Noise Reduction of Acoustical Materials—SAE J1400 MAY82 **1**:11.94
Flammability of Automotive Interior Materials—Horizontal Test Method—SAE J369a **1**:11.96
† Test Method for Determining Stiffness (Modulus of Bending) of Fiberboards—SAE J949 AUG81 . . . . **1**:11.98
Test Method for Determining Resistance to Snagging and Abrasion of Automotive Bodycloth—SAE J948a **1**:11.98
Test Method for Determining Visual Color Match to Master Specimen for Fabrics, Vinyls, Coated Fiberboards, and Other Automotive Trim Materials—SAE J361a **1**:11.99
Test Method of Stretch and Set of Textiles and Plastics—SAE J855 AUG80 . . . . **1**:11.100
Felts—Wool and Part Wool—SAE J314 MAY81 . . . **1**:11.102
* Automotive Rubber Mats—SAE J80 MAY82 . . . . **1**:11.104
Nonmetallic Automotive Gasket Materials—SAE J90b **1**:11.105
Rubber Rings for Automotive Applications—SAE J120a **1**:11.112
Engine Coolants—SAE J814c **1**:11.118
Engine Coolant Concentrate—Ethylene-Glycol Type—SAE J1034 . . . . **1**:11.122
Coolant System Hoses—SAE J20e **1**:11.123
† Fuel and Oil Hoses—SAE J30 JUN82 . . . . **1**:11.127
Power Steering Pressure Hose—High Volumetric Expansion Type—SAE J188 . . . . **1**:11.134
Power Steering Return Hose—Low Pressure—SAE J189 . . . . **1**:11.135
Power Steering Pressure Hose—Low Volumetric Expansion Type—SAE J191 . . . . **1**:11.137
Power Steering Pressure Hose—Wire Braid—SAE J190 . . . . **1**:11.138
Windshield Wiper Hose—SAE J50a **1**:11.139
Automotive Air Conditioning Hose—SAE J51b **1**:11.139
Windshield Washer Tubing—SAE J1037 . . . . **1**:11.141

VOLUME 2—PARTS AND COMPONENTS

THREADS, FASTENERS, AND COMMON PARTS

NOTE: Page numbers shown include the volume number in bold followed by the section number and page number within that section.

12 Threads

Screw Threads—SAE J475a **2**:12.01
Dryseal Pipe Threads—SAE J476a **2**:12.01

13 Fasteners

Hex Bolts—SAE J105 . . . . **2**:13.01
Hi-Head Finished Hex Bolts—SAE J871a **2**:13.04
Round Head Bolts—SAE J481 . . . . **2**:13.04
Slotted and Recessed Head Screws—SAE J478a . . **2**:13.07
Slotted Headless Setscrews—SAE J479a **2**:13.40
Square Head Setscrews—SAE J102 . . . . **2**:13.41
Flanged 12-Point Screws—SAE J58 . . . . **2**:13.42
Lag Screws—SAE J103 . . . . **2**:13.46
Square and Hex Nuts—SAE J104 . . . . **2**:13.47
Hexagon High Nuts—SAE J482a **2**:13.53
Alignment of Nut Slots—SAE J484 . . . . **2**:13.54
Crown (Blind, Acorn) Nuts—SAE J483a **2**:13.54
Spring Nuts—SAE J891a **2**:13.55
Push-On Spring Nuts—SAE J892a **2**:13.63
Steel Stamped Nuts of One Pitch Thread Design—SAE
    J1053 . . . . **2**:13.64
Plain Washers—SAE J488 . . . . **2**:13.68
Lock Washers—SAE J489b **2**:13.68
Conical Spring Washers—SAE J773b **2**:13.73
Nut and Conical Spring Washer Assemblies—SAE
    J238 . . . . **2**:13.74
Torque-Tension Test Procedure for Steel Threaded
    Fasteners—SAE J174 . . . . **2**:13.76
Cotter Pins—SAE J487a **2**:13.77
Holes in Bolt and Capscrew Shanks and Slots in Nuts
    for Cotter Pins—SAE J485 . . . . **2**:13.79
Straight Pins (Solid)—SAE J495 . . . . **2**:13.79
Grooved Straight Pins—SAE J494 . . . . **2**:13.80
Spring Type Straight Pins—SAE J496 . . . . **2**:13.82
Unhardened Ground Dowel Pins—SAE J497 . . . . . **2**:13.84
Rod Ends and Clevis Pins—SAE J493 . . . . **2**:13.84
Rivets and Riveting—SAE J492 . . . . **2**:13.85
Blind Rivets—Break Mandrel Type—SAE J1200 . . . **2**:13.95
Bolt and Capscrew Sizes for Use in Construction and
    Industrial Machinery—SAE J370 . . . . **2**:13.101
Hose Clamps—SAE J536b **2**:13.101

14 Ball Studs and Joints

Ball Studs and Ball Stud Socket Assemblies—SAE
    J491b **2**:14.01
Ball Stud and Socket Assembly Test Procedure—SAE
    J193 SEP79 . . . . **2**:14.06
Ball Joints—SAE J490 OCT81 . . . . **2**:14.08
Spherical Rod Ends—SAE J1120 SEP79 . . . . . . **2**:14.12
Metric Spherical Rod Ends—SAE J1259 APR80 . . . **2**:14.15
* Performance Test Procedure—Ball Joints and Spheri-
    cal Rod Ends—SAE J1367 SEP81 . . . . **2**:14.16

15 Splines

Involute Splines and Inspections—SAE J498c **2**:15.01
Parallel Side Splines for Soft Broached Holes in Fit-
    tings—SAE J499a **2**:15.01
Serrated Shaft Ends—SAE J500 . . . . **2**:15.03
Shaft Ends—SAE J501 . . . . **2**:15.04
Woodruff Keys—SAE J502 . . . . **2**:15.05
Woodruff Key Slots and Keyways—SAE J503 . . . . **2**:15.06

16 V-Belts

V-Belts and Pulleys—SAE J636c **2**:16.01
Automotive V-Belt Drives—SAE J637b **2**:16.04

SI (Metric) Synchronous Belts and Pulleys—SAE J1278
    OCT80 . . . . **2**:16.08
Automotive Synchronous Belt Drives—SAE J1313
    OCT80 . . . . **2**:16.12

17 Springs

Leaf Springs for Motor Vehicle Suspension—Metric
    Bar Sizes—SAE J1123a **2**:17.01
Leaf Springs for Motor Vehicle Suspension—SAE
    J510c **2**:17.01
Pneumatic Spring Terminology—SAE J511a **2**:17.08
Helical Compression and Extension Spring Terminol-
    ogy—SAE J1121 . . . . **2**:17.09
Helical Springs: Specification Check Lists—SAE
    J1122 . . . . **2**:17.14
Rated Spring Capacity—SAE J274 . . . . **2**:17.15

18 Speedometers and Tachometers

Factors Affecting Accuracy of Mechanically Driven Au-
    tomotive Speedometer-Odometers—SAE J862
    JUN81 . . . . **2**:18.01
Speedometers and Tachometers—Automotive—SAE
    J678e **2**:18.03
Speedometer Test Procedure—SAE J1059 . . . . . **2**:18.07
Electric Tachometer Specification—On Road—SAE
    J196 JUN80 . . . . **2**:18.08
Electric Tachometer Specification—Off Road—SAE
    J197 . . . . **2**:18.10
Automatic Vehicle Speed Control—Motor Vehicles—
    SAE J195 . . . . **2**:18.12

19 Tubing and Fittings

§ Coding Systems for Identification of Fluid Conductors
    and Connectors—SAE J846 FEB82 . . . . **2**:19.01
Automotive Tube Fittings—SAE J512 OCT80 . . . . **2**:19.04
Spherical and Flanged Sleeve (Compression) Tube Fit-
    tings—SAE J246 MAR81 . . . . **2**:19.18
Refrigeration Tube Fittings—SAE J513f **2**:19.26
Hydraulic Tube Fittings—SAE J514 APR80 . . . . . **2**:19.46
Hydraulic Hose Fittings—SAE J516 MAR81 . . . . **2**:19.72
Hose Push-On Fittings—SAE J1231 . . . . **2**:19.89
† Hydraulic Hose—SAE J517 JUN82 . . . . **2**:19.92
Selection, Installation, and Maintenance of Hose and
    Hose Assemblies—SAE J1273 SEP79 . . . . . . **2**:19.104
Tests and Procedures for SAE 100R Series Hydraulic
    Hose and Hose Assemblies—SAE J343 JUN80 . . **2**:19.105
Flex-Impulse Test Procedure for Hydraulic Hose As-
    semblies—SAE J1405 . . . . **2**:19.106
Tests and Procedures for High-Temperature Transmis-
    sion Oil Hose, Lubricating Oil Hose and Hose Assem-
    blies—SAE J1019 . . . . **2**:19.107
Hydraulic Flanged Tube, Pipe, and Hose Connections,
    4-Bolt Split Flange Type—SAE J518c **2**:19.107
Hydraulic "O" Ring—SAE J515a **2**:19.112
Formed Tube Ends for Hose Connections—SAE J962b **2**:19.112
Flares for Tubing—SAE J533b **2**:19.113
Seamless Low Carbon Steel Tubing Annealed for Bend-
    ing and Flaring—SAE J524 JAN80 . . . . **2**:19.115
Welded and Cold Drawn Low Carbon Steel Tubing An-
    nealed for Bending and Flaring—SAE J525 JAN80 **2**:19.115
Welded Low Carbon Steel Tubing—SAE J526 JAN80 **2**:19.116
Brazed Double Wall Low Carbon Steel Tubing—SAE
    J527 JAN80 . . . . **2**:19.117
Welded Flash Controlled Low Carbon Steel Tubing
    Normalized for Bending, Double Flaring, and Bead-
    ing—SAE J356 JAN80 . . . . **2**:19.118
Pressure Ratings for Hydraulic Tubing and Fittings—
    SAE J1065 . . . . **2**:19.119

* New
† Technical revision
§ Editorial change

NOTE: Page numbers shown include the volume number in bold followed by the section number and page number within that section.

Seamless Copper Tube—SAE J528 JAN80 . . . . . . 2:19.121
Metallic Air Brake System Tubing and Pipe—SAE J1149 . . . . 2:19.122
Nonmetallic Air Brake System Tubing—SAE J844 OCT80 . . . . 2:19.124
Performance Requirements for SAE J844d Nonmetallic Tubing and Fitting Assemblies Used in Automotive Air Brake Systems—SAE J1131 . . . . 2:19.126
Fuel Injection Tubing—SAE J529b 2:19.127
Automotive Pipe Fittings—SAE J530 JAN81 . . . . . 2:19.128
Automotive Pipe, Filler, and Drain Plugs—SAE J531 JAN81 . . . . 2:19.134
Automotive Straight Thread Filler and Drain Plugs— SAE J532 JAN81 . . . . 2:19.138
Lubrication Fittings—SAE J534 JAN81 . . . . 2:19.143

ELECTRICAL EQUIPMENT AND LIGHTING

20 Equipment

Nomenclature—Automotive Electrical Systems—SAE J831 . . . . 2:20.01
Ignition System Nomenclature and Terminology—SAE J139 . . . . 2:20.01
Ignition System Measurements Procedure—SAE J973a 2:20.02
† Storage Batteries—SAE J537 JUN82 . . . . 2:20.04
† Life Test for Automotive Storage Batteries—SAE J240 JUN82 . . . . 2:20.11
Grounding of Storage Batteries—SAE J538a 2:20.12
Voltage Drop for Starting Motor Circuits—SAE J541a 2:20.12
Voltages for Diesel Electrical Systems—SAE J539a . 2:20.12
Starting Motor Mountings—SAE J542c 2:20.13
Starting Motor Pinions and Ring Gears—SAE J543c 2:20.14
Generator Mountings—SAE J545b 2:20.14
† Electric Starting Motor Test Procedure—SAE J544 MAY82 . . . . 2:20.16
Low Temperature Cranking Load Requirements of an Engine—SAE J1253 . . . . 2:20.17
* Cranking Motor Application Considerations—SAE J1375 MAR82 . . . . 2:20.18
Electrical Generating System (Alternator Type) Performance Curve and Test Procedure—SAE J56 . . . . 2:20.18
Magneto Mountings—SAE J546 . . . . 2:20.19
Spark Plugs—SAE J548d 2:20.20
† Preignition Rating of Spark Plugs—SAE J549 JUN82 2:20.26
Performance Levels and Methods of Measurement of Electromagnetic Radiation from Vehicles and Devices (20–1000 MHz)—SAE J551 JUN81 . . . . . 2:20.26
Electric Fuses (Cartridge Type)—SAE J554b 2:20.32
Blade Type Electric Fuses—SAE J1284 DEC79 . . . 2:20.34
Circuit Breakers—SAE J553c 2:20.37
Circuit Breaker—Internal Mounted—Automatic Reset—SAE J258 . . . . 2:20.39
Ignition Switch—SAE J259 . . . . 2:20.39
§ Automobile, Truck, Truck-Tractor, Trailer, and Motor Coach Wiring—SAE J1292 OCT81 . . . . 2:20.39
Automotive Printed Circuits—SAE J771c 2:20.42
High Tension Ignition Cable—SAE J557 . . . . 2:20.46
Low Tension Wiring and Cable Terminals and Splice Clips—SAE J163 . . . . 2:20.48
Battery Cable—SAE J1127 JUN80 . . . . 2:20.48
Low Tension Primary Cable—SAE J1128 . . . . 2:20.50
Fusible Links—SAE J156a 2:20.55
Five Conductor Electrical Connectors for Automotive Type Trailers—SAE J895 . . . . 2:20.55
Four- and Eight-Conductor Rectangular Electrical Connectors for Automotive Type Trailers—SAE J1239 2:20.57

Seven-Conductor Electrical Connector for Truck-Trailer Jumper Cable—SAE J560b 2:20.60
Seven Conductor Jacketed Cable for Truck Trailer Connections—SAE J1067 . . . . 2:20.61
Electrical Terminals—Blade Type—SAE J858a 2:20.62
Electrical Terminals—Pin and Receptacle Type—SAE J928 JUN80 . . . . 2:20.63
Electrical Terminals—Eyelet and Spade Type—SAE J561 JUN80 . . . . 2:20.64
Nonmetallic Loom—SAE J562a 2:20.68
Electric Windshield Wiper Switch—SAE J112a . . . 2:20.69
Electric Windshield Washer Switch—SAE J234 . . . 2:20.69
Electric Blower Motor Switch—SAE J235 . . . . . . 2:20.70
Six- and Twelve-Volt Cigar Lighter Receptacles—SAE J563b 2:20.70
Performance Requirements for the Automotive Audio Cassette—SAE J1274 JUN80 . . . . 2:20.71
Testing Methods for Audio Cassettes—SAE J1275 JUN80 . . . . 2:20.72
Electromagnetic Susceptibility Procedures for Vehicle Components (Except Aircraft)—SAE J1113a 2:20.80
Recommended Environmental Practices for Electronic Equipment Design—SAE J1211 . . . . 2:20.92
Open Field Whole-Vehicle Radiated Susceptibility 10 kHz—18 GHz, Electric Field—SAE J1338 JUN81 2:20.109
Glossary of Automotive Electronic Terms—SAE J1213 2:20.120
Guide to Manifold Absolute Pressure Transducer Representative Test Method—SAE J1346 JUN81 . . . 2:20.125
Guide to Manifold Absolute Pressure Transducer Representative Specification—SAE J1347 JUN81 . . . 2:20.128

21 Lighting

Terminology—Motor Vehicle Lighting—SAE J387 . . 2:21.01
Preferred Conversion Values for Dimensions in Lighting—Inch-Pound Units/SI—SAE J1322 MAY81 . . 2:21.01
† Lighting Identification Code—SAE J759 MAR82 . . 2:21.03
Headlamp Beam Switching—SAE J564c 2:21.04
† Semiautomatic Headlamp Beam Switching Devices— SAE J565 JUN82 . . . . 2:21.04
Lamp Bulb Retention System—SAE J567c 2:21.06
Connectors and Plugs—SAE J856 . . . . 2:21.09
Dimensional Specifications for Sealed Beam Headlamp Units—SAE J571 FEB81 . . . . 2:21.11
142 mm × 200 mm Sealed Beam Headlamp Unit— SAE J1132 . . . . 2:21.18
Dimensional Specifications for General Service Sealed Lighting Units—SAE J760a 2:21.20
Lamp Bulbs and Sealed Beam Headlamp Units—SAE J573g 2:21.22
Service Performance Requirements and Test Procedures for Motor Vehicle Lamp Bulbs—SAE J1049 AUG79 . . . . 2:21.25
Tests for Motor Vehicle Lighting Devices and Components—SAE J575 JUN80 . . . . 2:21.26
Service Performance Requirements for Motor Vehicle Lighting Devices and Components—SAE J256b . . 2:21.28
§ Plastic Materials for Use in Optical Parts Such as Lenses and Reflectors of Motor Vehicle Lighting Devices—SAE J576 NOV81 . . . . 2:21.30
Color Specification for Electric Signal Lighting Devices—SAE J578d 2:21.30
Sealed Beam Headlamp Units for Motor Vehicles—SAE J579c 2:21.32
Service Performance Requirements for Sealed Beam Headlamp Units for Motor Vehicles—SAE J32a . . 2:21.33
Sealed Beam Headlamp Assembly—SAE J580 AUG79 2:21.34
Auxiliary Driving Lamps—SAE J581a 2:21.37
Front Fog Lamps—SAE J583 MAY81 . . . . 2:21.38

NOTE: Page numbers shown include the volume number in bold followed by the section number and page number within that section.

§ Auxiliary Low Beam Lamp—SAE J582 SEP81 . . . . **2**:21.38
Motorcycle Headlamps—SAE J584b **2**:21.39
Motorcycle Auxiliary Front Lamps—SAE J1306
JUN80 . . . . **2**:21.41
Motorcycle and Motor Driven Cycle Electrical System
(Maintenance of Design Voltage)—SAE J392 . . . **2**:21.41
Motorcycle Turn Signal Lamps—SAE J131a **2**:21.42
Tail Lamps (Rear Position Lamps)—SAE J585e **2**:21.42
Stop Lamps—SAE J586d **2**:21.43
Mechanical Stop Lamp Switch—SAE J249 . . . . . . **2**:21.44
† License Plate Lamps (Rear Registration Plate Lamps)—
SAE J587 OCT81 . . . . **2**:21.45
Turn Signal Lamps—SAE J588f **2**:21.46
Headlamp-Turn Signal Spacing—SAE J1221 . . . . . **2**:21.48
Supplemental High Mounted Stop and Rear Turn Signal
Lamps—SAE J186a **2**:21.52
Turn Signal Switch—SAE J589b **2**:21.53
Side Turn Signal Lamps—SAE J914b **2**:21.53
Cornering Lamps—SAE J852b **2**:21.54
* Rear Cornering Lamp—SAE J1373 JUN82 . . . **2**:21.55
Turn Signal Flashers—SAE J590e **2**:21.55
Service Performance Requirements for Turn Signal
Flashers—SAE J1055 . . . . **2**:21.56
Vehicular Hazard Warning Signal Flasher—SAE J945b **2**:21.58
Service Performance Requirements for Vehicular Haz-
ard Warning Flashers—SAE J1056 . . . . **2**:21.59
Warning Lamp Alternating Flashers—SAE J1054 . . **2**:21.60
Service Performance Requirements for Warning Lamp
Alternating Flashers—SAE J1104 . . . . **2**:21.60
Spot Lamps—SAE J591b **2**:21.62
Parking Lamps (Front Position Lamps)—SAE J222a . **2**:21.62
Clearance, Side Marker, and Identification Lamps—
SAE J592f **2**:21.63
† Backup Lamps (Reversing Lamps)—SAE J593
AUG81 . . . . **2**:21.64
Backup Lamp Switches—SAE J1076 . . . . **2**:21.64
Headlamp Switch—SAE J253 . . . . **2**:21.65
Reflex Reflectors—SAE J594f **2**:21.65
Emergency Warning Device—SAE J774c **2**:21.66
Flashing Warning Lamps for Authorized Emergency,
Maintenance and Service Vehicles—SAE J595b . **2**:21.67
Hazard Warning Signal Switch—SAE J910b **2**:21.68
360 Deg Emergency Warning Lamp—SAE J845 . . **2**:21.68
† School Bus Red Signal Lamps—SAE J887 MAY82 . **2**:21.69
School Bus Stop Arm—SAE J1133a **2**:21.70
Lighting Inspection Code—SAE J599 MAY81 . . . . **2**:21.71
Headlamp Testing Machines—SAE J600 MAY81 . . **2**:21.73
Headlamp Aiming Device for Mechanically Aimable
Sealed Beam Headlamp Units—SAE J602 OCT80 **2**:21.74
Flasher Test Equipment—SAE J823c **2**:21.77

BRAKES
22 Brakes

Road Vehicle—Hydraulic Brake Hose Assemblies for
Use with Non-Petroleum Base Hydraulic Fluids—SAE
J1401 JAN81 . . . . **2**:22.01
Automotive Air Brake Hose and Hose Assemblies—
SAE J1402 OCT80 . . . . **2**:22.07
Vacuum Brake Hose—SAE J1403a **2**:22.11
Application of Hydraulic Brake Hose to Motor Vehi-
cles—SAE J1406 MAR81 . . . . **2**:22.13
Rubber Seals for Hydraulic Disc Brake Cylinders—SAE
J1603 . . . . **2**:22.15
Brake Master Cylinder Reservoir Diaphragm Gasket—
SAE J1605 . . . . **2**:22.17

Rubber Boots for Drum Type Hydraulic Brake Wheel
Cylinders—SAE J1604 . . . . **2**:22.19
Hydraulic Wheel Cylinders for Automotive Drum
Brakes—SAE J101 MAR80 . . . . **2**:22.21
Hydraulic Master Cylinders for Motor Vehicle Brakes—
Test Procedure—SAE J1153 . . . . **2**:22.24
Hydraulic Master Cylinders for Motor Vehicle Brakes—
Performance Requirements—SAE J1154 . . . . . . **2**:22.28
Hydraulic Valves for Motor Vehicle Brake Systems Test
Procedure—SAE J1118 . . . . **2**:22.28
Hydraulic Valves for Motor Vehicle Brake Systems—
Performance Requirements—SAE J1137 . . . . . . **2**:22.32
Motor Vehicle Brake Fluid—Arctic—SAE J1702f . . **2**:22.33
Motor Vehicle Brake Fluid—SAE J1703 JAN80 . . . **2**:22.41
Motor Vehicle Brake Fluid Container Compatibility—
SAE J75 . . . . **2**:22.50
Labeling of Motor Vehicle Brake Fluid Containers—
SAE J988 . . . . **2**:22.50
Handling and Dispensing of Motor Vehicle Brake
Fluid—SAE J76 . . . . **2**:22.51
Service Maintenance of Motor Vehicle Brake Fluid in
Motor Vehicle Brake Actuating Systems—SAE J77 **2**:22.53
Automotive Brake Definitions and Nomenclature—SAE
J656g **2**:22.55
In-Service Brake Performance Test Procedure Passen-
ger Car and Light-Duty Truck—SAE J201 . . . . **2**:22.57
In-Service Brake Performance Test Procedure—Vehi-
cles Over 4500 kg (10 000 lb)—SAE J1250
FEB80 . . . . **2**:22.59
Gogan Hardness of Brake Lining—SAE J379a **2**:22.60
Specific Gravity of Brake Lining—SAE J380 . . . . . **2**:22.61
Friction Identification System for Brake Linings and
Brake Blocks for Motor Vehicles—SAE J866a . . . **2**:22.62
Swell, Growth, and Dimensional Stability of Brake Lin-
ings—SAE J160 JUN80 . . . . **2**:22.62
Brake Lining Quality Control Test Procedure—SAE
J661a **2**:22.63
Minimum Requirements for Motor Vehicle Brake Lin-
ings—SAE J998 . . . . **2**:22.65
Color Code for Location Identification of Combination
Linings of Two Different Materials or Two Shoe
Brakes—SAE J659 . . . . **2**:22.66
Brake Block Chamfer—SAE J662 . . . . **2**:22.66
Rivets for Brake Linings and Bolts for Brake Blocks—
SAE J663b **2**:22.66
Test Procedures for Brake Shoe and Lining Adhesives
and Bonds—SAE J840c **2**:22.67
Motor Vehicle Grade Parking Performance Test
Code—SAE J360 . . . . **2**:22.73
Vehicle Grade Parking Performance Requirements—
SAE J293 . . . . **2**:22.74
Service Brake Structural Integrity Requirements—Vehi-
cles Over 10 000 lb (4500 KG) GVWR—SAE
J1404 . . . . **2**:22.74
Brake Test Code—Inertia Dynamometer—SAE
J667 . . . . **2**:22.75
Brake System Road Test Code—Passenger Car and
Light-Duty Truck—SAE J843d **2**:22.77
Simulated Mountain Brake Performance Test Proce-
dure—SAE J1247 APR80 . . . . **2**:22.82
Service Brake System Performance Requirements—
Passenger Car—SAE J937b **2**:22.88
Brake System Dynamometer Test Procedure—Passen-
ger Car—SAE J212 JUN80 . . . . **2**:22.90
Service Brake System Performance Requirements—
Light-Duty Truck—SAE J155 . . . . **2**:22.94
Service Brake Structural Integrity Test Procedure—Pas-
senger Car—SAE J229 JUN80 . . . . **2**:22.96

* New
† Technical revision
§ Editorial change

Brake System Road Test Code—Passenger Car and Light Duty Truck-Trailer Combinations—SAE J134 JUN79 .... **2**:22.97

Service Brake System Performance Requirements—Passenger Car—Trailer Combinations—SAE J135a **2**:22.106

Brake System Road Test Code—Truck, Bus, and Combination of Vehicles—SAE J786a **2**:22.107

Brake System Performance Requirements—Truck, Bus, and Combination of Vehicles—SAE J992b **2**:22.113

Service Brake Structural Integrity Test Procedure—Vehicles Over 10 000 LB (4500 kg) GVWR—SAE J294 **2**:22.114

Brake System Road Test Code—Motorcycles—SAE J108a **2**:22.116

Service Brake System Performance Requirements—Motorcycles and Motor-Driven Cycles—SAE J109a **2**:22.118

Brake System Rating Test Code—Commercial Vehicles—SAE J880 MAY80 .... **2**:22.119

Brake System Torque Balance Test Code—Commercial Vehicles—SAE J225 JUN80 .... **2**:22.125

Brake Rating Test Code—Commercial Vehicle Inertia Dynamometer—SAE J971 .... **2**:22.126

Brake Rating Horsepower Requirements—Commercial Vehicles—SAE J257 JUN80 .... **2**:22.127

Emergency Air Brake Systems—Motor Vehicles and Vehicle Combinations—SAE J263 SEP80 ..... **2**:22.128

Automotive Air Brake Reservoir Volume—SAE J813 **2**:22.129

Test Code—Truck, Truck-Tractor, and Trailer Air Service Brake System Pneumatic Pressure and Time Levels—SAE J982 SEP80 .... **2**:22.129

Air Brake Gladhand Service (Control) and Emergency (Supply) Line Couplers—Trucks, Truck-Tractors, and Trailers—SAE J318 SEP80 .... **2**:22.130

Automotive and Off-Highway Air Brake Reservoir Performance and Identification Requirements—SAE J10 SEP80 .... **2**:22.131

Displacement of Pneumatic Brake Actuators—SAE J1155 SEP80 .... **2**:22.132

Stopping Distance Test Procedure—SAE J299 JAN80 .... **2**:22.132

Brake Disc and Drum Thermocouple Installation—SAE J79 .... **2**:22.133

Determination of Brake Fluid Temperature—SAE J291 JUN80 .... **2**:22.133

Wheel Slip Brake Control System Road Test Code—SAE J46 JUN80 .... **2**:22.134

Minimum Requirements for Wheel Slip Brake Control System Malfunction Signals—SAE J1230 OCT79 . **2**:22.138

Tubing—Motor Vehicle Brake System Hydraulic—SAE J1047 .... **2**:22.138

Automotive Hydraulic Brake System—Metric Tube Connections—SAE J1290 JUL80 .... **2**:22.141

Automotive Hydraulic Brake System—Metric Banjo Bolt Connections—SAE J1291 JUL80 .... **2**:22.146

Rubber Cups for Hydraulic Actuating Cylinders—SAE J1601 .... **2**:22.148

VOLUME 3—ENGINES, FUELS, LUBRICANTS, EMISSIONS, AND NOISE

FUELS AND LUBRICANTS

23 Fuels and Lubricants

Effective Dates of Revisions—SAE J301 .... **3**:23.01

Engine Oil Performance and Engine Service Classification—SAE J183 FEB80 .... **3**:23.01

Engine Oil Viscosity Classification—SAE J300 SEP80 **3**:23.05

§ Engine Oil Tests—SAE J304 JUN82 .... **3**:23.09

Physical and Chemical Properties of Engine Oils—SAE J357a **3**:23.11

Axle and Manual Transmission Lubricants—SAE J308c **3**:23.15

Axle and Manual Transmission Lubricant Viscosity Classification—SAE J306 MAY81 .... **3**:23.16

Automotive Lubricating Greases—SAE J310 MAR80 **3**:23.17

Fluid for Passenger Car Type Automatic Transmissions—SAE J311b **3**:23.20

Powershift Transmission Fluid Classification—SAE J1285 FEB80 .... **3**:23.22

Central Fluid Systems—SAE J71a **3**:23.23

† Automotive Gasolines—SAE J312 JUN82 ...... **3**:23.25

§ Diesel Fuels—SAE J313 APR82 .... **3**:23.34

† Alternative Automotive Fuels—SAE J1297 APR82 . **3**:23.39

The Lubricant Performance and Service Classification Maintenance Procedure—SAE J1146 NOV80 ... **3**:23.41

POWERPLANT COMPONENTS AND ACCESSORIES

24 Powerplant Components and Accessories

Engine Terminology and Nomenclature—General—SAE J604d **3**:24.01

Gas Turbine Engine Nomenclature—SAE J828 JAN80 **3**:24.02

Rotary-Trochoidal Engine Nomenclature and Terminology—SAE J1220 .... **3**:24.03

Turbocharger Nomenclature and Terminology—SAE J922 NOV79 .... **3**:24.07

Engine Power Test Code—Spark Ignition and Diesel—SAE J1349 DEC80 .... **3**:24.09

Procedure for Measuring Basic Highway Vehicle Engine Performance and Fuel Consumption—Spark Ignition and Diesel—SAE J1312 SEP80 .... **3**:24.11

Small Spark Ignition Engine Test Code—SAE J607a **3**:24.14

Gas Turbine Engine Test Code—SAE J116a **3**:24.16

Mounting Flanges and Power Take-Off Shafts for Small Engines—SAE J609a **3**:24.18

Valve Seat Inserts—Engine—SAE J610b **3**:24.20

Turbocharger Connections—SAE J1135 .... **3**:24.22

Ignition Timing—SAE J327 .... **3**:24.23

Engine Rotation and Cylinder Numbering—SAE J824 **3**:24.24

Piston Rings and Pistons—SAE J929a **3**:24.24

Piston Rings and Grooves (Metric)—SAE J1201 ... **3**:24.31

Sleeve Type Half Bearings—SAE J506b **3**:24.38

† Split Type Bushings—Design and Application—SAE J835 DEC81 .... **3**:24.45

Thrust Washers—Design and Application—SAE J924 JAN81 .... **3**:24.50

Air Cleaner Elements—SAE J1141 .... **3**:24.57

Air Cleaner Test Code—SAE J726 MAY81 ...... **3**:24.58

Engine and Transmission Dipstick Marking—SAE J614b **3**:24.68

Engine Mountings—SAE J615b **3**:24.69

Locating Ledge for Flat Pad Engine Mountings—SAE J832 .... **3**:24.69

Flywheels for Single-Plate Spring-Loaded Clutches—SAE J618 JUN80 .... **3**:24.70

Flywheels for Two-Plate Spring-Loaded Clutches—SAE J619 JUN80 .... **3**:24.71

Housing Internal Dimensions for Single and Two Plate Spring Loaded Clutches—SAE J373a **3**:24.72

Engine Flywheel Housings with Sealed Flanges—SAE J1172 .... **3**:24.72

Spring-Loaded Clutch Spin Test Procedure—SAE J1073 JUN80 .... **3**:24.72

Flywheel Spin Test Procedure—SAE J1240 ...... **3**:24.73

NOTE: Page numbers shown include the volume number in bold followed by the section number and page number within that section.

Filter Base Mounting—SAE J363 FEB80 . . . .   **3**:24.73
Water Connection Flanges—SAE J535 JAN80 . . . .   **3**:24.74
Airflow or Vacuum Governor Flanges—SAE J622
    JAN80 . . . .   **3**:24.75
Fuel Pump Mountings for Diaphragm Type Pumps—
    SAE J625 JUL80 . . . .   **3**:24.77
Fuel Injection Equipment Nomenclature—SAE J830b   **3**:24.78
Diesel Fuel Injection Pump Mountings—SAE J626b   **3**:24.80
Diesel Fuel Injection Nozzle Holder Assemblies—SAE
    J629b **3**:24.85
Diesel Fuel Injection Nozzle Holder Assembly (9.5
    mm)—SAE J347a **3**:24.87
Diesel Fuel Injection Nozzle and Holder Assembly (17
    mm Nominal Diameter)—SAE J265 . . . .   **3**:24.88
Fuel Injection Nozzle Gaskets—SAE J59 . . . . . .   **3**:24.88
Master Calibrating Fuel Injection Pump—SAE J981 .   **3**:24.89
Calibrating Nozzle and Holder Assembly for Diesel Fuel
    Injection Systems—SAE J968c **3**:24.90
Testing Techniques for Diesel Fuel Injection Systems—
    SAE J969b **3**:24.92
Test Stands for Diesel Fuel Injection Systems—SAE
    J970a **3**:24.92
Metric Thread Fuel Injection Tubing Connections—
    SAE J242a **3**:24.93
Fuel Injection Tubing Connections—SAE J521b . . .   **3**:24.94
Calibration Fluid for Diesel Injection Equipment—SAE
    J967d **3**:24.98
Glossary of Terms Related to Fluid Filters and Filter
    Testing—SAE J1124 . . . .   **3**:24.98
LP-Gas Fuel Systems Components—SAE J372a . . .   **3**:24.101
Pressure Relief for Cooling System—SAE J151 . . .   **3**:24.102
Multiposition Small Engine Exhaust System Fire Igni-
    tion Suppression—SAE J335b **3**:24.102
Spark Arrester Test Procedure for Large Size Engines—
    SAE J342 NOV80 . . . .   **3**:24.105
Spark Arrester Test Procedure for Medium Size En-
    gines—SAE J350 JAN80 . . . .   **3**:24.109
Spark Arrester Test Carbon—SAE J997 JAN80 . . .   **3**:24.112
Muffler Parts Nomenclature—SAE J261 . . . .   **3**:24.115
Resonator Parts Nomenclature—SAE J262 . . . . .   **3**:24.115
Engine Preheaters—SAE J226a **3**:24.116
Nomenclature for Exhaust System Parts—SAE J97   **3**:24.117
Carburetor Airflow Reference Standards—SAE J228
    JAN80 . . . .   **3**:24.118
† Radiator Caps and Filler Necks—SAE J164 MAR82   **3**:24.120
Large Size Radiator Filler Necks—SAE J868 . . . .   **3**:24.121
† Glossary of Engine Cooling System Terms—SAE
    J1004 SEP81 . . . .   **3**:24.121
† Radiator Nomenclature—SAE J631 FEB82 . . . . . .   **3**:24.123
Engine Charge Air Cooler Nomenclature—SAE
    J1148 . . . .   **3**:24.127
* Engine Cooling Fan Structural Analysis—SAE J1390
    APR82 . . . .   **3**:24.130
Oil Cooler Nomenclature and Glossary—SAE J1244
    JUN81 . . . .   **3**:24.133
Fan Hub Bolt-Circles and Pilot Holes—SAE J635a . .   **3**:24.141
Engine Coolant Pump Seals—SAE J780a **3**:24.142
† Guide to the Application and Use of Engine Coolant
    Pump Face Seals—SAE J1245 JUN82 . . . .   **3**:24.144
Fuel Tank Filler Cap and Cap Retainer—Threaded Pres-
    sure-Vacuum Type—SAE J1114 . . . .   **3**:24.150
Fuel Tank Filler Cap and Cap Retainer—SAE J829c   **3**:24.151
Filler Pipes and Openings of Motor Vehicle Fuel
    Tanks—SAE J1140 MAR80 . . . .   **3**:24.152
Fuel Tank Filler Conditions—Passenger Car, Multi-Pur-

pose Passenger Vehicles, and Light Duty Trucks—
    SAE J398b **3**:24.155
Gasoline Dispenser Nozzle Spouts—SAE J285 JUL81   **3**:24.156
Fuel Economy Measurement—Road Test Procedure—
    SAE J1082 SEP80 . . . .   **3**:24.156
Road Load Measurement and Dynamometer Simula-
    tion Using Coastdown Techniques—SAE J1263 .   **3**:24.165
Fuel Economy Measurement—Road Test Procedure—
    Cold Start and Warm-Up Fuel Economy—SAE
    J1256 JUN80 . . . .   **3**:24.188

EMISSIONS

25   Emissions

† Measurement of Carbon Dioxide, Carbon Monoxide,
    and Oxides of Nitrogen in Diesel Exhaust—SAE J177
    APR82 . . . .   **3**:25.01
Measurement of Intake Air or Exhaust Gas Flow of
    Diesel Engines—SAE J244 . . . .   **3**:25.11
Continuous Hydrocarbon Analysis of Diesel Emis-
    sions—SAE J215 JAN80 . . . .   **3**:25.21
Diesel Engine Emission Measurement Procedure—SAE
    J1003 . . . .   **3**:25.25
Diesel Emission Production Audit Test Procedure—
    SAE J1243 AUG79 . . . .   **3**:25.27
Diesel Engine Smoke Measurement—SAE J255a . .   **3**:25.32
Measurement Procedure for Evaluation of Full-Flow,
    Light Extinction Smokemeter Performance—SAE
    J1157 . . . .   **3**:25.40
Diesel Smoke Measurement Procedure—SAE J35 . .   **3**:25.51
Crankcase Emission Control Test Code—SAE J900
    NOV80 . . . .   **3**:25.54
Test Procedure for Measuring Carbon Monoxide Con-
    centrations in Vehicle Passenger Compartments—
    SAE J989a **3**:25.58
Determination of Sulfur Compounds in Automotive Ex-
    haust—SAE J1280 JAN80 . . . .   **3**:25.60
Measurement of Fuel Evaporative Emissions from Gas-
    oline Powered Passenger Cars and Light Trucks—
    SAE J170a **3**:25.78
† Measurement of Fuel Evaporative Emissions from Gas-
    oline Powered Passenger Cars and Light Trucks Us-
    ing the Enclosure Technique—SAE J171 JUN82 .   **3**:25.84
Instrumentation and Techniques for Exhaust Gas Emis-
    sions Measurement—SAE J254 . . . .   **3**:25.93
Constant Volume Sampler System for Exhaust Emis-
    sions Measurement—SAE J1094a **3**:25.102
Instrumentation and Techniques for Vehicle Refueling
    Emissions Measurement—SAE J1045 . . . .   **3**:25.124
Test Procedure for Measurement of Small Utility En-
    gine Exhaust Emissions—SAE J1088 . . . .   **3**:25.128
Determination of Emissions from Gas Turbine Powered
    Light Duty Surface Vehicles—SAE J1130 . . . . .   **3**:25.133
Emissions Terminology and Nomenclature—SAE
    J1145a **3**:25.143
Methane Measurement Using Gas Chromatography—
    SAE J1151 NOV79 . . . .   **3**:25.146

26   Sound Level

Maximum Sound Level Potential for Motorcycles—SAE
    J47 . . . .   **3**:26.01
Sound Levels for Motorcycles—SAE J331a **3**:26.02
Measurement of Exhaust Sound Levels of Stationary
    Motorcycles—SAE J1287 MAR82 . . . .   **3**:26.04
Instrumentation for Measuring Acoustic Impulses
    Within Vehicles—SAE J247 JUN80 . . . .   **3**:26.05
Qualifying a Sound Data Acquisition System—SAE
    J184a **3**:26.07

* New
† Technical revision
§ Editorial change

NOTE: Page numbers shown include the volume number in bold followed by the section number and page number within that section.

† Sound Level for Passenger Cars and Light Trucks— SAE J986 NOV81 . . . . 3:26.12

Maximum Sound Level for Passenger Cars and Light Trucks—SAE J1030 . . . . 3:26.14

Measurement of Light Vehicle Exhaust Sound Level Under Stationary Conditions—SAE J1169 . . . . . 3:26.16

Exterior Sound Level for Heavy Trucks and Buses— SAE J366b 3:26.18

Sound Level for Truck Cab Interior—SAE J336a . . . 3:26.19

Measurement of Exterior Sound Levels for Heavy Trucks Under Stationary Conditions—SAE J1096 . 3:26.20

Sound Level of Highway Truck Tires—SAE J57 JUL81 3:26.21

Measurement of Exterior Sound Level of Trucks with Auxiliary Equipment—SAE J1077 . . . . 3:26.23

Performance of Vehicle Traffic Horns—SAE J377 . . 3:26.24

Exterior Sound Level for Snowmobiles—SAE J192 APR80 . . . . 3:26.25

Operator Ear Sound Level Measurement Procedure for Snow Vehicles—SAE J1160 . . . . 3:26.26

Operational Sound Level Measurement Procedure for Snow Vehicles—SAE J1161 APR80 . . . . 3:26.28

Exterior Sound Level Measurement Procedure for Pleasure Motorboats—SAE J34a 3:26.29

Operator Sound Level Exposure Assessment Procedure for Pleasure Motorboats—SAE J1281 NOV79 . . 3:26.30

Alarm—Back Up—Electric—Performance, Test, and Application—SAE J994 SEP80 . . . . 3:26.32

Horn—Forward Warning—Electric—Performance, Test, and Application—SAE J1105 SEP80 . . . . . 3:26.34

Sound Measurement—Earthmoving Machinery—Operator—Singular Type—SAE J919 SEP80 . . . . . . 3:26.37

Sound Measurement—Earthmoving Machinery—Operator—Work Cycle—SAE J1166 SEP80 . . . . . . 3:26.39

Operator Ear Sound Level Measurement Procedure for Small Engine Powered Equipment—SAE J1174 . . 3:26.48

Bystander Sound Level Measurement Procedure for Small Engine Powered Equipment—SAE J1175 . . 3:26.49

Sound Measurement—Construction Site—SAE J1075 SEP80 . . . . 3:26.51

* Sound Power Determination—Earthmoving Machinery—Static Condition—SAE J1372 DEC81 . . . . 3:26.53

Sound Measurement—Earthmoving Machinery—Exterior—SAE J88 SEP80 . . . . 3:26.57

Sound Measurement—Trenching Equipment—SAE J1262 SEP80 . . . . 3:26.60

Sound Measurement—Self-Propelled Agricultural Equipment—Exterior—SAE J1008 SEP80 . . . . . 3:26.63

Engine Sound Level Measurement Procedure—SAE J1074 . . . . 3:26.64

§ Measurement Procedure for Determination of Silencer Effectiveness in Reducing Engine Intake or Exhaust Sound Level—SAE J1207 OCT81 . . . . 3:26.65

VOLUME 4—ON-HIGHWAY VEHICLES AND OFF-HIGHWAY MACHINERY

PASSENGER CARS, TRUCKS, BUSES, AND MOTORCYCLES

27 Vehicle Identification Numbers

† Vehicle Identification Number Systems—SAE J272 DEC81 . . . . 4:27.01

† Passenger Car Vehicle Identification Number System— SAE J273 DEC81 . . . . 4:27.02

† Passenger Car Identification Terminology—SAE J218 DEC81 . . . . 4:27.02

† Vehicle Identification Numbers—SAE J853 DEC81 . 4:27.03

† Engine and Transmission Identification Numbers—SAE J129 DEC81 . . . . 4:27.03

Vehicle Identification Numbers—Motorcycles—SAE J364a 4:27.03

† Truck Identification Terminology—SAE J1229 DEC81 4:27.04

Truck Vehicle Identification Numbers—SAE J187 . . 4:27.05

† World Manufacturer Identifier—SAE J1044 DEC81 4:27.05

§ Motor Vehicle License Plates—SAE J686 JUL81 . . 4:27.06

† Truck and Truck Tractor Vehicle Identification Number Systems—SAE J1108 DEC81 . . . . 4:27.07

28 Passenger Cars, Trucks, Buses and Motorcycles

Towability Design Criteria—Passenger Cars and Light Duty Trucks—SAE J1142a 4:28.01

Towed Vehicle/Wrecker Attachment Test Procedure—Passenger Cars and Light Duty Trucks—SAE J1143a 4:28.05

Towed Vehicle Drivetrain Test Procedure—Passenger Cars and Light Duty Trucks—SAE J1144a 4:28.07

Electric Vehicle Test Procedure—SAE J227a 4:28.09

29 Transmissions

† Symbols for Hydrodynamic Drives—SAE J640 DEC81 . . . . 4:29.01

Hydrodynamic Drives Terminology—SAE J641b . . . 4:29.02

Hydrodynamic Drive Test Code—SAE J643b 4:29.04

Automotive Transmission Terminology—SAE J645c . 4:29.07

Planetary Gear(s)—Terminology—SAE J646 JUL81 . 4:29.07

Transmissions—Schematic Diagrams—SAE J647 JUL81 . . . . 4:29.08

Automatic Transmission Hydraulic Control Systems— Terminology—SAE J648a 4:29.09

Automatic Transmission Functions—Terminology— SAE J649b 4:29.09

Passenger Car and Truck Automatic Transmission Test Code—SAE J651c 4:29.10

Automatic Transmissions—Manual Control Sequence—SAE J915 . . . . 4:29.14

Clearance Envelopes for Six- and Eight-Bolt Truck Transmission Mounted Power Take-Offs—SAE J772a 4:29.15

Openings for Six- and Eight-Bolt Truck Transmission Mounted Power Take-Offs—SAE J704b 4:29.16

Universal Joints and Driveshafts—Nomenclature and Terminology—SAE J901b 4:29.17

Axles—Nomenclature and Terminology—SAE J923 4:29.25

Axle Efficiency Test Procedure—SAE J1266 . . . . . 4:29.29

† One-Way Clutches—Nomenclature and Terminology— SAE J1087 AUG81 . . . . 4:29.33

Clutch Friction Test Machine (SAE No. 2)—Test Procedure—SAE J286 . . . . 4:29.35

Seals—Terminology of Radial Lip—SAE J111c 4:29.38

Seals—Application Guide to Radial Lip—SAE J946d 4:29.43

Seals—Evaluation of Elastohydrodynamic—SAE J1002 . . . . 4:29.54

Seals—Testing of Radial Lip—SAE J110c 4:29.57

Seals—Lathe Cut—SAE J654 . . . . 4:29.60

Cast Iron Sealing Rings—SAE J281 SEP80 . . . . . . 4:29.61

Cast Iron Sealing Rings (Metric)—SAE J1236 SEP80 4:29.63

30 Tires

Passenger Car Tire Performance Requirements and Test Procedures—SAE J918c 4:30.01

§ Rolling Resistance Measurement Procedure for Passenger Car Tires—SAE J1269 JUL81 . . . . 4:30.04

The Measurement of Passenger Car Tire Rolling Resistance—SAE J1270 OCT79 . . . . 4:30.06

NOTE: Page numbers shown include the volume number in bold followed by the section number and page number within that section.

* Rolling Resistance Measurement Procedure for Highway Truck and Bus Tires—SAE J1379 JUN82 . .   **4**:30.08

* The Measurement of Highway Truck and Bus Tire Rolling Resistance—SAE J1380 JUN82 . . . .   **4**:30.10

Wet or Dry Pavement Passenger Car Tire Peak and Locked Wheel Braking Traction—SAE J345a . . .   **4**:30.12

† Testing Machines for Measuring the Uniformity of Passenger Car and Light Truck Tires—SAE J332 AUG81 . . . .   **4**:30.14

Selection of Tires for Multipurpose Passenger Vehicles, Light-, Medium-, and Heavy-Duty Trucks, Buses, Trailers, and Semitrailers for Normal Highway Service—SAE J161a **4**:30.16

Truck and Bus Tire Performance Requirements and Test Procedures—SAE J341a **4**:30.17

Test Procedures for Measuring Truck Tire Revolutions per Mile—SAE J1025 . . . .   **4**:30.19

Test Procedure for Measuring Passenger Car Tire Revolutions per Mile—SAE J966 . . . .   **4**:30.19

Subjective Rating Scale for Evaluation of Noise and Ride Comfort Characteristics Related to Motor Vehicle Tires—SAE J1060 . . . .   **4**:30.20

Methods for Testing Snap-In Tubeless Tire Valves—SAE J1206 . . . .   **4**:30.21

Performance Requirements for Snap-In Tubeless Tire Valves—SAE J1205 . . . .   **4**:30.23

31 Wheels

Wheels—Passenger Cars—Performance Requirements and Test Procedures—SAE J328a **4**:31.01

Wheels—Passenger Cars—Impact Performance Requirements and Test Procedures—SAE J175 . . . .   **4**:31.02

Wheels—Recreational and Utility Trailer Test Procedures—SAE J1204 . . . .   **4**:31.03

Wheels/Rims—Trucks—Test Procedures and Performance Requirements—SAE J267a **4**:31.05

* Hub Fatigue Test Procedures—SAE J1095 JUN82   **4**:31.09

Labeling—Disc Wheels and Demountable Rims—Trucks—SAE J179a **4**:31.12

Nomenclature—Wheels and Rims—Trucks—SAE J393 . . . .   **4**:31.13

32 Bumpers

Bumper Jack Requirements—Motor Vehicles—SAE J979 . . . .   **4**:32.01

Bumper Jacking Test Procedure—Motor Vehicles—SAE J978 . . . .   **4**:32.01

Bumper Evaluation Test Procedure—Passenger Cars—SAE J980a **4**:32.02

Approach, Departure, and Ramp Breakover Angles—Passenger Car and Light Duty Trucks—SAE J689   **4**:32.03

33 Seat Belts

Seat Belt Hardware Test Procedure—SAE J140a . .   **4**:33.01

Seat Belt Hardware Performance Requirements—SAE J141 . . . .   **4**:33.03

Dynamic Test Procedure—Type 1 and Type 2 Seat Belt Assemblies—SAE J117 . . . .   **4**:33.04

Motor Vehicle Seat Belt Anchorages—Design Recommendations—SAE J383 . . . .   **4**:33.06

Motor Vehicle Seat Belt Anchorages Test Procedure—SAE J384 . . . .   **4**:33.08

Motor Vehicle Seat Belt Anchorages—Performance Requirements—SAE J385 . . . .   **4**:33.09

Motor Vehicle Seat Belt Assembly Installations—SAE J800c **4**:33.10

Seat Belt Assembly Webbing Abrasion Test Procedure—SAE J339a **4**:33.12

Seat Belt Assembly Webbing Abrasion Test Requirements—SAE J114 . . . .   **4**:33.12

Occupant Restraint System Evalution—Passenger Cars—SAE J128 . . . .   **4**:33.12

34 Passenger Car Components and Systems

† Vehicle Passenger Door Hinge Systems—SAE J934 JUL82 . . . .   **4**:34.01

† Passenger Car Side Door Latch Systems—SAE J839 JUL82 . . . .   **4**:34.02

† Vehicle Hood Latch Systems—SAE J362 JUL82 . .   **4**:34.05

Passenger Car Windshield Wiper Systems—SAE J903c **4**:34.06

Windshield Wiper Systems—Trucks, Buses, and Multipurpose Vehicles—SAE J198 . . . .   **4**:34.09

Passenger Car Windshield Washer Systems—SAE J942b **4**:34.11

Passenger Car Windshield Defrosting Systems—SAE J902b **4**:34.13

Windshield Defrosting Systems Test Procedure—Trucks, Buses, and Multipurpose Vehicles—SAE J381 . . . .   **4**:34.15

Windshield Defrosting Systems Performance Requirements—Trucks, Buses, and Multipurpose Vehicles—SAE J382 . . . .   **4**:34.17

Passenger Car Backlight Defogging System—SAE J953 . . . .   **4**:34.18

† Motor Vehicle Heater Test Procedure—SAE J638 JUN82 . . . .   **4**:34.20

† Safety Practices for Mechanical Vapor Compression Refrigeration Equipment or Systems Used to Cool Passenger Compartment of Motor Vehicles—SAE J639 OCT81 . . . .   **4**:34.26

Devices for Use in Defining and Measuring Vehicle Seating Accommodation—SAE J826 APR80 . . .   **4**:34.27

Motor Vehicle Seating Systems—SAE J879b **4**:34.31

Dynamic Flex Fatigue Test for Slab Polyurethane Foam—SAE J388 . . . .   **4**:34.34

Urethane for Automotive Seating—SAE J954 . . .   **4**:34.35

Load Deflection Testing of Urethane Foams for Automotive Seating—SAE J815 MAY81 . . . .   **4**:34.36

Automotive Safety Glazing—SAE J673b **4**:34.36

Light Transmittance of Automotive Windshields Safety Glazing Materials—SAE J1203 . . . .   **4**:34.38

Safety Glazing Materials—Motor Vehicles—SAE J674a **4**:34.39

Passenger Car Glazing—Electrical Circuits—SAE J216   **4**:34.40

Passenger Car Glazing Shade Bands—SAE J100 . .   **4**:34.40

Drop Test for Evaluating Laminated Safety Glass for Use in Automotive Windshields—SAE J938a . . .   **4**:34.41

Test Procedure for Determining Reflectivity of Rear View Mirrors—SAE J964a **4**:34.41

* Measuring the Radius of Curvature of Convex Mirrors—SAE J1246 MAY82 . . . .   **4**:34.42

Vision Factors Considerations in Rear View Mirror Design—SAE J985 . . . .   **4**:34.44

Passenger Car Rear Vision—SAE J834a **4**:34.45

Motor Vehicle Dimensions—SAE J1100 JUL79 . . .   **4**:34.49

Motor Vehicle Driver's Eye Range—SAE J941 MAR81 . . . .   **4**:34.66

Driver Hand Control Reach—SAE J287 FEB80 . . .   **4**:34.72

Design Criteria—Driver Hand Controls Location for Passenger Cars, Multi-Purpose Passenger Vehicles, and Trucks (10 000 GVW and Under)—SAE J1138   **4**:34.105

Supplemental Information—Driver Hand Controls Location for Passenger Cars, Multi-Purpose Passenger

* New
† Technical revision
§ Editorial change

Vehicles, and Trucks (10 000 GVW and Under)—
SAE J1139 . . . . 4:34.107

Describing and Measuring the Driver's Field of View—
SAE J1050a 4:34.108

Vision Glossary—SAE J264 . . . . 4:34.119

Motor Vehicle Fiducial Marks—SAE J182a 4:34.121

Motor Vehicle Driver and Passenger Head Position—
SAE J1052 . . . . 4:34.122

Synthetic Skins for Automotive Testing—SAE J202 . 4:34.124

Collision Deformation Classification—SAE J224
MAR80 . . . . 4:34.125

Film Analysis Guides for Dynamic Studies of Test Subjects—SAE J138 . . . . 4:34.135

Instrumentation for Impact Tests—SAE J211 JUN80 4:34.137

Moving Barrier Collision Tests—SAE J972 JUN80 . 4:34.138

Barrier Collision Tests—SAE J850 JUN80 . . . . . 4:34.142

Roll-Over Tests without Collision—SAE J857 JUN80 4:34.143

Inverted Vehicle Drop Test Procedure—SAE J996
JUN80 . . . . 4:34.146

Passenger Car Roof Crush Test Procedure—SAE J374
JUN80 . . . . 4:34.147

Passenger Car Door System Crush Test Procedure—
SAE J367 JUN80 . . . . 4:34.148

Bodyforms for Use in Motor Vehicle Passenger Compartment Impact Development—SAE J984 JUN80 4:34.149

Steering Control System—Passenger Car—Laboratory
Test Procedure—SAE J944 JUN80 . . . . 4:34.150

Rear Underride Guard Test Procedure—SAE J260
JUN80 . . . . 4:34.152

Symbols for Motor Vehicle Controls, Indicators and
Tell-Tales—SAE J1048 MAR80 . . . . 4:34.153

35 Trailers

Trailer Couplings, Hitches and Safety Chains—Automotive Type—SAE J684f 4:35.01

Tire to Body Clearance Check for Recreational Vehicles—SAE J1214 . . . . 4:35.03

36 Truck and Bus

Nomenclature—Truck, Bus, Trailer—SAE J687c . . . 4:36.01

Truck Ability Prediction Procedure—SAE J688 . . . 4:36.02

Joint RCCC/SAE Fuel Consumption Test Procedure
(Short Term-In-Service Vehicle) Type I—SAE
J1264 . . . . 4:36.05

* Joint TMC/SAE Fuel Consumption Test Procedure—
Type II—SAE J1321 OCT81 . . . . 4:36.08

* Test Method for Measuring Power Consumption of
Cooling Fans for Trucks and Buses—SAE J1339
JUL81 . . . . 4:36.27

* Test Method for Measuring Power Consumption of Air
Conditioning and Air Brake Compressors for Trucks
and Buses—SAE J1340 JUL81 . . . . 4:36.29

* Test Method for Measuring Power Consumption of Hydraulic Pumps for Trucks and Buses—SAE J1341
JUL81 . . . . 4:36.29

* Test Method for Measuring Power Consumption of Fan
Drive Systems for Trucks and Buses—SAE J1342
JUL81 . . . . 4:36.30

* Information Relating to Duty Cycles and Average
Power Requirements of Truck and Bus Engine Accessories—SAE J1343 JUL81 . . . . 4:36.32

§ SAE Wind Tunnel Test Procedure for Trucks and
Buses—SAE J1252 JUL81 . . . . 4:36.33

Certificates of Maximum Net Horsepower for Motor
Trucks and Truck Tractors—SAE J690 . . . . . . 4:36.37

Motor Truck CA Dimensions—SAE J691 . . . . . . 4:36.38

Average Vehicle Dimensions for Use in Designing
Docking Facilities for Motor Vehicles—SAE J699a 4:36.39

Turning Ability and Off Tracking—Motor Vehicles—
SAE J695b 4:36.39

Truck Tractor Semitrailer Interchange Coupling Dimensions—SAE J701a 4:36.43

† Fifth Wheel Kingpin Performance—Commercial Trailers and Semitrailers—SAE J133 JAN82 . . . . . 4:36.46

† Fifth Wheel Kingpin—Commercial Trailers and Semitrailers—SAE J700 JAN82 . . . . 4:36.48

Fifth Wheel Kingpin, Heavy Duty—Commercial Trailers
and Semitrailers—SAE J848a 4:36.49

Connection and Accessory Locations for Towing Doubles Trailers and Multi-Axle Trailers—SAE J849b 4:36.49

Full Trailer Tow Bar Eye—SAE J847 . . . . 4:36.51

Safety Chain of Full Trailers or Converter Dollies—SAE
J697a 4:36.51

Recommended Tolerances for Spoke-Type Wheels,
Demountable Rims, and Rim Spacers—Trucks and
Trailers—SAE J851 . . . . 4:36.52

Commercial Vehicle Disc Wheels—SAE J694a . . . 4:36.52

Extra Wide Single Tire Rim and Wheel Mounting for
Rear Axles—SAE J876a 4:36.53

Truck Overall Widths Across Dual Tires—SAE J693a 4:36.53

Trailer Axle Alignment—SAE J875 . . . . 4:36.54

Brake Flange Mounting—On-Highway Vehicles—SAE
J337 . . . . 4:36.54

SAE Nodal Mount—SAE J1134 . . . . 4:36.55

Brake and Electrical Connection Locations—Truck-
Tractor and Truck-Trailer—SAE J702b 4:36.55

Brake Diaphragm Maintenance—Tractor and Semitrailer—SAE J666 . . . . 4:36.56

Tire Chain Clearance—Trucks, Buses, and Combinations of Vehicles—SAE J683a 4:36.56

Passenger and Light Truck Tire Traction Device Profile
Determination and Classification—SAE J1232 . . 4:36.57

Rating of Winches—SAE J706a 4:36.58

Rating of Truck Power Take-Offs—SAE J705b . . . 4:36.59

Rear Wheel Splash and Stone Throw Protection—SAE
J682 . . . . 4:36.60

† Location and Operation of Instruments and Controls
in Motor Truck Cabs—SAE J680 JUN82 . . . . . 4:36.60

Wheel Chocks—SAE J348 . . . . 4:36.62

37 Motorcycles

Definitions—Motorcycles—SAE J213a 4:37.01

Operator Controls and Displays on Motorcycles—SAE
J107 APR80 . . . . 4:37.01

† Rear View Mirrors—Motorcycles—SAE J268 MAY82 4:37.03

Motorcycle Stop Lamp Switch—SAE J1167 . . . . 4:37.03

Motorcycle Bank Angle Measurement Procedure—
SAE J1168 . . . . 4:37.04

Fuel and Lubricant Tanks for Motorcycles—SAE
J1241 . . . . 4:37.05

OFF-HIGHWAY MACHINES AND VEHICLES

38 Snowmobiles

Snowmobile Definitions and Nomenclature—General—SAE J33a 4:38.01

Vehicle Identification Numbers—Snowmobile and All-
Terrain Vehicles—SAE J64 FEB81 . . . . 4:38.03

Maintenance of Design Voltage—Snowmobile Electrical Systems—SAE J277 . . . . 4:38.04

Snowmobile Headlamps—SAE J280 . . . . 4:38.04

Snowmobile Stop Lamp—SAE J278 . . . . 4:38.05

Snowmobile Tail Lamp (Rear Position Lamp)—SAE
J279 . . . . 4:38.06

Snowmobile and Snowmobile Cutter Lamps, Reflective
Devices, and Associated Equipment—SAE J292 . 4:38.07

NOTE: Page numbers shown include the volume number in bold followed by the section number and page number within that section.

Tests for Snowmobile Switching Devices and Components—SAE J68 OCT79 . . . . **4**:38.08

Snowmobile Passenger Handgrips—SAE J1062 . . . **4**:38.09

Snowmobile Brake Control Systems—SAE J1282 SEP80 . . . . **4**:38.10

Service Brake System Performance Requirements—Snowmobiles—SAE J44 . . . . . . **4**:38.11

Brake System Test Procedure—Snowmobiles—SAE J45 . . . . **4**:38.11

Dynamic Cushioning Performance Criteria for Snowmobile Seats—SAE J89a **4**:38.13

Snowmobile and All-Terrain Vehicle Pulley Guards and Shields—SAE J93 . . . . . . **4**:38.15

Metallic and Nonmetallic Nonpressure Integral Fuel Tank—Snowmobile—SAE J288a **4**:38.17

Snowmobile Throttle Control Systems—SAE J92 . . **4**:38.18

Speed Control Assurance for Snowmobiles—SAE J1222 FEB81 . . . . . **4**:38.19

Recommendations for Children's Snowmobile—SAE J1038 FEB80 . . . . . **4**:38.20

39   Agricultural Equipment

Agricultural Tractor Test Code—SAE J708 JUN80 . **4**:39.01

Terminology for Agricultural Equipment—SAE J1150 **4**:39.05

Agricultural Tractor Tire Loadings, Torque Factors, and Inflation Pressures—SAE J709d **4**:39.05

Liquid Ballast Table for Drive Tires of Agricultural Machines—SAE J884 MAY80 . . . . **4**:39.10

Tire Selection Tables for Agricultural and Light Industrial Machines of Future Design—SAE J711c . . . **4**:39.12

Agricultural Tractor Tire Dynamic Indices—SAE J1261 FEB79 . . . . . **4**:39.13

Lawn and Garden Tractors Load and Inflation Pressures and Tire Selection Table for Future Design—SAE J344 . . . . **4**:39.14

Brake Test Procedure and Brake Performance Criteria for Agricultural Equipment—SAE J1041 . . . . . . **4**:39.15

Three-Point Hitch, Implement Quick-Attaching Coupler, Agricultural Tractors—SAE J909 APR80 . . . **4**:39.17

Three-Point Free-Link Hitch Attachment of Implements to Agricultural Wheeled Tractors—SAE J715 MAY80 . . . . **4**:39.19

Test Procedure for Measuring Hydraulic Lift Force Capacity on Agricultural Tractors Equipped with Three-Point Hitch—SAE J283 . . . . **4**:39.22

Application of Hydraulic Remote Control to Agricultural Tractors and Trailing Type Agricultural Implements—SAE J716a **4**:39.24

Dimensional Standard for Cylindrical Hydraulic Couplers for Agricultural Tractors—SAE J1036 . . . . **4**:39.26

Rear Power Take-Off for Agricultural Tractors—SAE J1170 JUN80 . . . . **4**:39.27

Operating Requirements for Tractors and Power Take-Off Driven Implements—SAE J721 JUN80 . . . . **4**:39.30

Auxiliary Power Take-Off Drives for Agricultural Tractors—SAE J717 MAY80 . . . . **4**:39.31

Power Take-Off Definitions and Terminology for Agricultural Tractors—SAE J722 MAY80 . . . . **4**:39.32

Tractor Belt Speed and Pulley Width—SAE J720 MAY80 . . . . **4**:39.32

Industrial and Agricultural Disc Wheels—SAE J712a **4**:39.32

Wheel Mounting Elements for Industrial and Agricultural Disc Wheels—SAE J714b **4**:39.36

T-Hook Slots for Securement in Shipment of Agricultural Equipment—SAE J39 . . . . **4**:39.37

Headlamps for Agricultural Equipment—SAE J975 MAY80 . . . . **4**:39.38

Flashing Warning Lamp for Agricultural Equipment—SAE J974 MAY80 . . . . **4**:39.38

Lighting and Marking of Agricultural Equipment on Highways—SAE J137c **4**:39.39

Combination Tail and Floodlamp for Agricultural Equipment—SAE J976 MAY80 . . . . . . **4**:39.39

Slow-Moving Vehicle Identification Emblem—SAE J943a **4**:39.40

Mounting Brackets and Socket for Warning Lamp and Slow-Moving Vehicle (SMV) Identification Emblem—SAE J725 MAY80 . . . . **4**:39.41

Performance Test for Air Conditioned Agricultural Equipment—SAE J1006 MAR80 . . . . . **4**:39.41

Agricultural Equipment Enclosure Pressurization System Test Procedure—SAE J1012 MAR80 . . . . . **4**:39.43

Safety Alert Symbol for Agricultural, Construction and Industrial Equipment—SAE J284a **4**:39.43

Safety for Agricultural Equipment—SAE J208d . . . **4**:39.44

Operator Controls on Agricultural Equipment—SAE J841 MAY80 . . . . **4**:39.46

Universal Symbols for Operator Controls on Agricultural Equipment—SAE J389b **4**:39.47

Roll-Over Protective Structures (ROPS) for Wheeled Agricultural Tractors—SAE J1194 . . . . . **4**:39.49

Overhead Protection for Agricultural Tractors—Test Procedures and Performance Requirements—SAE J167 JUN81 . . . . **4**:39.56

Measurement of Whole Body Vibration of the Seated Operator of Off-Highway Work Machines—SAE J1013 JAN80 . . . . . **4**:39.57

Development of a Frequency Weighted Portable Ride Meter—SAE J1225 . . . . **4**:39.60

Technical Publications for Agricultural Equipment—SAE J1035 JUN80 . . . . . **4**:39.65

40   Construction and Industrial Equipment

Categories of Off-Road Self-Propelled Work Machines—SAE J1116 JUN81 . . . . . **4**:40.01

Product Identification Numbering System of Off-Road Work Machines—SAE J1360 JUN81 . . . . . **4**:40.03

Identification Terminology of Earthmoving Machines—SAE J1057 JUN81 . . . . . **4**:40.04

Specification Definitions—Off-Road Work Machines—SAE J1234 . . . . **4**:40.12

Identification Terminology of Mobile Forestry Machines—SAE J1209 . . . . **4**:40.14

Format for Commercial Literature Specifications—Off-Road Work Machines—SAE J1233 . . . . . . **4**:40.17

Component Nomenclature—Crawler Tractor—SAE J727 MAY80 . . . . **4**:40.18

Component Nomenclature—Industrial Tractors (Wheel)—SAE J1092 . . . . **4**:40.19

Component Nomenclature—Two and Four-Wheel Tractors—SAE J869a **4**:40.19

Component Nomenclature—Scrapers—SAE J728a . **4**:40.21

Component Nomenclature—Graders—SAE J870 . . **4**:40.23

Nomenclature—Dozer—SAE J729 MAY80 . . . . . **4**:40.24

Specification Definitions—Dozers—SAE J173 JAN80 **4**:40.26

Component Nomenclature—Loader—SAE J731d . . **4**:40.27

* Classification, Nomenclature and Specification Definitions for Trenching Machines—SAE J1382 MAY82 **4**:40.29

Nomenclature—Rippers, Rooters, Scarifiers—SAE J733b **4**:40.33

Component Nomenclature—Dumper Trailer—SAE J734c **4**:40.34

Component Nomenclature—Dumpers—SAE J1016 **4**:40.35

* New
† Technical revision
§ Editorial change

NOTE: Page numbers shown include the volume number in bold followed by the section number and page number within that section.

Component Nomenclature—Rollers/Compactors—SAE J1017 . . . . 4:40.36

Classification and Nomenclature Towing Winch for Skidders and Crawler Tractors—SAE J1014 OCT79 4:40.38

Nomenclature and Dimensions for Crane Shovels—SAE J958 MAR81 . . . . 4:40.40

Identification Terminology—Pipelayers—SAE J1295 JUN80 . . . . 4:40.42

Nomenclature and Dimensions for Hydraulic Excavators—SAE J1193 MAR81 . . . . 4:40.42

Component Nomenclature—Articulated Log Skidder, Rubber-Tired—SAE J1109 APR80 . . . . 4:40.45

Component Nomenclature—Feller Buncher—SAE J1254 . . . . 4:40.45

Component Nomenclature—Skidder-Grapple—SAE J1111 MAR81 . . . . 4:40.47

Specification Definitions—Loaders—SAE J732 FEB80 . . . . 4:40.48

Specification Definitions—Hydraulic Backhoes—SAE J49 APR80 . . . . 4:40.50

Specification Definitions—Articulated, Rubber-Tired Log Skidder—SAE J1110 APR80 . . . . 4:40.53

Specification Definitions—Skidder-Grapple—SAE J1112 APR80 . . . . 4:40.55

Felling Head Terminology and Nomenclature—SAE J1272 OCT79 . . . . 4:40.57

Specification Definitions—Winches for Crawler Tractors and Skidders—SAE J1158 . . . . 4:40.59

Specification Definitions—Feller/Buncher—SAE J1255 . . . . 4:40.60

Fire Prevention on Forestry Equipment—SAE J1212 4:40.62

Unauthorized Starting or Movement of Machines—SAE J1083 FEB80 . . . . 4:40.63

Minimum Performance Criteria for Braking Systems for Rubber-Tired Skidders—SAE J1178 . . . . 4:40.63

Definitions for Machine Availability (Construction and Industrial)—SAE J1032 APR80 . . . . 4:40.64

Operating Load for Loaders—SAE J818b 4:40.66

§ Lubrication Chart—Construction and Industrial Machinery—SAE J753 JUN82 . . . . 4:40.67

Lubricant Types—Construction and Industrial Machinery—SAE J754a 4:40.67

Maintenance Interval—Construction Equipment—SAE J752b 4:40.68

Oil Change System for Quick Service of Off-Road Self-Propelled Work Machines—SAE J1069 JUN81 . . 4:40.68

Dry-Break Fueling Installation for Construction Machinery—SAE J176a 4:40.69

Guidelines for Fluid Level Indicators—SAE J48 . . . . 4:40.69

Symbols and Color Codes for Maintenance Instructions, Container and Filler Identification—SAE J223 APR80 . . . . 4:40.70

Assessing Cleanliness of Hydraulic Fluid Power Components and Systems—SAE J1227 . . . . 4:40.70

Hydraulic Systems Diagnostic Port Sizes and Locations—SAE J1298 OCT80 . . . . 4:40.76

Hydraulic Power Pump Test Procedure—SAE J745 OCT80 . . . . 4:40.76

Hydraulic Power Pumps—SAE J744 OCT80 . . . . . 4:40.78

Hydraulic Directional Control Valves, 3000 psi Maximum—SAE J748 OCT80 . . . . 4:40.80

Method of Measuring and Reporting the Pressure Differential-Flow Characteristics of a Hydraulic Fluid Power Valve—SAE J1117 SEP80 . . . . 4:40.81

Measuring and Reporting the Internal Leakage of a Hydraulic Fluid Power Valve—SAE J1235 SEP80 . . 4:40.84

Standardized Fluid for Hydraulic Component Tests—SAE J1276 AUG79 . . . . 4:40.85

Reporting Cleanliness Levels of Hydraulic Fluids—SAE J1165 OCT80 . . . . 4:40.85

* Method for Assessing the Cleanliness Level of New Hydraulic Fluid—SAE J1277 MAY82 . . . . 4:40.86

Hydraulic Motor Test Procedure—SAE J746 OCT80 4:40.87

Hydraulic Control Valve Test Procedure—SAE J747 OCT80 . . . . 4:40.89

Hydraulic Power Circuit Filtration—SAE J931a 4:40.92

Hydraulic Cylinder Test Procedure—SAE J214 OCT80 4:40.94

Cylinder Rod Wiper Seal Ingression Test—SAE J1195 4:40.96

External Leakage Classifications for Hydraulic Systems—SAE J1176 . . . . 4:40.98

Reserve Tractive Ability Test Code—SAE J872 OCT80 4:40.98

Machine Drag Test Code—SAE J873 APR80 . . . . 4:40.100

Center of Gravity Test Code—SAE J874 MAR81 . . 4:40.101

Gradeability Test Code—SAE J950 APR80 . . . . . 4:40.105

Engine Cooling System Field Test (Air-to-Boil)—SAE J819 MAR80 . . . . 4:40.106

Machine Slope Operation Test Code—SAE J897 . . 4:40.107

Loading Ability Test Code—Scrapers—SAE J764 APR80 . . . . 4:40.108

Crane Structures—Method of Test—SAE J987 OCT80 . . . . 4:40.110

Cantilevered Boom Crane Structures—Method of Test—SAE J1063 OCT80 . . . . 4:40.115

Rating Chart for Cantilevered Boom Cranes—SAE J1257 OCT80 . . . . 4:40.121

Crane Hoist Line Speed and Power Test Code—SAE J820 OCT80 . . . . 4:40.141

Crane Load Stability Test Code—SAE J765 OCT80 4:40.142

Crane Boomstop—SAE J220 OCT80 . . . . 4:40.144

Telescopic Boom Length Indicating System—SAE J1180 OCT80 . . . . 4:40.144

Radius-of-Load and Boom Angle Measuring System—SAE J375 OCT80 . . . . 4:40.145

Load Indicating Devices in Lifting Crane Service—SAE J376 OCT80 . . . . 4:40.146

Crane Boom Hoist Disengaging Device—SAE J999 OCT80 . . . . 4:40.147

Crane Load Moment System—SAE J159 OCT80 . . 4:40.147

Lifting Crane, Wire-Rope Strength Factors—SAE J959 OCT80 . . . . 4:40.148

Crane and Cable Excavator Basic Operating Control Arrangements—SAE J983 OCT80 . . . . 4:40.150

Mobile Crane Working Area Definitions—SAE J1028 OCT80 . . . . 4:40.152

Mobile Crane Stability Ratings—SAE J1289 APR81 4:40.153

Pipelayers and Side Booms, Tractor-Mounted—Specifications and Test—SAE J743 DEC80 . . . . 4:40.153

* Rope Drum Rotation Indicating Device—SAE J1332 OCT81 . . . . 4:40.157

Lifting Crane Sheave and Drum Sizes—SAE J881 OCT80 . . . . 4:40.158

Hole Spacing for Scraper and Bulldozer Cutting Edges—SAE J737b 4:40.158

Hole Placement on Dozer End Bits—SAE J63 FEB80 4:40.158

Grader Cutting Edge—SAE J739b 4:40.160

Scraper and Bulldozer Cutting Edge Cross Sections, Rolled, Cast, Forged or Machined—SAE J738b . . 4:40.160

Dozer Capacity—SAE J1265 FEB80 . . . . 4:40.161

Countersunk Square Holes for Cutting Edges and End Bits—SAE J740b 4:40.163

Overcenter Clutch Spin Test Procedure—SAE J1079 4:40.163

Industrial Power Take-Offs with Driving Ring Type Overcenter Clutches—SAE J621d 4:40.164

Procedure for Measuring Bore Eccentricity and Face Deviation of Flywheels, Flywheel Housings, and Flywheel Housing Adapters—SAE J1033 . . . . 4:40.165

NOTE: Page numbers shown include the volume number in bold followed by the section number and page number within that section.

Engine Flywheel Housings—SAE J617c 4:40.166
Engine Foot Mounting (Front and Rear)—SAE J616c   4:40.168
Mounting Flanges for Engine Accessory Drives—SAE
  J896 . . . .   4:40.168
Flywheels for Engine Mounted Torque Converters—
  SAE J927b 4:40.169
Exhaust Flanges—Industrial Engines—SAE J624a . .   4:40.170
Flywheels for Single Bearing Engine Mounted Power
  Generators—SAE J162a 4:40.170
Flywheels for Industrial Engines Used with Industrial
  Power Take-Offs Equipped with Driving-Ring Type
  Overcenter Clutches and Engine Mounted Marine
  Gears—SAE J620d 4:40.172
Drain, Fill, and Level Plugs for Earthmoving Machin-
  ery—SAE J371a 4:40.173
Electrical Connector for Auxiliary Starting of Construc-
  tion, Agricultural, and Off-Road Machinery—SAE
  J1283 JUN80 . . . .   4:40.175
Sealed Lighting Units for Construction and Industrial
  Machinery—SAE J598 APR80 . . . .   4:40.179
Dimensional Specifications for Sealed Lighting Unit for
  Construction and Industrial Machinery—SAE J572a   4:40.180
Flashing Warning Lamp for Industrial Equipment—SAE
  J96 . . . .   4:40.181
Headlamps for Industrial Equipment—SAE J95 APR80   4:40.182
Combination Tail and Floodlamp for Industrial Equip-
  ment—SAE J94 APR80 . . . .   4:40.182
Lighting and Marking of Construction and Industrial
  Machinery—SAE J1029 APR80 . . . .   4:40.182
Lighting and Marking of Industrial Equipment on High-
  ways—SAE J99 APR80 . . . .   4:40.183
Electrical System for Construction and Industrial Ma-
  chinery—SAE J821a 4:40.184
Electrical Charging Systems for Construction and In-
  dustrial Machinery—SAE J180 APR80 . . . . . .   4:40.186
*Electrical Propulsion Rotating Equipment—Off-Road
  Dumper—SAE J1317 JUN82 . . . .   4:40.190
Wiring Identification System for Industrial and Con-
  struction Equipment—SAE J210 . . . .   4:40.192
†Braking Performance—In-Service Crawler Tractors and
  Crawler Loaders—SAE J1026 JUN82 . . . .   4:40.192
Braking Performance—Rubber-Tired Construction Ma-
  chines—SAE J1152 APR80 . . . .   4:40.193
†Braking Performance—New Off-Highway Dumpers—
  SAE J1224 JUN82 . . . .   4:40.199
Braking Performance—Rollers and Compactors—SAE
  J1136 SEP79 . . . .   4:40.201
Off-Highway Tire and Rim Classification—SAE J751
  APR80 . . . .   4:40.203
Off-Road Tire and Rim Selection and Application—SAE
  J1315 MAY81 . . . .   4:40.209
Ton-Mile Per Hour Test Procedure—SAE J1015 . . .   4:40.210
Ton Mile Per Hour Application Practice—SAE J1098
  APR80 . . . .   4:40.213
Drawbars—Crawler Tractor—SAE J749a 4:40.214
Capacity Ratings—Scraper, Dumper Body and Trailer
  Body—SAE J741b 4:40.215
Elevating Scrapers—Capacity Rating—SAE J957 . .   4:40.216
Shovel Dipper, Clam Bucket, and Dragline Bucket Rat-
  ing—SAE J67 OCT80 . . . .   4:40.216
Capacity Rating—Loader Bucket—SAE J742 OCT79   4:40.217
Nomenclature—Hydraulic Backhoes—SAE J326
  SEP80 . . . .   4:40.218
Excavator Hoe Bucket Rating—SAE J296 OCT80 . .   4:40.219
Hydraulic Backhoe Lift Capacity—SAE J31 . . . . . .   4:40.220

Axle Rating for Industrial Wheel Loaders and Loader-
  Backhoes—SAE J43 . . . .   4:40.222
Hydraulic Excavator Lift Capacity Rating—SAE J1097
  OCT80 . . . .   4:40.222
Hydraulic Excavator Digging Forces—SAE J1179
  OCT80 . . . .   4:40.226
Hydraulic Excavator Operator Controls—SAE J1177
  OCT80 . . . .   4:40.227
Excavator Hand Signals—SAE J1307 MAY81 . . . .   4:40.229
Tire Guards for Protection of Operator of Earthmoving
  Haulage Machines—SAE J321b 4:40.233
Lift Arm Safety Device for Loaders—SAE J38 . . . .   4:40.234
Steering Frame Lock for Articulated Loaders and Trac-
  tors—SAE J276 JUN81 . . . .   4:40.234
Performance Criteria for Rollover Protective Structures
  (ROPS) for Construction, Earthmoving, Forestry, and
  Mining Machines—SAE J1040c 4:40.235
Labeling of ROPS and FOPS—SAE J1164 . . . . .   4:40.243
Operator Protection for Industrial Equipment—SAE
  J1042 APR80 . . . .   4:40.243
Deflection Limiting Volume—ROPS/FOPS Laboratory
  Evaluation—SAE J397b 4:40.244
Minimum Performance Criteria for Falling Object Pro-
  tective Structure (FOPS)—SAE J231 JAN81 . . . .   4:40.245
Minimum Performance Criteria for Falling Object Pro-
  tective Structure (FOPS) for Industrial Equipment—
  SAE J1043 APR80 . . . .   4:40.246
Operator Protective Structure Performance Criteria for
  Certain Forestry Equipment—SAE J1084 APR80   4:40.247
Steel Products for Rollover Protective Structures
  (ROPS) and Falling Object Protective Structures
  (FOPS)—SAE J1119 APR80 . . . .   4:40.248
Performance Prediction of Roll-Over Protective Struc-
  tures (ROPS) Through Analytical Methods—SAE
  J1215 . . . .   4:40.254
USA Human Physical Dimensions—SAE J833 JAN80   4:40.255
Minimum Access Dimensions for Construction and In-
  dustrial Machinery—SAE J925 . . . .   4:40.258
Access Systems for Off-Road Machines—SAE J185
  JUN81 . . . .   4:40.260
Deflection of Seat Cushions for Off-Road Work Ma-
  chines—SAE J1051 JAN80 . . . .   4:40.264
Determining Operator Seat Location on Off-Road Work
  Machines—SAE J1163 JAN80 . . . .   4:40.265
Operator's Seat Dimensions for Off-Road Self-Pro-
  pelled Work Machines—SAE J899 OCT80 . . . . .   4:40.267
Control Locations for Construction and Industrial
  Equipment Design—SAE J898 APR80 . . . .   4:40.269
Operator Enclosures Human Factor Design Consider-
  ations—SAE J154a 4:40.270
Instrument Face Design and Location for Construction
  and Industrial Equipment—SAE J209 APR80 . . .   4:40.272
Universal Symbols for Operator Controls on Industrial
  Equipment—SAE J298 . . . .   4:40.274
Operator Controls on Industrial Equipment—SAE J297
  APR80 . . . .   4:40.276
Operator Controls for Graders—SAE J1071 . . . .   4:40.277
Safety Considerations for the Operator—SAE J153 .   4:40.277
Safety for Industrial Wheeled Equipment—SAE J98
  DEC80 . . . .   4:40.278
Nomenclature—Industrial Mowers—SAE J990 . . . .   4:40.279
Industrial Rotary Mowers—SAE J232 . . . .   4:40.281
Safety for Industrial Flail Mowers—SAE J1001 DEC80   4:40.282
Seat Belts for Construction Machines—SAE J386
  APR80 . . . .   4:40.283
Safety Signs—SAE J115 SEP79 . . . .   4:40.285
Fuel-Fired Heaters—Air Heating—for Construction and
  Industrial Machinery—SAE J1024 APR80 . . . . .   4:40.287

* New
† Technical revision
§ Editorial change

NOTE: Page numbers shown include the volume number in bold followed by the section number and page number within that section.

* Selection and Application Guidelines for Diesel, Gasoline, and Propane Fired Liquid Cooled Engine Pre-Heaters—SAE J1350 DEC81 . . . .   **4**:40.287

Electric Engine Preheaters and Battery Warmers for Diesel Engines—SAE J1310 APR81 . . . .   **4**:40.291

Design Guidelines for Air Conditioning Systems for Construction and Industrial Equipment Cabs—SAE J169 APR80 . . . .   **4**:40.301

Operator Cab Environment for Heated, Ventilated, and Air Conditioned Construction and Industrial Equipment—SAE J1129 . . . .   **4**:40.302

Remote and Automatic Control Systems for Construction and Industrial Machinery—SAE J956 . . . . . .   **4**:40.303

Minimum Performance Criteria for Emergency Steering of Wheeled Earthmoving Construction Machines—SAE J53 . . . .   **4**:40.305

Engineering Design Serviceability Guide Lines—Construction and Industrial Machinery—SAE J817a . .   **4**:40.307

Format for Construction Equipment Manuals—SAE J920a **4**:40.313

Storage Batteries for Construction and Industrial Machinery—SAE J930b **4**:40.314

MARINE EQUIPMENT
41 Marine Equipment

† Marine Propeller-Shaft Couplings—SAE J756 AUG81   **4**:41.01

Marine Push-Pull Control Cables—SAE J917 JUN80   **4**:41.02

Marine Control Cable Connection—Engine Clutch Lever—SAE J960 JUN80 . . . .   **4**:41.03

Marine Control Cable Connection—Engine Throttle Lever—SAE J961 JUN80 . . . .   **4**:41.04

† Static Electric Outboard Thrust—SAE J1286 NOV81   **4**:41.04

Marine Propeller-Shaft Ends and Hubs—SAE J755 JUN80 . . . .   **4**:41.05

Marine Engine Mountings Direct Drive Transmission—SAE J233 JUN80 . . . .   **4**:41.08

External Ignition Protection of Marine Electrical Devices—SAE J1171 . . . .   **4**:41.08

Marine Engine Rating Code—SAE J1228 MAR80 . .   **4**:41.11

Ignition Distributors—Marine—SAE J1294 APR80 .   **4**:41.15

Marine Engine Wiring—SAE J378c **4**:41.16

High Tension Ignition Cable Assemblies—Marine—SAE J1191 . . . .   **4**:41.19

Marine Carburetors—SAE J1223 DEC80 . . . .   **4**:41.21

Marine Electrical Switches—SAE J1320 JUN81 . . .   **4**:41.22

NOTE: Page numbers shown include the volume number in bold followed by the section number and page number within that section.

NUMERICAL INDEX

NUMERICAL INDEX FOR SAE STANDARDS, RECOMMENDED PRACTICES, AND INFORMATION REPORTS

Each surface vehicle Standard, Recommended Practice, or Information Report has a designation consisting of the letter "J" combined with a number. The letter "J" is combined with a nonsignificant number to eliminate any possible confusion between the report number and the SAE numbers within the reports.

The page number shown for each document includes the volume number in bold followed by the section number and page number within that section.

Effective with the 1981 SAE Handbook, revisions of reports are now indicated by the month and year of revision, for example, J1159 AUG79. This new system will be phased in over a five year period. A lower case "a," "b," etc., appended to the report designation number indicates successive revisions of older reports.

Special Note:

Reports which have been cancelled and superseded, and the superseding documents, are listed by J number following this index.

Reports which have been cancelled and not replaced after 1977 are also listed by J number following this index.

SAE J NO.

10 SEP80	Automotive and Off-Highway Air Brake Reservoir Performance and Identification Requirements	2:22.131
17 OCT79	Latex Foam Rubbers	1:11.37
18 DEC79	Sponge- and Expanded Cellular-Rubber Products	1:11.40
19 NOV80	Latex Dipped Goods and Coatings for Automotive Applications	1:11.45
20e	Coolant System Hoses	1:11.123
30 JUN82	Fuel and Oil Hoses	1:11.127
31	Hydraulic Backhoe Lift Capacity	4:40.220
32a	Service Performance Requirements for Sealed Beam Headlamp Units for Motor Vehicles	2:21.33
33a	Snowmobile Definitions and Nomenclature—General	4:38.01
34a	Exterior Sound Level Measurement Procedure for Pleasure Motorboats	3:26.29
35	Diesel Smoke Measurement Procedure	3:25.51
38	Lift Arm Safety Device for Loaders	4:40.234
39	T-Hook Slots for Securement in Shipment of Agricultural Equipment	4:39.37
43	Axle Rating for Industrial Wheel Loaders and Loader-Backhoes	4:40.222
44	Service Brake System Performance Requirements—Snowmobiles	4:38.11
45	Brake System Test Procedure—Snowmobiles	4:38.11
46 JUN80	Wheel Slip Brake Control System Road Test Code	2:22.134
47	Maximum Sound Level Potential for Motorcycles	3:26.01
48	Guidelines for Fluid Level Indicators	4:40.69
49 APR80	Specification Definitions—Hydraulic Backhoes	4:40.50
50a	Windshield Wiper Hose	1:11.139
51b	Automotive Air Conditioning Hose	1:11.139
53	Minimum Performance Criteria for Emergency Steering of Wheeled Earthmoving Construction Machines	4:40.305
56	Electrical Generating System (Alternator Type) Performance Curve and Test Procedure	2:20.18
57 JUL81	Sound Level of Highway Truck Tires	3:26.21
58	Flanged 12-Point Screws	2:13.42
59	Fuel Injection Nozzle Gaskets	3:24.88

SAE J NO.

63 FEB80	Hole Placement on Dozer End Bits	4:40.158
64 FEB81	Vehicle Identification Numbers—Snowmobile and All-Terrain Vehicles	4:38.03
67 OCT80	Shovel Dipper, Clam Bucket, and Dragline Bucket Rating	4:40.216
68 OCT79	Tests for Snowmobile Switching Devices and Components	4:38.08
71a	Central Fluid Systems	3:23.23
75	Motor Vehicle Brake Fluid Container Compatibility	2:22.50
76	Handling and Dispensing of Motor Vehicle Brake Fluid	2:22.51
77	Service Maintenance of Motor Vehicle Brake Fluid in Motor Vehicle Brake Actuating Systems	2:22.53
78 JUN79	Steel Self-Drilling Tapping Screws	1:4.21
79	Brake Disc and Drum Thermocouple Installation	2:22.133
80 MAY82	Automotive Rubber Mats	1:11.104
81 JUN79	Thread Rolling Screws	1:4.26
82 JUN79	Mechanical and Quality Requirements for Machine Screws	1:4.14
88 SEP80	Sound Measurement—Earthmoving Machinery—Exterior	3:26.57
89a	Dynamic Cushioning Performance Criteria for Snowmobile Seats	4:38.13
90b	Nonmetallic Automotive Gasket Materials	1:11.105
92	Snowmobile Throttle Control Systems	4:38.18
93	Snowmobile and All-Terrain Vehicle Pulley Guards and Shields	4:38.15
94 APR80	Combination Tail and Floodlamp for Industrial Equipment	4:40.182
95 APR80	Headlamps for Industrial Equipment	4:40.182
96	Flashing Warning Lamp for Industrial Equipment	4:40.181
97	Nomenclature for Exhaust System Parts	3:24.117
98 DEC80	Safety for Industrial Wheeled Equipment	4:40.278
99 APR80	Lighting and Marking of Industrial Equipment on Highways	4:40.183
100	Passenger Car Glazing Shade Bands	4:34.40
101 MAR80	Hydraulic Wheel Cylinders for Automotive Drum Brakes	2:22.21
102	Square Head Setscrews	2:13.41
103	Lag Screws	2:13.46
104	Square and Hex Nuts	2:13.47

NOTE: Page numbers shown include the volume number in bold followed by the section number and page number within that section.

SAE J NO.

105	Hex Bolts	2:13.01
107 APR80	Operator Controls and Displays on Motorcycles	4:37.01
108a	Brake System Road Test Code—Motorcycles	2:22.116
109a	Service Brake System Performance Requirements—Motorcycles and Motor-Driven Cycles	2:22.118
110c	Seals—Testing of Radial Lip	4:29.57
111c	Seals—Terminology of Radial Lip	4:29.38
112a	Electric Windshield Wiper Switch	2:20.69
113	Hard Drawn Mechanical Spring Wire and Springs	1:5.04
114	Seat Belt Assembly Webbing Abrasion Test Requirements	4:33.12
115 SEP79	Safety Signs	4:40.285
116a	Gas Turbine Engine Test Code	3:24.16
117	Dynamic Test Procedure—Type 1 and Type 2 Seat Belt Assemblies	4:33.04
118a	Formerly Standard SAE Carbon Steels	1:1.16
119 JAN82	Fiberboard Crease Bending Test	1:11.86
120a	Rubber Rings for Automotive Applications	1:11.112
121a	Decarburization in Hardened and Tempered Threaded Fasteners	1:4.44
122a	Surface Discontinuities on Nuts	1:4.40
123c	Surface Discontinuities on Bolts, Screws, and Studs	1:4.37
125	Elevated Temperature Properties of Cast Irons	1:6.08
126 JUN81	Selecting and Specifying Hot and Cold Rolled Steel Sheet and Strip	1:3.19
128	Occupant Restraint System Evalution—Passenger Cars	4:33.12
129 DEC81	Engine and Transmission Identification Numbers	4:27.03
131a	Motorcycle Turn Signal Lamps	2:21.42
132	Oil Tempered Chromium-Vanadium Valve Spring Quality Wire and Springs	1:5.03
133 JAN82	Fifth Wheel Kingpin Performance—Commercial Trailers and Semitrailers	4:36.46
134 JUN79	Brake System Road Test Code—Passenger Car and Light Duty Truck-Trailer Combinations	2:22.97
135a	Service Brake System Performance Requirements—Passenger Car—Trailer Combinations	2:22.106
137c	Lighting and Marking of Agricultural Equipment on Highways	4:39.39
138	Film Analysis Guides for Dynamic Studies of Test Subjects	4:34.135
139	Ignition System Nomenclature and Terminology	2:20.01
140a	Seat Belt Hardware Test Procedure	4:33.01
141	Seat Belt Hardware Performance Requirements	4:33.03
151	Pressure Relief for Cooling System	3:24.102
153	Safety Considerations for the Operator	4:40.277
154a	Operator Enclosures Human Factor Design Considerations	4:40.270
155	Service Brake System Performance Requirements—Light-Duty Truck	2:22.94
156a	Fusible Links	2:20.55
157	Oil Tempered Chromium–Silicon Alloy Steel Wire and Springs	1:5.05
158a	Automotive Malleable Iron Castings	1:6.04
159 OCT80	Crane Load Moment System	4:40.147
160 JUN80	Swell, Growth, and Dimensional Stability of Brake Linings	2:22.62
161a	Selection of Tires for Multipurpose Passenger Vehicles, Light-, Medium-, and Heavy-Duty Trucks, Buses, Trailers, and Semitrailers for Normal Highway Service	4:30.16

SAE J NO.

162a	Flywheels for Single Bearing Engine Mounted Power Generators	4:40.170
163	Low Tension Wiring and Cable Terminals and Splice Clips	2:20.48
164 MAR82	Radiator Caps and Filler Necks	3:24.120
167 JUN81	Overhead Protection for Agricultural Tractors—Test Procedures and Performance Requirements	4:39.56
169 APR80	Design Guidelines for Air Conditioning Systems for Construction and Industrial Equipment Cabs	4:40.301
170a	Measurement of Fuel Evaporative Emissions from Gasoline Powered Passenger Cars and Light Trucks	3:25.78
171 JUN82	Measurement of Fuel Evaporative Emissions from Gasoline Powered Passenger Cars and Light Trucks Using the Enclosure Technique	3:25.84
172	Hard Drawn Carbon Steel Valve Spring Quality Wire and Springs	1:5.06
173 JAN80	Specification Definitions—Dozers	4:40.26
174	Torque-Tension Test Procedure for Steel Threaded Fasteners	2:13.76
175	Wheels—Passenger Cars—Impact Performance Requirements and Test Procedures	4:31.02
176a	Dry-Break Fueling Installation for Construction Machinery	4:40.69
177 APR82	Measurement of Carbon Dioxide, Carbon Monoxide, and Oxides of Nitrogen in Diesel Exhaust	3:25.01
178	Music Steel Spring Wire and Springs	1:5.09
179a	Labeling—Disc Wheels and Demountable Rims—Trucks	4:31.12
180 APR80	Electrical Charging Systems for Construction and Industrial Machinery	4:40.186
182a	Motor Vehicle Fiducial Marks	4:34.121
183 FEB80	Engine Oil Performance and Engine Service Classification	3:23.01
184a	Qualifying a Sound Data Acquisition System	3:26.07
185 JUN81	Access Systems for Off-Road Machines	4:40.260
186a	Supplemental High Mounted Stop and Rear Turn Signal Lamps	2:21.52
187	Truck Vehicle Identification Numbers	4:27.05
188	Power Steering Pressure Hose—High Volumetric Expansion Type	1:11.134
189	Power Steering Return Hose—Low Pressure	1:11.135
190	Power Steering Pressure Hose—Wire Braid	1:11.138
191	Power Steering Pressure Hose—Low Volumetric Expansion Type	1:11.137
192 APR80	Exterior Sound Level for Snowmobiles	3:26.25
193 SEP79	Ball Stud and Socket Assembly Test Procedure	2:14.06
195	Automatic Vehicle Speed Control—Motor Vehicles	2:18.12
196 JUN80	Electric Tachometer Specification—On Road	2:18.08
197	Electric Tachometer Specification—Off Road	2:18.10
198	Windshield Wiper Systems—Trucks, Buses, and Multipurpose Vehicles	4:34.09
200 APR80	Classification System for Rubber Materials for Automotive Applications	1:11.01
201	In-Service Brake Performance Test Procedure Passenger Car and Light-Duty Truck	2:22.57
202	Synthetic Skins for Automotive Testing	4:34.124
207	Electroplating of Nickel and Chromium on Metal Parts—Automotive Ornamentation and Hardware	1:10.137
208d	Safety for Agricultural Equipment	4:39.44

NOTE: Page numbers shown include the volume number in bold followed by the section number and page number within that section.

SAE J NO.

209 APR80	Instrument Face Design and Location for Construction and Industrial Equipment	**4**:40.272
210	Wiring Identification System for Industrial and Construction Equipment	**4**:40.192
211 JUN80	Instrumentation for Impact Tests	**4**:34.137
212 JUN80	Brake System Dynamometer Test Procedure—Passenger Car	**2**:22.90
213a	Definitions—Motorcycles	**4**:37.01
214 OCT80	Hydraulic Cylinder Test Procedure	**4**:40.94
215 JAN80	Continuous Hydrocarbon Analysis of Diesel Emissions	**3**:25.21
216	Passenger Car Glazing—Electrical Circuits	**4**:34.40
217	Stainless Steel 17-7 PH Spring Wire and Springs	**1**:5.07
218 DEC81	Passenger Car Identification Terminology	**4**:27.02
220 OCT80	Crane Boomstop	**4**:40.144
222a	Parking Lamps (Front Position Lamps)	**2**:21.62
223 APR80	Symbols and Color Codes for Maintenance Instructions, Container and Filler Identification	**4**:40.70
224 MAR80	Collision Deformation Classification	**4**:34.125
225 JUN80	Brake System Torque Balance Test Code—Commercial Vehicles	**2**:22.125
226a	Engine Preheaters	**3**:24.116
227a	Electric Vehicle Test Procedure	**4**:28.09
228 JAN80	Carburetor Airflow Reference Standards	**3**:24.118
229 JUN80	Service Brake Structural Integrity Test Procedure—Passenger Car	**2**:22.96
230	Stainless Steel, SAE 30302, Spring Wire and Springs	**1**:5.08
231 JAN81	Minimum Performance Criteria for Falling Object Protective Structure (FOPS)	**4**:40.245
232	Industrial Rotary Mowers	**4**:40.281
233 JUN80	Marine Engine Mountings Direct Drive Transmission	**4**:41.08
234	Electric Windshield Washer Switch	**2**:20.69
235	Electric Blower Motor Switch	**2**:20.70
238	Nut and Conical Spring Washer Assemblies	**2**:13.74
240 JUN82	Life Test for Automotive Storage Batteries	**2**:20.11
242a	Metric Thread Fuel Injection Tubing Connections	**3**:24.93
243	Methods of Tests for Automotive-Type Sealers, Adhesives, and Deadeners	**1**:11.46
244	Measurement of Intake Air or Exhaust Gas Flow of Diesel Engines	**3**:25.11
246 MAR81	Spherical and Flanged Sleeve (Compression) Tube Fittings	**2**:19.18
247 JUN80	Instrumentation for Measuring Acoustic Impulses Within Vehicles	**3**:26.05
249	Mechanical Stop Lamp Switch	**2**:21.44
250	Synthetic Resin Plastic Sealers, Nondrying Type	**1**:11.45
253	Headlamp Switch	**2**:21.65
254	Instrumentation and Techniques for Exhaust Gas Emissions Measurement	**3**:25.93
255a	Diesel Engine Smoke Measurement	**3**:25.32
256b	Service Performance Requirements for Motor Vehicle Lighting Devices and Components	**2**:21.28
257 JUN80	Brake Rating Horsepower Requirements—Commercial Vehicles	**2**:22.127
258	Circuit Breaker—Internal Mounted—Automatic Reset	**2**:20.39
259	Ignition Switch	**2**:20.39
260 JUN80	Rear Underride Guard Test Procedure	**4**:34.152
261	Muffler Parts Nomenclature	**3**:24.115
262	Resonator Parts Nomenclature	**3**:24.115
263 SEP80	Emergency Air Brake Systems—Motor Vehicles and Vehicle Combinations	**2**:22.128
264	Vision Glossary	**4**:34.119

SAE J NO.

265	Diesel Fuel Injection Nozzle and Holder Assembly (17 mm Nominal Diameter)	**3**:24.88
267a	Wheels/Rims—Trucks—Test Procedures and Performance Requirements	**4**:31.05
268 MAY82	Rear View Mirrors—Motorcycles	**4**:37.03
271	Special Quality High Tensile, Hard Drawn Mechanical Spring Wire and Springs	**1**:5.04
272 DEC81	Vehicle Identification Number Systems	**4**:27.01
273 DEC81	Passenger Car Vehicle Identification Number System	**4**:27.02
274	Rated Spring Capacity	**2**:17.15
275	Test Method for Determining Window Fogging Resistance of Interior Trim Materials	**1**:11.62
276 JUN81	Steering Frame Lock for Articulated Loaders and Tractors	**4**:40.234
277	Maintenance of Design Voltage—Snowmobile Electrical Systems	**4**:38.04
278	Snowmobile Stop Lamp	**4**:38.05
279	Snowmobile Tail Lamp (Rear Position Lamp)	**4**:38.06
280	Snowmobile Headlamps	**4**:38.04
281 SEP80	Cast Iron Sealing Rings	**4**:29.61
283	Test Procedure for Measuring Hydraulic Lift Force Capacity on Agricultural Tractors Equipped with Three-Point Hitch	**4**:39.22
284a	Safety Alert Symbol for Agricultural, Construction and Industrial Equipment	**4**:39.43
285 JUL81	Gasoline Dispenser Nozzle Spouts	**3**:24.156
286	Clutch Friction Test Machine (SAE No. 2)—Test Procedure	**4**:29.35
287 FEB80	Driver Hand Control Reach	**4**:34.72
288a	Metallic and Nonmetallic Nonpressure Integral Fuel Tank—Snowmobile	**4**:38.17
291 JUN80	Determination of Brake Fluid Temperature	**2**:22.133
292	Snowmobile and Snowmobile Cutter Lamps, Reflective Devices, and Associated Equipment	**4**:38.07
293	Vehicle Grade Parking Performance Requirements	**2**:22.74
294	Service Brake Structural Integrity Test Procedure—Vehicles Over 10 000 LB (4500 kg) GVWR	**2**:22.114
296 OCT80	Excavator Hoe Bucket Rating	**4**:40.219
297 APR80	Operator Controls on Industrial Equipment	**4**:40.276
298	Universal Symbols for Operator Controls on Industrial Equipment	**4**:40.274
299 JAN80	Stopping Distance Test Procedure	**2**:22.132
300 SEP80	Engine Oil Viscosity Classification	**3**:23.05
301	Effective Dates of Revisions	**3**:23.01
304 JUN82	Engine Oil Tests	**3**:23.09
306 MAY81	Axle and Manual Transmission Lubricant Viscosity Classification	**3**:23.16
308c	Axle and Manual Transmission Lubricants	**3**:23.15
310 MAR80	Automotive Lubricating Greases	**3**:23.17
311b	Fluid for Passenger Car Type Automatic Transmissions	**3**:23.20
312 JUN82	Automotive Gasolines	**3**:23.25
313 APR82	Diesel Fuels	**3**:23.34
314 MAY81	Felts—Wool and Part Wool	**1**:11.102
315 SEP80	Fiberboard Test Procedure	**1**:11.78
316	Oil Tempered Carbon Steel Spring Wire and Springs	**1**:5.01
318 SEP80	Air Brake Gladhand Service (Control) and Emergency (Supply) Line Couplers—Trucks, Truck-Tractors, and Trailers	**2**:22.130
321b	Tire Guards for Protection of Operator of Earthmoving Haulage Machines	**4**:40.233
322	Nonmetallic Trim Materials—Test Method for Determining the Staining Resistance to Hydrogen Sulfide Gas	**1**:11.61

NOTE: Page numbers shown include the volume number in bold followed by the section number and page number within that section.

SAE J NO.

323	Test Method for Determining Cold Cracking of Flexible Plastic Materials	**1**:11.60
326 SEP80	Nomenclature—Hydraulic Backhoes . .	**4**:40.218
327	Ignition Timing	**3**:24.23
328a	Wheels—Passenger Cars—Performance Requirements and Test Procedures .	**4**:31.01
331a	Sound Levels for Motorcycles	**3**:26.02
332 AUG81	Testing Machines for Measuring the Uniformity of Passenger Car and Light Truck Tires	**4**:30.14
335b	Multiposition Small Engine Exhaust System Fire Ignition Suppression	**3**:24.102
336a	Sound Level for Truck Cab Interior . . .	**3**:26.19
337	Brake Flange Mounting—On-Highway Vehicles	**4**:36.54
339a	Seat Belt Assembly Webbing Abrasion Test Procedure	**4**:33.12
341a	Truck and Bus Tire Performance Requirements and Test Procedures . . .	**4**:30.17
342 NOV80	Spark Arrester Test Procedure for Large Size Engines	**3**:24.105
343 JUN80	Tests and Procedures for SAE 100R Series Hydraulic Hose and Hose Assemblies	**2**:19.105
344	Lawn and Garden Tractors Load and Inflation Pressures and Tire Selection Table for Future Design	**4**:39.14
345a	Wet or Dry Pavement Passenger Car Tire Peak and Locked Wheel Braking Traction	**4**:30.12
347a	Diesel Fuel Injection Nozzle Holder Assembly (9.5 mm)	**3**:24.87
348	Wheel Chocks	**4**:36.62
349 JUN80	Detection of Surface Imperfections in Ferrous Rods, Bars, Tubes, and Wires	**1**:3.42
350 JAN80	Spark Arrester Test Procedure for Medium Size Engines	**3**:24.109
351	Oil Tempered Carbon Steel Valve Spring Quality Wire and Springs	**1**:5.02
356 JAN80	Welded Flash Controlled Low Carbon Steel Tubing Normalized for Bending, Double Flaring, and Beading	**2**:19.118
357a	Physical and Chemical Properties of Engine Oils	**3**:23.11
358 JAN80	Nondestructive Tests	**1**:3.45
359 JUN81	Infrared Testing	**1**:3.47
360	Motor Vehicle Grade Parking Performance Test Code	**2**:22.73
361a	Test Method for Determining Visual Color Match to Master Specimen for Fabrics, Vinyls, Coated Fiberboards, and Other Automotive Trim Materials	**1**:11.99
362 JUL82	Vehicle Hood Latch Systems	**4**:34.05
363 FEB80	Filter Base Mounting	**3**:24.73
364a	Vehicle Identification Numbers—Motorcycles	**4**:27.03
365a	Method of Testing Resistance to Scuffing of Trim Materials	**1**:11.83
366b	Exterior Sound Level for Heavy Trucks and Buses	**3**:26.18
367 JUN80	Passenger Car Door System Crush Test Procedure	**4**:34.148
368a	High Strength, Quenched, and Tempered Structural Steels	**1**:1.79
369a	Flammability of Automotive Interior Materials—Horizontal Test Method	**1**:11.96
370	Bolt and Capscrew Sizes for Use in Construction and Industrial Machinery . .	**2**:13.101
371a	Drain, Fill, and Level Plugs for Earthmoving Machinery	**4**:40.173
372a	LP-Gas Fuel Systems Components . . .	**3**:24.101
373a	Housing Internal Dimensions for Single and Two Plate Spring Loaded Clutches	**3**:24.72

SAE J NO.

374 JUN80	Passenger Car Roof Crush Test Procedure	**4**:34.147
375 OCT80	Radius-of-Load and Boom Angle Measuring System	**4**:40.145
376 OCT80	Load Indicating Devices in Lifting Crane Service	**4**:40.146
377	Performance of Vehicle Traffic Horns . .	**3**:26.24
378c	Marine Engine Wiring	**4**:41.16
379a	Gogan Hardness of Brake Lining	**2**:22.60
380	Specific Gravity of Brake Lining	**2**:22.61
381	Windshield Defrosting Systems Test Procedure—Trucks, Buses, and Multipurpose Vehicles	**4**:34.15
382	Windshield Defrosting Systems Performance Requirements—Trucks, Buses, and Multipurpose Vehicles	**4**:34.17
383	Motor Vehicle Seat Belt Anchorages—Design Recommendations	**4**:33.06
384	Motor Vehicle Seat Belt Anchorages Test Procedure	**4**:33.08
385	Motor Vehicle Seat Belt Anchorages—Performance Requirements	**4**:33.09
386 APR80	Seat Belts for Construction Machines . .	**4**:40.283
387	Terminology—Motor Vehicle Lighting .	**2**:21.01
388	Dynamic Flex Fatigue Test for Slab Polyurethane Foam	**4**:34.34
389b	Universal Symbols for Operator Controls on Agricultural Equipment	**4**:39.47
391 JUL81	Definition for Particle Size	**1**:3.56
392	Motorcycle and Motor Driven Cycle Electrical System (Maintenance of Design Voltage)	**2**:21.41
393	Nomenclature—Wheels and Rims—Trucks	**4**:31.13
397b	Deflection Limiting Volume—ROPS/FOPS Laboratory Evaluation	**4**:40.244
398b	Fuel Tank Filler Conditions—Passenger Car, Multi-Purpose Passenger Vehicles, and Light Duty Trucks	**3**:24.155
399a	Anodized Aluminum Automotive Parts .	**1**:10.27
400 JUN80	Test for Chip Resistance of Surface Coatings	**1**:11.64
401 APR81	Selection and Use of Steels	**1**:1.05
402 JUN81	SAE Numbering System for Wrought or Rolled Steel	**1**:1.07
403 SEP80	Chemical Compositions of SAE Carbon Steels	**1**:1.08
404 OCT80	Chemical Compositions of SAE Alloy Steels	**1**:1.11
405d	Chemical Compositions of SAE Wrought Stainless Steels	**1**:1.13
406c	Methods of Determining Hardenability of Steels	**1**:1.17
408 JUN79	Methods of Sampling Steel for Chemical Analysis	**1**:1.71
409c	Permissible Variations from Specified Ladle Chemical Ranges and Limits for Steels	**1**:1.72
410c	High Strength, Low Alloy Steel	**1**:1.74
411 JUN81	Carbon and Alloy Steels	**1**:2.01
412h	General Characteristics and Heat Treatments of Steels	**1**:2.05
413b	Mechanical Properties of Heat Treated Wrought Steels	**1**:2.13
414a	Estimated Mechanical Properties and Machinability of Hot Rolled and Cold Drawn Carbon Steel Bars	**1**:2.15
415 JUN82	Definitions of Heat Treating Terms . . .	**1**:2.21
416 JUN79	Tensile Test Specimens	**1**:3.01
417b	Hardness Tests and Hardness Number Conversions	**1**:3.03
418a	Grain Size Determination of Steels . . .	**1**:3.07
419	Methods of Measuring Decarburization	**1**:3.10
420 MAR81	Magnetic Particle Inspection	**1**:3.47

NOTE: Page numbers shown include the volume number in bold followed by the section number and page number within that section.

SAE J NO.

421 APR82	Cleanliness Rating of Steels by the Magnetic Particle Method	**1**:3.37
422 JUN79	Microscopic Determination of Inclusions in Steels	**1**:3.39
423a	Methods of Measuring Case Depth	**1**:3.43
424 OCT81	Method for Determining Breakage Allowances for Sheet Steel	**1**:3.45
425 MAR81	Eddy Current Testing by Electromagnetic Methods	**1**:3.48
426c	Liquid Penetrant Test Methods	**1**:3.52
427b	Penetrating Radiation Inspection	**1**:3.53
428b	Ultrasonic Inspection	**1**:3.55
429 JAN80	Mechanical and Material Requirements for Externally Threaded Fasteners	**1**:4.01
430	Mechanical and Chemical Requirements for Nonthreaded Fasteners	**1**:4.18
431 AUG79	Automotive Gray Iron Castings	**1**:6.01
434c	Automotive Ductile (Nodular) Iron Castings	**1**:6.06
435c	Automotive Steel Castings	**1**:6.12
437a	Selection and Heat Treatment of Tool and Die Steels	**1**:7.02
438b	Tool and Die Steels	**1**:7.01
439a	Sintered Carbide Tools	**1**:7.07
441	Cut Steel Wire Shot	**1**:8.05
442 AUG79	Test Strip, Holder and Gage for Shot Peening	**1**:8.05
443	Procedures for Using Standard Shot Peening Test Strip	**1**:8.07
444a	Cast Shot and Grit Size Specifications for Peening and Cleaning	**1**:8.09
445a	Metallic Shot and Grit Mechanical Testing	**1**:8.10
446a	Preferred Thicknesses for Uncoated Flat Metals (Thru 12 mm)	**1**:9.07
448a	Surface Texture	**1**:9.03
449a	Surface Texture Control	**1**:9.05
450	Use of the Terms Yield Point and Yield Strength	**1**:9.01
451b	Aluminum Alloys—Fundamentals	**1**:10.01
452c	General Information on SAE Aluminum Casting Alloys	**1**:10.05
453c	Chemical Compositions and Mechanical and Physical Properties of SAE Aluminum Casting Alloys	**1**:10.08
454 JUL81	General Data on Wrought Aluminum Alloys	**1**:10.11
457j	Chemical Compositions, Mechanical Property Limits, and Dimensional Tolerances of SAE Wrought Aluminum Alloys	**1**:10.26
459c	Bearing and Bushing Alloys (Information Report)	**1**:10.28
460e	Bearing and Bushing Alloys (Standard)	**1**:10.28
461 SEP81	Wrought and Cast Copper Alloys	**1**:10.30
462 SEP81	Cast Copper Alloys	**1**:10.64
463 SEP81	Wrought Copper and Copper Alloys	**1**:10.67
464c	Magnesium Alloys	**1**:10.106
465c	Magnesium Casting Alloys	**1**:10.106
466c	Magnesium Wrought Alloys	**1**:10.111
467b	Special Purpose Alloys ("Superalloys")	**1**:10.115
468b	Zinc Alloy Ingot and Die Casting Compositions	**1**:10.126
469a	Zinc Die Casting Alloys	**1**:10.127
470c	Wrought Nickel and Nickel-Related Alloys	**1**:10.127
471d	Sintered Powder Metal Parts: Ferrous	**1**:8.01
473a	Solders	**1**:10.142
474b	Electroplating and Related Finishes	**1**:10.143
475a	Screw Threads	**2**:12.01
476a	Dryseal Pipe Threads	**2**:12.01
478a	Slotted and Recessed Head Screws	**2**:13.07
479a	Slotted Headless Setscrews	**2**:13.40
481	Round Head Bolts	**2**:13.04

SAE J NO.

482a	Hexagon High Nuts	**2**:13.53
483a	Crown (Blind, Acorn) Nuts	**2**:13.54
484	Alignment of Nut Slots	**2**:13.54
485	Holes in Bolt and Capscrew Shanks and Slots in Nuts for Cotter Pins	**2**:13.79
487a	Cotter Pins	**2**:13.77
488	Plain Washers	**2**:13.68
489b	Lock Washers	**2**:13.68
490 OCT81	Ball Joints	**2**:14.08
491b	Ball Studs and Ball Stud Socket Assemblies	**2**:14.01
492	Rivets and Riveting	**2**:13.85
493	Rod Ends and Clevis Pins	**2**:13.84
494	Grooved Straight Pins	**2**:13.80
495	Straight Pins (Solid)	**2**:13.79
496	Spring Type Straight Pins	**2**:13.82
497	Unhardened Ground Dowel Pins	**2**:13.84
498c	Involute Splines and Inspections	**2**:15.01
499a	Parallel Side Splines for Soft Broached Holes in Fittings	**2**:15.01
500	Serrated Shaft Ends	**2**:15.03
501	Shaft Ends	**2**:15.04
502	Woodruff Keys	**2**:15.05
503	Woodruff Key Slots and Keyways	**2**:15.06
506b	Sleeve Type Half Bearings	**3**:24.38
510c	Leaf Springs for Motor Vehicle Suspension	**2**:17.01
511a	Pneumatic Spring Terminology	**2**:17.08
512 OCT80	Automotive Tube Fittings	**2**:19.04
513f	Refrigeration Tube Fittings	**2**:19.26
514 APR80	Hydraulic Tube Fittings	**2**:19.46
515a	Hydraulic "O" Ring	**2**:19.112
516 MAR81	Hydraulic Hose Fittings	**2**:19.72
517 JUN82	Hydraulic Hose	**2**:19.92
518c	Hydraulic Flanged Tube, Pipe, and Hose Connections, 4-Bolt Split Flange Type	**2**:19.107
521b	Fuel Injection Tubing Connections	**3**:24.94
524 JAN80	Seamless Low Carbon Steel Tubing Annealed for Bending and Flaring	**2**:19.115
525 JAN80	Welded and Cold Drawn Low Carbon Steel Tubing Annealed for Bending and Flaring	**2**:19.115
526 JAN80	Welded Low Carbon Steel Tubing	**2**:19.116
527 JAN80	Brazed Double Wall Low Carbon Steel Tubing	**2**:19.117
528 JAN80	Seamless Copper Tube	**2**:19.121
529b	Fuel Injection Tubing	**2**:19.127
530 JAN81	Automotive Pipe Fittings	**2**:19.128
531 JAN81	Automotive Pipe, Filler, and Drain Plugs	**2**:19.134
532 JAN81	Automotive Straight Thread Filler and Drain Plugs	**2**:19.138
533b	Flares for Tubing	**2**:19.113
534 JAN81	Lubrication Fittings	**2**:19.143
535 JAN80	Water Connection Flanges	**3**:24.74
536b	Hose Clamps	**2**:13.101
537 JUN82	Storage Batteries	**2**:20.04
538a	Grounding of Storage Batteries	**2**:20.12
539a	Voltages for Diesel Electrical Systems	**2**:20.12
541a	Voltage Drop for Starting Motor Circuits	**2**:20.12
542c	Starting Motor Mountings	**2**:20.13
543c	Starting Motor Pinions and Ring Gears	**2**:20.14
544 MAY82	Electric Starting Motor Test Procedure	**2**:20.16
545b	Generator Mountings	**2**:20.14
546	Magneto Mountings	**2**:20.19
548d	Spark Plugs	**2**:20.20
549 JUN82	Preignition Rating of Spark Plugs	**2**:20.26
551 JUN81	Performance Levels and Methods of Measurement of Electromagnetic Radiation from Vehicles and Devices (20–1000 MHz)	**2**:20.26
553c	Circuit Breakers	**2**:20.37
554b	Electric Fuses (Cartridge Type)	**2**:20.32
557	High Tension Ignition Cable	**2**:20.46

NOTE: Page numbers shown include the volume number in bold followed by the section number and page number within that section.

SAE J NO.

560b	Seven-Conductor Electrical Connector for Truck-Trailer Jumper Cable	**2**:20.60
561 JUN80	Electrical Terminals—Eyelet and Spade Type	**2**:20.64
562a	Nonmetallic Loom	**2**:20.68
563b	Six- and Twelve-Volt Cigar Lighter Receptacles	**2**:20.70
564c	Headlamp Beam Switching	**2**:21.04
565 JUN82	Semiautomatic Headlamp Beam Switching Devices	**2**:21.04
567c	Lamp Bulb Retention System	**2**:21.06
571 FEB81	Dimensional Specifications for Sealed Beam Headlamp Units	**2**:21.11
572a	Dimensional Specifications for Sealed Lighting Unit for Construction and Industrial Machinery	**4**:40.180
573g	Lamp Bulbs and Sealed Beam Headlamp Units	**2**:21.22
575 JUN80	Tests for Motor Vehicle Lighting Devices and Components	**2**:21.26
576 NOV81	Plastic Materials for Use in Optical Parts Such as Lenses and Reflectors of Motor Vehicle Lighting Devices	**2**:21.30
578d	Color Specification for Electric Signal Lighting Devices	**2**:21.30
579c	Sealed Beam Headlamp Units for Motor Vehicles	**2**:21.32
580 AUG79	Sealed Beam Headlamp Assembly . . .	**2**:21.34
581a	Auxiliary Driving Lamps	**2**:21.37
582 SEP81	Auxiliary Low Beam Lamp	**2**:21.38
583 MAY81	Front Fog Lamps	**2**:21.38
584b	Motorcycle Headlamps	**2**:21.39
585e	Tail Lamps (Rear Position Lamps)	**2**:21.42
586d	Stop Lamps	**2**:21.43
587 OCT81	License Plate Lamps (Rear Registration Plate Lamps)	**2**:21.45
588f	Turn Signal Lamps	**2**:21.46
589b	Turn Signal Switch	**2**:21.53
590e	Turn Signal Flashers	**2**:21.55
591b	Spot Lamps	**2**:21.62
592f	Clearance, Side Marker, and Identification Lamps	**2**:21.63
593 AUG81	Backup Lamps (Reversing Lamps)	**2**:21.64
594f	Reflex Reflectors	**2**:21.65
595b	Flashing Warning Lamps for Authorized Emergency, Maintenance and Service Vehicles	**2**:21.67
598 APR80	Sealed Lighting Units for Construction and Industrial Machinery	**4**:40.179
599 MAY81	Lighting Inspection Code	**2**:21.71
600 MAY81	Headlamp Testing Machines	**2**:21.73
602 OCT80	Headlamp Aiming Device for Mechanically Aimable Sealed Beam Headlamp Units	**2**:21.74
604d	Engine Terminology and Nomenclature—General	**3**:24.01
607a	Small Spark Ignition Engine Test Code .	**3**:24.14
609a	Mounting Flanges and Power Take-Off Shafts for Small Engines	**3**:24.18
610b	Valve Seat Inserts—Engine	**3**:24.20
614b	Engine and Transmission Dipstick Marking	**3**:24.68
615b	Engine Mountings	**3**:24.69
616c	Engine Foot Mounting (Front and Rear)	**4**:40.168
617c	Engine Flywheel Housings	**4**:40.166
618 JUN80	Flywheels for Single-Plate Spring-Loaded Clutches	**3**:24.70
619 JUN80	Flywheels for Two-Plate Spring-Loaded Clutches	**3**:24.71
620d	Flywheels for Industrial Engines Used with Industrial Power Take-Offs Equipped with Driving-Ring Type Overcenter Clutches and Engine Mounted Marine Gears	**4**:40.172

SAE J NO.

621d	Industrial Power Take-Offs with Driving Ring Type Overcenter Clutches	**4**:40.164
622 JAN80	Airflow or Vacuum Governor Flanges .	**3**:24.75
624a	Exhaust Flanges—Industrial Engines . .	**4**:40.170
625 JUL80	Fuel Pump Mountings for Diaphragm Type Pumps	**3**:24.77
626b	Diesel Fuel Injection Pump Mountings .	**3**:24.80
629b	Diesel Fuel Injection Nozzle Holder Assemblies	**3**:24.85
631 FEB82	Radiator Nomenclature	**3**:24.123
635a	Fan Hub Bolt-Circles and Pilot Holes . .	**3**:24.141
636c	V-Belts and Pulleys	**2**:16.01
637b	Automotive V-Belt Drives	**2**:16.04
638 JUN82	Motor Vehicle Heater Test Procedure .	**4**:34.20
639 OCT81	Safety Practices for Mechanical Vapor Compression Refrigeration Equipment or Systems Used to Cool Passenger Compartment of Motor Vehicles . . .	**4**:34.26
640 DEC81	Symbols for Hydrodynamic Drives . . .	**4**:29.01
641b	Hydrodynamic Drives Terminology . . .	**4**:29.02
643b	Hydrodynamic Drive Test Code	**4**:29.04
645c	Automotive Transmission Terminology .	**4**:29.07
646 JUL81	Planetary Gear(s)—Terminology	**4**:29.07
647 JUL81	Transmissions—Schematic Diagrams . .	**4**:29.08
648a	Automatic Transmission Hydraulic Control Systems—Terminology	**4**:29.09
649b	Automatic Transmission Functions—Terminology	**4**:29.09
651c	Passenger Car and Truck Automatic Transmission Test Code	**4**:29.10
654	Seals—Lathe Cut	**4**:29.60
656g	Automotive Brake Definitions and Nomenclature	**2**:22.55
659	Color Code for Location Identification of Combination Linings of Two Different Materials or Two Shoe Brakes	**2**:22.66
661a	Brake Lining Quality Control Test Procedure	**2**:22.63
662	Brake Block Chamfer	**2**:22.66
663b	Rivets for Brake Linings and Bolts for Brake Blocks	**2**:22.66
666	Brake Diaphragm Maintenance—Tractor and Semitrailer	**4**:36.56
667	Brake Test Code—Inertia Dynamometer	**2**:22.75
671 APR82	Vibration Damping Materials and Underbody Coatings	**1**:11.56
673b	Automotive Safety Glazing	**4**:34.36
674a	Safety Glazing Materials—Motor Vehicles	**4**:34.39
678e	Speedometers and Tachometers—Automotive	**2**:18.03
680 JUN82	Location and Operation of Instruments and Controls in Motor Truck Cabs . .	**4**:36.60
682	Rear Wheel Splash and Stone Throw Protection	**4**:36.60
683a	Tire Chain Clearance—Trucks, Buses, and Combinations of Vehicles	**4**:36.56
684f	Trailer Couplings, Hitches and Safety Chains—Automotive Type	**4**:35.01
686 JUL81	Motor Vehicle License Plates	**4**:27.06
687c	Nomenclature—Truck, Bus, Trailer . . .	**4**:36.01
688	Truck Ability Prediction Procedure . . .	**4**:36.02
689	Approach, Departure, and Ramp Breakover Angles—Passenger Car and Light Duty Trucks	**4**:32.03
690	Certificates of Maximum Net Horsepower for Motor Trucks and Truck Tractors	**4**:36.37
691	Motor Truck CA Dimensions	**4**:36.38
693a	Truck Overall Widths Across Dual Tires	**4**:36.53
694a	Commercial Vehicle Disc Wheels	**4**:36.52
695b	Turning Ability and Off Tracking—Motor Vehicles	**4**:36.39

NOTE: Page numbers shown include the volume number in bold followed by the section number and page number within that section.

SAE J NO.

697a	Safety Chain of Full Trailers or Converter Dollies	**4**:36.51
699a	Average Vehicle Dimensions for Use in Designing Docking Facilities for Motor Vehicles	**4**:36.39
700 JAN82	Fifth Wheel Kingpin—Commercial Trailers and Semitrailers	**4**:36.48
701a	Truck Tractor Semitrailer Interchange Coupling Dimensions	**4**:36.43
702b	Brake and Electrical Connection Locations—Truck-Tractor and Truck-Trailer	**4**:36.55
704b	Openings for Six- and Eight-Bolt Truck Transmission Mounted Power Take-Offs	**4**:29.16
705b	Rating of Truck Power Take-Offs	**4**:36.59
706a	Rating of Winches	**4**:36.58
708 JUN80	Agricultural Tractor Test Code	**4**:39.01
709d	Agricultural Tractor Tire Loadings, Torque Factors, and Inflation Pressures	**4**:39.05
711c	Tire Selection Tables for Agricultural and Light Industrial Machines of Future Design	**4**:39.12
712a	Industrial and Agricultural Disc Wheels	**4**:39.32
714b	Wheel Mounting Elements for Industrial and Agricultural Disc Wheels	**4**:39.36
715 MAY80	Three-Point Free-Link Hitch Attachment of Implements to Agricultural Wheeled Tractors	**4**:39.19
716a	Application of Hydraulic Remote Control to Agricultural Tractors and Trailing Type Agricultural Implements	**4**:39.24
717 MAY80	Auxiliary Power Take-Off Drives for Agricultural Tractors	**4**:39.31
720 MAY80	Tractor Belt Speed and Pulley Width	**4**:39.32
721 JUN80	Operating Requirements for Tractors and Power Take-Off Driven Implements	**4**:39.30
722 MAY80	Power Take-Off Definitions and Terminology for Agricultural Tractors	**4**:39.32
725 MAY80	Mounting Brackets and Socket for Warning Lamp and Slow-Moving Vehicle (SMV) Identification Emblem	**4**:39.41
726 MAY81	Air Cleaner Test Code	**3**:24.58
727 MAY80	Component Nomenclature—Crawler Tractor	**4**:40.18
728a	Component Nomenclature—Scrapers	**4**:40.21
729 MAY80	Nomenclature—Dozer	**4**:40.24
731d	Component Nomenclature—Loader	**4**:40.27
732 FEB80	Specification Definitions—Loaders	**4**:40.48
733b	Nomenclature—Rippers, Rooters, Scarifiers	**4**:40.33
734c	Component Nomenclature—Dumper Trailer	**4**:40.34
737b	Hole Spacing for Scraper and Bulldozer Cutting Edges	**4**:40.158
738b	Scraper and Bulldozer Cutting Edge Cross Sections, Rolled, Cast, Forged or Machined	**4**:40.160
739b	Grader Cutting Edge	**4**:40.160
740b	Countersunk Square Holes for Cutting Edges and End Bits	**4**:40.163
741b	Capacity Ratings—Scraper, Dumper Body and Trailer Body	**4**:40.215
742 OCT79	Capacity Rating—Loader Bucket	**4**:40.217
743 DEC80	Pipelayers and Side Booms, Tractor-Mounted—Specifications and Test	**4**:40.153
744 OCT80	Hydraulic Power Pumps	**4**:40.78
745 OCT80	Hydraulic Power Pump Test Procedure	**4**:40.76
746 OCT80	Hydraulic Motor Test Procedure	**4**:40.87
747 OCT80	Hydraulic Control Valve Test Procedure	**4**:40.89
748 OCT80	Hydraulic Directional Control Valves, 3000 psi Maximum	**4**:40.80
749a	Drawbars—Crawler Tractor	**4**:40.214
751 APR80	Off-Highway Tire and Rim Classification	**4**:40.203

SAE J NO.

752b	Maintenance Interval—Construction Equipment	**4**:40.68
753 JUN82	Lubrication Chart—Construction and Industrial Machinery	**4**:40.67
754a	Lubricant Types—Construction and Industrial Machinery	**4**:40.67
755 JUN80	Marine Propeller-Shaft Ends and Hubs	**4**:41.05
756 AUG81	Marine Propeller-Shaft Couplings	**4**:41.01
759 MAR82	Lighting Identification Code	**2**:21.03
760a	Dimensional Specifications for General Service Sealed Lighting Units	**2**:21.20
763 JAN82	Aging of Carbon Steel Sheet and Strip	**1**:2.20
764 APR80	Loading Ability Test Code—Scrapers	**4**:40.108
765 OCT80	Crane Load Stability Test Code	**4**:40.142
770c	Alloy Steel Machinability Ratings	**1**:2.24
771c	Automotive Printed Circuits	**2**:20.42
772a	Clearance Envelopes for Six- and Eight-Bolt Truck Transmission Mounted Power Take-Offs	**4**:29.15
773b	Conical Spring Washers	**2**:13.73
774c	Emergency Warning Device	**2**:21.66
775 JUL80	Engine Poppet Valve Materials	**1**:1.80
778 OCT80	Formerly Standard SAE Alloy Steels	**1**:1.15
780a	Engine Coolant Pump Seals	**3**:24.142
786a	Brake System Road Test Code—Truck, Bus, and Combination of Vehicles	**2**:22.107
800c	Motor Vehicle Seat Belt Assembly Installations	**4**:33.10
810 JUN80	Classification of Common Imperfections in Sheet Steel	**1**:3.24
813	Automotive Air Brake Reservoir Volume	**2**:22.129
814c	Engine Coolants	**1**:11.118
815 MAY81	Load Deflection Testing of Urethane Foams for Automotive Seating	**4**:34.36
817a	Engineering Design Serviceability Guide Lines—Construction and Industrial Machinery	**4**:40.307
818b	Operating Load for Loaders	**4**:40.66
819 MAR80	Engine Cooling System Field Test (Air-to-Boil)	**4**:40.106
820 OCT80	Crane Hoist Line Speed and Power Test Code	**4**:40.141
821a	Electrical System for Construction and Industrial Machinery	**4**:40.184
823c	Flasher Test Equipment	**2**:21.77
824	Engine Rotation and Cylinder Numbering	**3**:24.24
826 APR80	Devices for Use in Defining and Measuring Vehicle Seating Accommodation	**4**:34.27
827	Cast Steel Shot	**1**:8.08
828 JAN80	Gas Turbine Engine Nomenclature	**3**:24.02
829c	Fuel Tank Filler Cap and Cap Retainer	**3**:24.151
830b	Fuel Injection Equipment Nomenclature	**3**:24.78
831	Nomenclature—Automotive Electrical Systems	**2**:20.01
832	Locating Ledge for Flat Pad Engine Mountings	**3**:24.69
833 JAN80	USA Human Physical Dimensions	**4**:40.255
834a	Passenger Car Rear Vision	**4**:34.45
835 DEC81	Split Type Bushings—Design and Application	**3**:24.45
839 JUL82	Passenger Car Side Door Latch Systems	**4**:34.02
840c	Test Procedures for Brake Shoe and Lining Adhesives and Bonds	**2**:22.67
841 MAY80	Operator Controls on Agricultural Equipment	**4**:39.46
843d	Brake System Road Test Code—Passenger Car and Light-Duty Truck	**2**:22.77
844 OCT80	Nonmetallic Air Brake System Tubing	**2**:19.124
845	360 Deg Emergency Warning Lamp	**2**:21.68
846 FEB82	Coding Systems for Identification of Fluid Conductors and Connectors	**2**:19.01
847	Full Trailer Tow Bar Eye	**4**:36.51
848a	Fifth Wheel Kingpin, Heavy Duty—Commercial Trailers and Semitrailers	**4**:36.49

NOTE: Page numbers shown include the volume number in bold followed by the section number and page number within that section.

SAE J NO.

849b	Connection and Accessory Locations for Towing Doubles Trailers and Multi-Axle Trailers	**4**:36.49
850 JUN80	Barrier Collision Tests	**4**:34.142
851	Recommended Tolerances for Spoke-Type Wheels, Demountable Rims, and Rim Spacers—Trucks and Trailers	**4**:36.52
852b	Cornering Lamps	**2**:21.54
853 DEC81	Vehicle Identification Numbers	**4**:27.03
855 AUG80	Test Method of Stretch and Set of Textiles and Plastics	**1**:11.100
856	Connectors and Plugs	**2**:21.09
857 JUN80	Roll-Over Tests without Collision	**4**:34.143
858a	Electrical Terminals—Blade Type	**2**:20.62
859	Numbering System for Designating Grades of Cast Ferrous Materials	**1**:6.01
860	Test Method for Measuring Weight of Organic Trim Materials	**1**:11.59
861	Method of Testing Resistance to Crocking of Organic Trim Materials	**1**:11.59
862 JUN81	Factors Affecting Accuracy of Mechanically Driven Automotive Speedometer-Odometers	**2**:18.01
863 DEC81	Methods of Determining Plastic Deformation in Sheet Metal Stampings	**1**:3.14
864 JUN79	Surface Hardness Testing with Files	**1**:3.02
866a	Friction Identification System for Brake Linings and Brake Blocks for Motor Vehicles	**2**:22.62
868	Large Size Radiator Filler Necks	**3**:24.121
869a	Component Nomenclature—Two and Four-Wheel Tractors	**4**:40.19
870	Component Nomenclature—Graders	**4**:40.23
871a	Hi-Head Finished Hex Bolts	**2**:13.04
872 OCT80	Reserve Tractive Ability Test Code	**4**:40.98
873 APR80	Machine Drag Test Code	**4**:40.100
874 MAR81	Center of Gravity Test Code	**4**:40.101
875	Trailer Axle Alignment	**4**:36.54
876a	Extra Wide Single Tire Rim and Wheel Mounting for Rear Axles	**4**:36.53
877	Properties of Low Carbon Steel Sheets and Strip and Their Relationship to Formability	**1**:3.17
879b	Motor Vehicle Seating Systems	**4**:34.31
880 MAY80	Brake System Rating Test Code—Commercial Vehicles	**2**:22.119
881 OCT80	Lifting Crane Sheave and Drum Sizes	**4**:40.158
882	Test Method for Measuring Thickness of Automotive Textiles and Plastics	**1**:11.60
883	Test Method for Determining Dimensional Stability of Automotive Textile Materials	**1**:11.59
884 MAY80	Liquid Ballast Table for Drive Tires of Agricultural Machines	**4**:39.10
887 MAY82	School Bus Red Signal Lamps	**2**:21.69
891a	Spring Nuts	**2**:13.55
892a	Push-On Spring Nuts	**2**:13.63
895	Five Conductor Electrical Connectors for Automotive Type Trailers	**2**:20.55
896	Mounting Flanges for Engine Accessory Drives	**4**:40.168
897	Machine Slope Operation Test Code	**4**:40.107
898 APR80	Control Locations for Construction and Industrial Equipment Design	**4**:40.269
899 OCT80	Operator's Seat Dimensions for Off-Road Self-Propelled Work Machines	**4**:40.267
900 NOV80	Crankcase Emission Control Test Code	**3**:25.54
901b	Universal Joints and Driveshafts—Nomenclature and Terminology	**4**:29.17
902b	Passenger Car Windshield Defrosting Systems	**4**:34.13
903c	Passenger Car Windshield Wiper Systems	**4**:34.06

SAE J NO.

909 APR80	Three-Point Hitch, Implement Quick-Attaching Coupler, Agricultural Tractors	**4**:39.17
910b	Hazard Warning Signal Switch	**2**:21.68
911 OCT81	Surface Texture Measurement of Cold Rolled Sheet Steel	**1**:9.01
912a	Test Method for Determining Blocking Resistance and Associated Characteristics of Automotive Trim Materials	**1**:11.85
913a	Test Method for Wicking of Automotive Fabrics and Fibrous Materials	**1**:11.83
914b	Side Turn Signal Lamps	**2**:21.53
915	Automatic Transmissions—Manual Control Sequence	**4**:29.14
916 JUN82	Rules for SAE Use of SI (Metric) Units	**INDEX** 89
917 JUN80	Marine Push-Pull Control Cables	**4**:41.02
918c	Passenger Car Tire Performance Requirements and Test Procedures	**4**:30.01
919 SEP80	Sound Measurement—Earthmoving Machinery—Operator—Singular Type	**3**:26.37
920a	Format for Construction Equipment Manuals	**4**:40.313
922 NOV79	Turbocharger Nomenclature and Terminology	**3**:24.07
923	Axles—Nomenclature and Terminology	**4**:29.25
924 JAN81	Thrust Washers—Design and Application	**3**:24.50
925	Minimum Access Dimensions for Construction and Industrial Machinery	**4**:40.258
927b	Flywheels for Engine Mounted Torque Converters	**4**:40.169
928 JUN80	Electrical Terminals—Pin and Receptacle Type	**2**:20.63
929a	Piston Rings and Pistons	**3**:24.24
930b	Storage Batteries for Construction and Industrial Machinery	**4**:40.314
931a	Hydraulic Power Circuit Filtration	**4**:40.92
932	Definitions for Macrostrain and Microstrain	**1**:3.57
933 JUN79	Mechanical and Quality Requirements for Tapping Screws	**1**:4.19
934 JUL82	Vehicle Passenger Door Hinge Systems	**4**:34.01
935 JUL81	High Strength Carbon and Alloy Die Drawn Steels	**1**:2.04
937b	Service Brake System Performance Requirements—Passenger Car	**2**:22.88
938a	Drop Test for Evaluating Laminated Safety Glass for Use in Automotive Windshields	**4**:34.41
940 JAN82	Glossary of Carbon Steel Sheet and Strip Terms	**1**:2.18
941 MAR81	Motor Vehicle Driver's Eye Range	**4**:34.66
942b	Passenger Car Windshield Washer Systems	**4**:34.11
943a	Slow-Moving Vehicle Identification Emblem	**4**:39.40
944 JUN80	Steering Control System—Passenger Car—Laboratory Test Procedure	**4**:34.150
945b	Vehicular Hazard Warning Signal Flasher	**2**:21.58
946d	Seals—Application Guide to Radial Lip	**4**:29.43
947 JUL80	Glossary of Fiberboard Terminology	**1**:11.76
948a	Test Method for Determining Resistance to Snagging and Abrasion of Automotive Bodycloth	**1**:11.98
949 AUG81	Test Method for Determining Stiffness (Modulus of Bending) of Fiberboards	**1**:11.98
950 APR80	Gradeability Test Code	**4**:40.105
951 FEB80	Florida Exposure of Automotive Finishes	**1**:11.67
953	Passenger Car Backlight Defogging System	**4**:34.18
954	Urethane for Automotive Seating	**4**:34.35
956	Remote and Automatic Control Systems for Construction and Industrial Machinery	**4**:40.303
957	Elevating Scrapers—Capacity Rating	**4**:40.216

NOTE: Page numbers shown include the volume number in bold followed by the section number and page number within that section.

SAE J NO.

958 MAR81	Nomenclature and Dimensions for Crane Shovels	**4**:40.40
959 OCT80	Lifting Crane, Wire-Rope Strength Factors	**4**:40.148
960 JUN80	Marine Control Cable Connection—Engine Clutch Lever	**4**:41.03
961 JUN80	Marine Control Cable Connection—Engine Throttle Lever	**4**:41.04
962b	Formed Tube Ends for Hose Connections	**2**:19.112
964a	Test Procedure for Determining Reflectivity of Rear View Mirrors	**4**:34.41
966	Test Procedure for Measuring Passenger Car Tire Revolutions per Mile	**4**:30.19
967d	Calibration Fluid for Diesel Injection Equipment	**3**:24.98
968c	Calibrating Nozzle and Holder Assembly for Diesel Fuel Injection Systems	**3**:24.90
969b	Testing Techniques for Diesel Fuel Injection Systems	**3**:24.92
970a	Test Stands for Diesel Fuel Injection Systems	**3**:24.92
971	Brake Rating Test Code—Commercial Vehicle Inertia Dynamometer	**2**:22.126
972 JUN80	Moving Barrier Collision Tests	**4**:34.138
973a	Ignition System Measurements Procedure	**2**:20.02
974 MAY80	Flashing Warning Lamp for Agricultural Equipment	**4**:39.38
975 MAY80	Headlamps for Agricultural Equipment	**4**:39.38
976 MAY80	Combination Tail and Floodlamp for Agricultural Equipment	**4**:39.39
978	Bumper Jacking Test Procedure—Motor Vehicles	**4**:32.01
979	Bumper Jack Requirements—Motor Vehicles	**4**:32.01
980a	Bumper Evaluation Test Procedure—Passenger Cars	**4**:32.02
981	Master Calibrating Fuel Injection Pump	**3**:24.89
982 SEP80	Test Code—Truck, Truck-Tractor, and Trailer Air Service Brake System Pneumatic Pressure and Time Levels	**2**:22.129
983 OCT80	Crane and Cable Excavator Basic Operating Control Arrangements	**4**:40.150
984 JUN80	Bodyforms for Use in Motor Vehicle Passenger Compartment Impact Development	**4**:34.149
985	Vision Factors Considerations in Rear View Mirror Design	**4**:34.44
986 NOV81	Sound Level for Passenger Cars and Light Trucks	**3**:26.12
987 OCT80	Crane Structures—Method of Test	**4**:40.110
988	Labeling of Motor Vehicle Brake Fluid Containers	**2**:22.50
989a	Test Procedure for Measuring Carbon Monoxide Concentrations in Vehicle Passenger Compartments	**3**:25.58
990	Nomenclature—Industrial Mowers	**4**:40.279
992b	Brake System Performance Requirements—Truck, Bus, and Combination of Vehicles	**2**:22.113
993b	Alloy and Temper Designation Systems for Aluminum	**1**:10.02
994 SEP80	Alarm—Back Up—Electric—Performance, Test, and Application	**3**:26.32
995 JUN79	Mechanical and Material Requirements for Steel Nuts	**1**:4.15
996 JUN80	Inverted Vehicle Drop Test Procedure	**4**:34.146
997 JAN80	Spark Arrester Test Carbon	**3**:24.112
998	Minimum Requirements for Motor Vehicle Brake Linings	**2**:22.65
999 OCT80	Crane Boom Hoist Disengaging Device	**4**:40.147
1001 DEC80	Safety for Industrial Flail Mowers	**4**:40.282
1002	Seals—Evaluation of Elastohydrodynamic	**4**:29.54

SAE J NO.

1003	Diesel Engine Emission Measurement Procedure	**3**:25.25
1004 SEP81	Glossary of Engine Cooling System Terms	**3**:24.121
1006 MAR80	Performance Test for Air Conditioned Agricultural Equipment	**4**:39.41
1008 SEP80	Sound Measurement—Self-Propelled Agricultural Equipment—Exterior	**3**:26.63
1012 MAR80	Agricultural Equipment Enclosure Pressurization System Test Procedure	**4**:39.43
1013 JAN80	Measurement of Whole Body Vibration of the Seated Operator of Off-Highway Work Machines	**4**:39.57
1014 OCT79	Classification and Nomenclature Towing Winch for Skidders and Crawler Tractors	**4**:40.38
1015	Ton-Mile Per Hour Test Procedure	**4**:40.210
1016	Component Nomenclature—Dumpers	**4**:40.35
1017	Component Nomenclature—Rollers/Compactors	**4**:40.36
1019	Tests and Procedures for High-Temperature Transmission Oil Hose, Lubricating Oil Hose and Hose Assemblies	**2**:19.107
1024 APR80	Fuel-Fired Heaters—Air Heating—for Construction and Industrial Machinery	**4**:40.287
1025	Test Procedures for Measuring Truck Tire Revolutions per Mile	**4**:30.19
1026 JUN82	Braking Performance—In-Service Crawler Tractors and Crawler Loaders	**4**:40.192
1028 OCT80	Mobile Crane Working Area Definitions	**4**:40.152
1029 APR80	Lighting and Marking of Construction and Industrial Machinery	**4**:40.182
1030	Maximum Sound Level for Passenger Cars and Light Trucks	**3**:26.14
1032 APR80	Definitions for Machine Availability (Construction and Industrial)	**4**:40.64
1033	Procedure for Measuring Bore Eccentricity and Face Deviation of Flywheels, Flywheel Housings, and Flywheel Housing Adapters	**4**:40.165
1034	Engine Coolant Concentrate—Ethylene-Glycol Type	**1**:11.122
1035 JUN80	Technical Publications for Agricultural Equipment	**4**:39.65
1036	Dimensional Standard for Cylindrical Hydraulic Couplers for Agricultural Tractors	**4**:39.26
1037	Windshield Washer Tubing	**1**:11.141
1038 FEB80	Recommendations for Children's Snowmobile	**4**:38.20
1040c	Performance Criteria for Rollover Protective Structures (ROPS) for Construction, Earthmoving, Forestry, and Mining Machines	**4**:40.235
1041	Brake Test Procedure and Brake Performance Criteria for Agricultural Equipment	**4**:39.15
1042 APR80	Operator Protection for Industrial Equipment	**4**:40.243
1043 APR80	Minimum Performance Criteria for Falling Object Protective Structure (FOPS) for Industrial Equipment	**4**:40.246
1044 DEC81	World Manufacturer Identifier	**4**:27.05
1045	Instrumentation and Techniques for Vehicle Refueling Emissions Measurement	**3**:25.124
1047	Tubing—Motor Vehicle Brake System Hydraulic	**2**:22.138
1048 MAR80	Symbols for Motor Vehicle Controls, Indicators and Tell-Tales	**4**:34.153
1049 AUG79	Service Performance Requirements and Test Procedures for Motor Vehicle Lamp Bulbs	**2**:21.25
1050a	Describing and Measuring the Driver's Field of View	**4**:34.108

NOTE: Page numbers shown include the volume number in bold followed by the section number and page number within that section.

32

SAE J NO.		
1051 JAN80	Deflection of Seat Cushions for Off-Road Work Machines	**4**:40.264
1052	Motor Vehicle Driver and Passenger Head Position	**4**:34.122
1053	Steel Stamped Nuts of One Pitch Thread Design	**2**:13.64
1054	Warning Lamp Alternating Flashers . . .	**2**:21.60
1055	Service Performance Requirements for Turn Signal Flashers	**2**:21.56
1056	Service Performance Requirements for Vehicular Hazard Warning Flashers .	**2**:21.59
1057 JUN81	Identification Terminology of Earthmoving Machines	**4**:40.04
1058	Sheet Steel Thickness and Profile	**1**:3.16
1059	Speedometer Test Procedure	**2**:18.07
1060	Subjective Rating Scale for Evaluation of Noise and Ride Comfort Characteristics Related to Motor Vehicle Tires	**4**:30.20
1061a	Surface Discontinuities on General Application Bolts, Screws, and Studs	**1**:4.33
1062	Snowmobile Passenger Handgrips . . .	**4**:38.09
1063 OCT80	Cantilevered Boom Crane Structures—Method of Test	**4**:40.115
1065	Pressure Ratings for Hydraulic Tubing and Fittings	**2**:19.119
1067	Seven Conductor Jacketed Cable for Truck Trailer Connections	**2**:20.61
1069 JUN81	Oil Change System for Quick Service of Off-Road Self-Propelled Work Machines	**4**:40.68
1071	Operator Controls for Graders	**4**:40.277
1072	Sintered Tool Materials	**1**:7.12
1073 JUN80	Spring-Loaded Clutch Spin Test Procedure	**3**:24.72
1074	Engine Sound Level Measurement Procedure	**3**:26.64
1075 SEP80	Sound Measurement—Construction Site	**3**:26.51
1076	Backup Lamp Switches	**2**:21.64
1077	Measurement of Exterior Sound Level of Trucks with Auxiliary Equipment . . .	**3**:26.23
1079	Overcenter Clutch Spin Test Procedure	**4**:40.163
1081 JUN81	Chemical Compositions of SAE Experimental Steels	**1**:1.14
1082 SEP80	Fuel Economy Measurement—Road Test Procedure	**3**:24.156
1083 FEB80	Unauthorized Starting or Movement of Machines	**4**:40.63
1084 APR80	Operator Protective Structure Performance Criteria for Certain Forestry Equipment	**4**:40.247
1085a	Test for Dynamic Properties of Elastomeric Isolators	**1**:11.34
1086	Numbering Metals and Alloys	**1**:1.01
1087 AUG81	One-Way Clutches—Nomenclature and Terminology	**4**:29.33
1088	Test Procedure for Measurement of Small Utility Engine Exhaust Emissions	**3**:25.128
1092	Component Nomenclature—Industrial Tractors (Wheel)	**4**:40.19
1094a	Constant Volume Sampler System for Exhaust Emissions Measurement . . .	**3**:25.102
1095 JUN82	Hub Fatigue Test Procedures	**4**:31.09
1096	Measurement of Exterior Sound Levels for Heavy Trucks Under Stationary Conditions	**3**:26.20
1097 OCT80	Hydraulic Excavator Lift Capacity Rating	**4**:40.222
1098 APR80	Ton Mile Per Hour Application Practice	**4**:40.213
1099	Technical Report on Fatigue Properties	**1**:3.57
1100 JUL79	Motor Vehicle Dimensions	**4**:34.49
1102	Mechanical and Material Requirements for Wheel Bolts	**1**:4.18
1104	Service Performance Requirements for Warning Lamp Alternating Flashers .	**2**:21.60

SAE J NO.		
1105 SEP80	Horn—Forward Warning—Electric—Performance, Test, and Application . . .	**3**:26.34
1108 DEC81	Truck and Truck Tractor Vehicle Identification Number Systems	**4**:27.07
1109 APR80	Component Nomenclature—Articulated Log Skidder, Rubber-Tired	**4**:40.45
1110 APR80	Specification Definitions—Articulated, Rubber-Tired Log Skidder	**4**:40.53
1111 MAR81	Component Nomenclature—Skidder-Grapple	**4**:40.47
1112 APR80	Specification Definitions—Skidder-Grapple	**4**:40.55
1113a	Electromagnetic Susceptibility Procedures for Vehicle Components (Except Aircraft)	**2**:20.80
1114	Fuel Tank Filler Cap and Cap Retainer—Threaded Pressure-Vacuum Type . . .	**3**:24.150
1115	Guidelines for Developing and Revising SAE Nomenclature and Definitions . .	**INDEX** 101
1116 JUN81	Categories of Off-Road Self-Propelled Work Machines	**4**:40.01
1117 SEP80	Method of Measuring and Reporting the Pressure Differential-Flow Characteristics of a Hydraulic Fluid Power Valve	**4**:40.81
1118	Hydraulic Valves for Motor Vehicle Brake Systems Test Procedure	**2**:22.28
1119 APR80	Steel Products for Rollover Protective Structures (ROPS) and Falling Object Protective Structures (FOPS)	**4**:40.248
1120 SEP79	Spherical Rod Ends	**2**:14.12
1121	Helical Compression and Extension Spring Terminology	**2**:17.09
1122	Helical Springs: Specification Check Lists	**2**:17.14
1123a	Leaf Springs for Motor Vehicle Suspension—Metric Bar Sizes	**2**:17.01
1124	Glossary of Terms Related to Fluid Filters and Filter Testing	**3**:24.98
1127 JUN80	Battery Cable	**2**:20.48
1128	Low Tension Primary Cable	**2**:20.50
1129	Operator Cab Environment for Heated, Ventilated, and Air Conditioned Construction and Industrial Equipment . .	**4**:40.302
1130	Determination of Emissions from Gas Turbine Powered Light Duty Surface Vehicles	**3**:25.133
1131	Performance Requirements for SAE J844d Nonmetallic Tubing and Fitting Assemblies Used in Automotive Air Brake Systems	**2**:19.126
1132	142 mm × 200 mm Sealed Beam Headlamp Unit	**2**:21.18
1133a	School Bus Stop Arm	**2**:21.70
1134	SAE Nodal Mount	**4**:36.55
1135	Turbocharger Connections	**3**:24.22
1136 SEP79	Braking Performance—Rollers and Compactors	**4**:40.201
1137	Hydraulic Valves for Motor Vehicle Brake Systems—Performance Requirements	**2**:22.32
1138	Design Criteria—Driver Hand Controls Location for Passenger Cars, Multi-Purpose Passenger Vehicles, and Trucks (10 000 GVW and Under)	**4**:34.105
1139	Supplemental Information—Driver Hand Controls Location for Passenger Cars, Multi-Purpose Passenger Vehicles, and Trucks (10 000 GVW and Under) . . .	**4**:34.107
1140 MAR80	Filler Pipes and Openings of Motor Vehicle Fuel Tanks	**3**:24.152
1141	Air Cleaner Elements	**3**:24.57
1142a	Towability Design Criteria—Passenger Cars and Light Duty Trucks	**4**:28.01
1143a	Towed Vehicle/Wrecker Attachment Test Procedure—Passenger Cars and Light Duty Trucks	**4**:28.05

NOTE: Page numbers shown include the volume number in bold followed by the section number and page number within that section.

SAE J NO.

1144a	Towed Vehicle Drivetrain Test Procedure—Passenger Cars and Light Duty Trucks	4:28.07
1145a	Emissions Terminology and Nomenclature	3:25.143
1146 NOV80	The Lubricant Performance and Service Classification Maintenance Procedure	3:23.41
1147	Welding, Brazing, and Soldering—Materials and Practices	1:9.07
1148	Engine Charge Air Cooler Nomenclature	3:24.127
1149	Metallic Air Brake System Tubing and Pipe	2:19.122
1150	Terminology for Agricultural Equipment	4:39.05
1151 NOV79	Methane Measurement Using Gas Chromatography	3:25.146
1152 APR80	Braking Performance—Rubber-Tired Construction Machines	4:40.193
1153	Hydraulic Master Cylinders for Motor Vehicle Brakes—Test Procedure	2:22.24
1154	Hydraulic Master Cylinders for Motor Vehicle Brakes—Performance Requirements	2:22.28
1155 SEP80	Displacement of Pneumatic Brake Actuators	2:22.132
1157	Measurement Procedure for Evaluation of Full-Flow, Light Extinction Smokemeter Performance	3:25.40
1158	Specification Definitions—Winches for Crawler Tractors and Skidders	4:40.59
1159 AUG79	Preparation of SAE Technical Reports—Surface Vehicles and Machines: Standards, Recommended Practices, Information Reports	**INDEX** 86
1160	Operator Ear Sound Level Measurement Procedure for Snow Vehicles	3:26.26
1161 APR80	Operational Sound Level Measurement Procedure for Snow Vehicles	3:26.28
1163 JAN80	Determining Operator Seat Location on Off-Road Work Machines	4:40.265
1164	Labeling of ROPS and FOPS	4:40.243
1165 OCT80	Reporting Cleanliness Levels of Hydraulic Fluids	4:40.85
1166 SEP80	Sound Measurement—Earthmoving Machinery—Operator—Work Cycle	3:26.39
1167	Motorcycle Stop Lamp Switch	4:37.03
1168	Motorcycle Bank Angle Measurement Procedure	4:37.04
1169	Measurement of Light Vehicle Exhaust Sound Level Under Stationary Conditions	3:26.16
1170 JUN80	Rear Power Take-Off for Agricultural Tractors	4:39.27
1171	External Ignition Protection of Marine Electrical Devices	4:41.08
1172	Engine Flywheel Housings with Sealed Flanges	3:24.72
1173	Size Classification and Characteristics of Glass Beads for Peening	1:8.11
1174	Operator Ear Sound Level Measurement Procedure for Small Engine Powered Equipment	3:26.48
1175	Bystander Sound Level Measurement Procedure for Small Engine Powered Equpiment	3:26.49
1176	External Leakage Classifications for Hydraulic Systems	4:40.98
1177 OCT80	Hydraulic Excavator Operator Controls	4:40.227
1178	Minimum Performance Criteria for Braking Systems for Rubber-Tired Skidders	4:40.63
1179 OCT80	Hydraulic Excavator Digging Forces	4:40.226
1180 OCT80	Telescopic Boom Length Indicating System	4:40.144

SAE J NO.

1183	Recommended Guidelines for Fatigue Testing of Elastomeric Materials and Components	1:11.29
1184	Definitions of Acoustical Terms	1:11.89
1191	High Tension Ignition Cable Assemblies—Marine	4:41.19
1193 MAR81	Nomenclature and Dimensions for Hydraulic Excavators	4:40.42
1194	Roll-Over Protective Structures (ROPS) for Wheeled Agricultural Tractors	4:39.49
1195	Cylinder Rod Wiper Seal Ingression Test	4:40.96
1199	Mechanical and Material Requirements for Metric Externally Threaded Steel Fasteners	1:4.06
1200	Blind Rivets—Break Mandrel Type	2:13.95
1201	Piston Rings and Grooves (Metric)	3:24.31
1203	Light Transmittance of Automotive Windshields Safety Glazing Materials	4:34.38
1204	Wheels—Recreational and Utility Trailer Test Procedures	4:31.03
1205	Performance Requirements for Snap-In Tubeless Tire Valves	4:30.23
1206	Methods for Testing Snap-In Tubeless Tire Valves	4:30.21
1207 OCT81	Measurement Procedure for Determination of Silencer Effectiveness in Reducing Engine Intake or Exhaust Sound Level	3:26.65
1209	Identification Terminology of Mobile Forestry Machines	4:40.14
1211	Recommended Environmental Practices for Electronic Equipment Design	2:20.92
1212	Fire Prevention on Forestry Equipment	4:40.62
1213	Glossary of Automotive Electronic Terms	2:20.120
1214	Tire to Body Clearance Check for Recreational Vehicles	4:35.03
1215	Performance Prediction of Roll-Over Protective Structures (ROPS) Through Analytical Methods	4:40.254
1216	Test Methods for Metric Threaded Fasteners	1:4.11
1220	Rotary-Trochoidal Engine Nomenclature and Terminology	3:24.03
1221	Headlamp-Turn Signal Spacing	2:21.48
1222 FEB81	Speed Control Assurance for Snowmobiles	4:38.19
1223 DEC80	Marine Carburetors	4:41.21
1224 JUN82	Braking Performance—New Off-Highway Dumpers	4:40.199
1225	Development of a Frequency Weighted Portable Ride Meter	4:39.60
1227	Assessing Cleanliness of Hydraulic Fluid Power Components and Systems	4:40.70
1228 MAR80	Marine Engine Rating Code	4:41.11
1229 DEC81	Truck Identification Terminology	4:27.04
1230 OCT79	Minimum Requirements for Wheel Slip Brake Control System Malfunction Signals	2:22.138
1231	Hose Push-On Fittings	2:19.89
1232	Passenger and Light Truck Tire Traction Device Profile Determination and Classification	4:36.57
1233	Format for Commercial Literature Specifications—Off-Road Work Machines	4:40.17
1234	Specification Definitions—Off-Road Work Machines	4:40.12
1235 SEP80	Measuring and Reporting the Internal Leakage of a Hydraulic Fluid Power Valve	4:40.84
1236 SEP80	Cast Iron Sealing Rings (Metric)	4:29.63
1237	Metric Thread Rolling Screws	1:4.29
1239	Four- and Eight-Conductor Rectangular Electrical Connectors for Automotive Type Trailers	2:20.57

NOTE: Page numbers shown include the volume number in bold followed by the section number and page number within that section.

SAE J NO.

1240	Flywheel Spin Test Procedure	3:24.73
1241	Fuel and Lubricant Tanks for Motorcycles	4:37.05
1242	Acoustic Emission Test Methods	**1**:3.56
1243 AUG79	Diesel Emission Production Audit Test Procedure	3:25.27
1244 JUN81	Oil Cooler Nomenclature and Glossary	3:24.133
1245 JUN82	Guide to the Application and Use of Engine Coolant Pump Face Seals	3:24.144
1246 MAY82	Measuring the Radius of Curvature of Convex Mirrors	4:34.42
1247 APR80	Simulated Mountain Brake Performance Test Procedure	2:22.82
1250 FEB80	In-Service Brake Performance Test Procedure—Vehicles Over 4500 kg (10 000 lb)	2:22.59
1252 JUL81	SAE Wind Tunnel Test Procedure for Trucks and Buses	4:36.33
1253	Low Temperature Cranking Load Requirements of an Engine	2:20.17
1254	Component Nomenclature—Feller Buncher	4:40.45
1255	Specification Definitions—Feller/Buncher	4:40.60
1256 JUN80	Fuel Economy Measurement—Road Test Procedure—Cold Start and Warm-Up Fuel Economy	3:24.188
1257 OCT80	Rating Chart for Cantilevered Boom Cranes	4:40.121
1259 APR80	Metric Spherical Rod Ends	2:14.15
1261 FEB79	Agricultural Tractor TireDynamic Indices	4:39.13
1262 SEP80	Sound Measurement—Trenching Equipment	3:26.60
1263	Road Load Measurement and Dynamometer Simulation Using Coastdown Techniques	3:24.165
1264	Joint RCCC/SAE Fuel Consumption Test Procedure (Short Term-In-Service Vehicle) Type I	4:36.05
1265 FEB80	Dozer Capacity	4:40.161
1266	Axle Efficiency Test Procedure	4:29.29
1267	Leakage Testing	1:3.50
1268 JUN81	Hardenability Bands for Carbon and Alloy H Steels	1:1.26
1269 JUL81	Rolling Resistance Measurement Procedure for Passenger Car Tires	4:30.04
1270 OCT79	The Measurement of Passenger Car Tire Rolling Resistance	4:30.06
1271 AUG79	Technical Committee Guideposts	**INDEX** 81
1272 OCT79	Felling Head Terminology and Nomenclature	4:40.57
1273 SEP79	Selection, Installation, and Maintenance of Hose and Hose Assemblies	2:19.104
1274 JUN80	Performance Requirements for the Automotive Audio Cassette	2:20.71
1275 JUN80	Testing Methods for Audio Cassettes	2:20.72
1276 AUG79	Standardized Fluid for Hydraulic Component Tests	4:40.85
1277 MAY82	Method for Assessing the Cleanliness Level of New Hydraulic Fluid	4:40.86
1278 OCT80	SI (Metric) Synchronous Belts and Pulleys	2:16.08
1280 JAN80	Determination of Sulfur Compounds in Automotive Exhaust	3:25.60
1281 NOV79	Operator Sound Level Exposure Assessment Procedure for Pleasure Motorboats	3:26.30
1282 SEP80	Snowmobile Brake Control Systems	4:38.10
1283 JUN80	Electrical Connector for Auxiliary Starting of Construction, Agricultural, and Off-Road Machinery	4:40.175
1284 DEC79	Blade Type Electric Fuses	2:20.34
1285 FEB80	Powershift Transmission Fluid Classification	3:23.22
1286 NOV81	Static Electric Outboard Thrust	4:41.04

SAE J NO.

1287 MAR82	Measurement of Exhaust Sound Levels of Stationary Motorcycles	3:26.04
1289 APR81	Mobile Crane Stability Ratings	4:40.153
1290 JUL80	Automotive Hydraulic Brake System—Metric Tube Connections	2:22.141
1291 JUL80	Automotive Hydraulic Brake System—Metric Banjo Bolt Connections	2:22.146
1292 OCT81	Automobile, Truck, Truck-Tractor, Trailer, and Motor Coach Wiring	2:20.39
1293 JAN80	Undervehicle Corrosion Test	1:3.34
1294 APR80	Ignition Distributors—Marine	4:41.15
1295 JUN80	Identification Terminology—Pipelayers	4:40.42
1297 APR82	Alternative Automotive Fuels	3:23.39
1298 OCT80	Hydraulic Systems Diagnostic Port Sizes and Locations	4:40.76
1306 JUN80	Motorcycle Auxiliary Front Lamps	2:21.41
1307 MAY81	Excavator Hand Signals	4:40.229
1310 APR81	Electric Engine Preheaters and Battery Warmers for Diesel Engines	4:40.291
1312 SEP80	Procedure for Measuring Basic Highway Vehicle Engine Performance and Fuel Consumption—Spark Ignition and Diesel	3:24.11
1313 OCT80	Automotive Synchronous Belt Drives	2:16.12
1315 MAY81	Off-Road Tire and Rim Selection and Application	4:40.209
1317 JUN82	Electrical Propulsion Rotating Equipment—Off-Road Dumper	4:40.190
1320 JUN81	Marine Electrical Switches	4:41.22
1321 OCT81	Joint TMC/SAE Fuel Consumption Test Procedure—Type II	4:36.08
1322 MAY81	Preferred Conversion Values for Dimensions in Lighting—Inch-Pound Units/SI	2:21.01
1323 AUG80	Standard Classification System for Fiberboards	1:11.81
1324 DEC81	Heat Insulation Materials Test Procedure	1:11.56
1325 SEP80	Test Method for Measuring the Relative Drapeability of Flexible Insulation Materials	1:11.89
1326 AUG80	Test Method for Measuring Wet Color Transfer Characteristics	1:11.89
1332 OCT81	Rope Drum Rotation Indicating Device	4:40.157
1338 JUN81	Open Field Whole-Vehicle Radiated Susceptibility 10 kHz—18 GHz, Electric Field	2:20.109
1339 JUL81	Test Method for Measuring Power Consumption of Cooling Fans for Trucks and Buses	4:36.27
1340 JUL81	Test Method for Measuring Power Consumption of Air Conditioning and Air Brake Compressors for Trucks and Buses	4:36.29
1341 JUL81	Test Method for Measuring Power Consumption of Hydraulic Pumps for Trucks and Buses	4:36.29
1342 JUL81	Test Method for Measuring Power Consumption of Fan Drive Systems for Trucks and Buses	4:36.30
1343 JUL81	Information Relating to Duty Cycles and Average Power Requirements of Truck and Bus Engine Accessories	4:36.32
1344 OCT80	Marking of Plastic Parts	1:11.68
1345 FEB82	Automotive Plastic Parts Specification	1:11.71
1346 JUN81	Guide to Manifold Absolute Pressure Transducer Representative Test Method	2:20.125
1347 JUN81	Guide to Manifold Absolute Pressure Transducer Representative Specification	2:20.128
1349 DEC80	Engine Power Test Code—Spark Ignition and Diesel	3:24.09
1350 DEC81	Selection and Application Guidelines for Diesel, Gasoline, and Propane Fired Liquid Cooled Engine Pre-Heaters	4:40.287

NOTE: Page numbers shown include the volume number in bold followed by the section number and page number within that section.

SAE J NO.

1351 JUL81	Hot Odor Test for Insulation Materials .	**1**:11.92
1352 MAY81	Compression and Recovery of Insulation Paddings	**1**:11.92
1355 MAR81	Test Method for Measuring Thickness of Resilient Insulating Paddings	**1**:11.90
1360 JUN81	Product Identification Numbering System of Off-Road Work Machines	**4**:40.03
1361 APR81	Hot Plate Method for Evaluating Heat Resistance and Thermal Insulation Properties of Materials	**1**:11.91
1367 SEP81	Performance Test Procedure—Ball Joints and Spherical Rod Ends	**2**:14.16
1372 DEC81	Sound Power Determination—Earthmoving Machinery—Static Condition	**3**:26.53
1373 JUN82	Rear Cornering Lamp	**2**:21.55
1375 MAR82	Cranking Motor Application Considerations	**2**:20.18
1379 JUN82	Rolling Resistance Measurement Procedure for Highway Truck and Bus Tires	**4**:30.08
1380 JUN82	The Measurement of Highway Truck and Bus Tire Rolling Resistance	**4**:30.10
1382 MAY82	Classification, Nomenclature and Specification Definitions for Trenching Machines	**4**:40.29
1389 MAY82	Corrosion Test for Insulation Materials .	**1**:11.93
1390 APR82	Engine Cooling Fan Structural Analysis	**3**:24.130
1392 MAY82	Steel, High Strength, Hot Rolled Sheet and Strip, Cold Rolled Sheet, and Coated Sheet	**1**:1.76

SAE J NO.

1400 MAY82	Laboratory Measurement of the Airborne Noise Reduction of Acoustical Materials	**1**:11.94
1401 JAN81	Road Vehicle—Hydraulic Brake Hose Assemblies for Use with Non-Petroleum Base Hydraulic Fluids	**2**:22.01
1402 OCT80	Automotive Air Brake Hose and Hose Assemblies	**2**:22.07
1403a	Vacuum Brake Hose	**2**:22.11
1404	Service Brake Structural Integrity Requirements—Vehicles Over 10 000 lb (4500 KG) GVWR	**2**:22.74
1405	Flex-Impulse Test Procedure for Hydraulic Hose Assemblies	**2**:19.106
1406 MAR81	Application of Hydraulic Brake Hose to Motor Vehicles	**2**:22.13
1500 JUN80	Universal Symbols for Operator Controls	**INDEX** 102
1601	Rubber Cups for Hydraulic Actuating Cylinders	**2**:22.148
1603	Rubber Seals for Hydraulic Disc Brake Cylinders	**2**:22.15
1604	Rubber Boots for Drum Type Hydraulic Brake Wheel Cylinders	**2**:22.19
1605	Brake Master Cylinder Reservoir Diaphragm Gasket	**2**:22.17
1702f	Motor Vehicle Brake Fluid—Arctic	**2**:22.33
1703 JAN80	Motor Vehicle Brake Fluid	**2**:22.41

NOTE: Page numbers shown include the volume number in bold followed by the section number and page number within that section.

CANCELLED AND SUPERSEDED REPORTS

CANCELLED STANDARDS, RECOMMENDED PRACTICES, AND INFORMATION REPORTS

SAE reports listed below in "J number" order are those reports which have been cancelled after 1977 as a result of technical committee action. These reports have not been superseded by other reports.

Copies of cancelled reports can be obtained by contacting the Library, SAE, 400 Commonwealth Drive, Warrendale, PA 15096 (412)776-4841. A charge will be made for this service. Questions regarding reports cancelled prior to 1978 should be addressed to the Technical Division at the above address.

SAE J Report Number	Title	Year Cancelled
14	Specifications for Elastomer Compounds for Automotive Applications	1980
15	Flexible Foams Made from Polymers or Co-polymers of Vinyl Chloride	1978
29	Plastic Material for Use in Housings of Motor Vehicle Lighting Devices	1983
52	Steering Wheel Rim Faceform Impact Test Procedure	1981
106	Soil Type and Strength Classification	1982
136	Simplified Method for Simulating Glancing Blow Impacts—Motor Vehicles	1981
152	Engine Specification Tag	1980
165	Fan Blast Deflectors for Earthmoving Machines	1982
168	Protective Enclosures for Agricultural Tractors—Test Procedures and Performance Requirements	1978
194	Drawbar for Forestry Tractors	1978
245	Engine Rating Code—Spark Ignition	1982
248	Crane Overload Indicating System Test Procedure	1978
270	Engine Rating Code—Diesel	1982
282	Automotive Gasoline Performance and Information System	1979
333	Operator Protection for Wheel Type Agricultural Tractors	1978
334	Protective Frame for Agricultural Tractors—Test Procedures and Performance Requirements	1978
338	Motor Vehicle Instrument Panel Laboratory Impact Test Procedure—Knee-Leg Area	1981
346	Motor Vehicle Seatback Assembly Laboratory Impact Test Procedure—Head Area	1981
352	External Ignition-Proofing of Marine Engine Alternators	1979
353	External Ignition-Proofing of Marine Engine Regulators	1979
354	External Ignition-Proofing of Marine Engine Distributors	1979
355	External Ignition-Proofing of Marine Engine Cranking Motors	1979
407	Hardenability Bands for Alloy H Steels	1981
520	Fuel Supply Connections	1978
552	External Electromagnetic Radiation Suppressor	1982

SAE J Report Number	Title	Year Cancelled
555	Truck, Truck-Tractor, Trailer, and Motor Coach Wiring	1981
556	Automobile Wiring	1981
568	Sockets Receiving Prefocus Base Lamps	1978
577	Vibration Test Machine	1980
596	Electric Emergency Lanterns	1979
597	Liquid Burning Emergency Flares	1979
603	Incandescent Lamp Impact Test	1981
623	Automotive Carburetor Flanges	1983
634	Water Thermostat Pockets	1983
652	Truck Transmissions—Test Code	1980
660	Brake Linings	1980
685	Data Plate—Automotive Type Trailers	1981
703	Fuel Systems—Truck and Truck Tractors	1980
718	540-RPM Power Take-Off for Farm Tractors	1978
719	1000-RPM Power Take-Off for Farm Tractors	1978
736	Mechanical Power Outlet Test Code	1979
776	Hardenability Bands for Carbon H Steels	1981
779	Tractor Protection Valve Control	1983
816	Engine Test Code—Spark Ignition and Diesel	1982
885	Human Tolerance to Impact Conditions as Related to Motor Vehicle Design	1981
893	Vehicle Fuel Consumption Test Code	1979
921	Motor Vehicle Instrument Panel Laboratory Impact Test Procedure—Head Area	1981
963	Anthropomorphic Test Device for Use in Dynamic Testing of Motor Vehicles	1979
991	Soil-Machine Terminology	1982
1010	Emission Control Hose	1983
1018	Recreational Trailer Vehicle Identification Number System	1981
1039	Size Classification for Crawler Tractors	1980
1046	Exterior Sound Level Measurement Procedure for Small Engine Powered Equipment	1982
1089	Lateral Impact Test Procedure for Vehicle Interiors	1981
1258	Automotive Hydraulic Brake System—Metric Connections	1982

CANCELLED AND SUPERSEDED STANDARDS, RECOMMENDED PRACTICES, AND INFORMATION REPORTS

SAE reports listed below in "J number" order are those reports which have been cancelled as a result of technical committee action and superseded by other reports.

Copies of cancelled reports can be obtained by contacting the Library, SAE, 400 Commonwealth Drive, Warrendale, PA 15096 (412)776-4841. A charge will be made for this service.

SAE J Report Number	Title	Year Cancelled	Superseded By
4	Motor Vehicle Seat Belt Assemblies	1974	J114, 117, 140a, 141, 339a, 800c
40	Automotive Brake Hoses	1969	J1400 Series
60	Rubber Cups for Hydraulic Actuating Cylinders	1977	J1600 Series
70	Hydraulic Brake Fluid	1968	J1700 Series
320	Minimum Performance Criteria for Roll-Over Protective System for Rubber-Tired, Self-Propelled Scrapers	1974	J1040
394	Minimum Performance Criteria for Roll-Over Protective Structure for Rubber-Tired Front End Loaders and Rubber-Tired Dozers	1976	J1040
395	Minimum Performance Criteria for Roll-Over Protective Structure for Crawler Tractors and Crawler-Type Loaders	1974	J1040
396	Minimum Performance Criteria for Roll-Over Protective Structures for Motor Graders	1974	J1040
507	Helical Compression Springs Hot-Coiled for General Automotive Use	1977	J1121
508	Helical Compression and Extension Springs Cold-Coiled for General Automotive Use	1977	J1121
509	Helical Springs for Motor-Vehicle Suspension	1977	J1121
558	Low Tension Cable	1978	J1127, 1128
653	Form for Transmission Compression Spring	1976	J1122
787	Motor Vehicle Seat Belt Anchorage	1977	J383, 384, 385
878	Low Tension Cable Thermosetting Insulation	1978	J1128
894	Terminology—Construction and Industrial Machinery	1978	J1234
926	Hydraulic Pipe Fittings	1979	J514 (Section IV)
977	Instrumentation for Laboratory Impact Tests	1973	J211a
1011	Performance Criteria for Roll-Over Protective Structures for Rubber Tired, Off-Highway, Non-Trailed Hauling Units with Rear or Side Dump Bodies	1974	J1040

SUBJECT INDEX

SUBJECT INDEX

ABRASION

Seat Belt Assembly Webbing Abrasion Test Procedure—SAE J339a ... **4**:33.12

Seat Belt Assembly Webbing Abrasion Test Requirements—SAE J114 ... **4**:33.12

Test Method for Determining Resistance to Snagging and Abrasion of Automotive Bodycloth—SAE J948a ... **1**:11.98

ACOUSTICS

See Also: SOUND

Acoustic Emission Test Methods—SAE J1242 ... **1**:3.56

Definitions of Acoustical Terms—SAE J1184 ... **1**:11.89

Instrumentation for Measuring Acoustic Impulses Within Vehicles—SAE J247 JUN80 ... **3**:26.05

Laboratory Measurement of the Airborne Noise Reduction of Acoustical Materials—SAE J1400 MAY82 ... **1**:11.94

Test Method for Measuring the Relative Drapeability of Flexible Insulation Materials—SAE J1325 SEP80 ... **1**:11.89

Test Method for Measuring Thickness of Resilient Insulating Paddings—SAE J1355 MAR81 ... **1**:11.90

ADHESIVES

Methods of Tests for Automotive-Type Sealers, Adhesives, and Deadeners—SAE J243 ... **1**:11.46

Test Procedures for Brake Shoe and Lining Adhesives and Bonds—SAE J840c ... **2**:22.67

AGRICULTURAL MACHINERY

Agricultural Equipment Enclosure Pressurization System Test Procedure—SAE J1012 MAR80 ... **4**:39.43

Agricultural Tractor Test Code—SAE J708 JUN80 ... **4**:39.01

Application of Hydraulic Remote Control to Agricultural Tractors and Trailing Type Agricultural Implements—SAE J716a ... **4**:39.24

Categories of Off-Road Self-Propelled Work Machines—SAE J1116 JUN81 ... **4**:40.01

Deflection of Seat Cushions for Off-Road Work Machines—SAE J1051 JAN80 ... **4**:40.264

Determining Operator Seat Location on Off-Road Work Machines—SAE J1163 JAN80 ... **4**:40.265

Development of a Frequency Weighted Portable Ride Meter—SAE J1225 ... **4**:39.60

Dimensional Standard for Cylindrical Hydraulic Couplers for Agricultural Tractors—SAE J1036 ... **4**:39.26

Electrical Connector for Auxiliary Starting of Construction, Agricultural, and Off-Road Machinery—SAE J1283 JUN80 ... **4**:40.175

Measurement of Whole Body Vibration of the Seated Operator of Off-Highway Work Machines—SAE J1013 JAN80 ... **4**:39.57

Performance Test for Air Conditioned Agricultural Equipment—SAE J1006 MAR80 ... **4**:39.41

Product Identification Numbering System of Off-Road Work Machines—SAE J1360 JUN81 ... **4**:40.03

Slow-Moving Vehicle Identification Emblem—SAE J943a ... **4**:39.40

Sound Measurement—Self-Propelled Agricultural Equipment—Exterior—SAE J1008 SEP80 ... **3**:26.63

Technical Publications for Agricultural Equipment—SAE J1035 JUN80 ... **4**:39.65

Terminology for Agricultural Equipment—SAE J1150 ... **4**:39.05

Test Procedure for Measuring Hydraulic Lift Force Capacity on Agricultural Tractors Equipped with Three-Point Hitch—SAE J283 ... **4**:39.22

T-Hook Slots for Securement in Shipment of Agricultural Equipment—SAE J39 ... **4**:39.37

Tractor Belt Speed and Pulley Width—SAE J720 MAY80 ... **4**:39.32

Brake Systems

Brake Test Procedure and Brake Performance Criteria for Agricultural Equipment—SAE J1041 ... **4**:39.15

Implements

Operating Requirements for Tractors and Power Take-Off Driven Implements—SAE J721 JUN80 ... **4**:39.30

Three-Point Free-Link Hitch Attachment of Implements to Agricultural Wheeled Tractors—SAE J715 MAY80 ... **4**:39.19

Three-Point Hitch, Implement Quick-Attaching Coupler, Agricultural Tractors—SAE J909 APR80 ... **4**:39.17

Lamps

Combination Tail and Floodlamp for Agricultural Equipment—SAE J976 MAY80 ... **4**:39.39

Flashing Warning Lamp for Agricultural Equipment—SAE J974 MAY80 ... **4**:39.38

Headlamps for Agricultural Equipment—SAE J975 MAY80 ... **4**:39.38

Operator Controls

Operator Controls on Agricultural Equipment—SAE J841 MAY80 ... **4**:39.46

Universal Symbols for Operator Controls—SAE J1500 JUN80 ... **INDEX** 102

Universal Symbols for Operator Controls on Agricultural Equipment—SAE J389b ... **4**:39.47

Operator Protective Structures

Overhead Protection for Agricultural Tractors—Test Procedures and Performance Requirements—SAE J167 JUN81 ... **4**:39.56

Roll-Over Protective Structures (ROPS) for Wheeled Agricultural Tractors—SAE J1194 ... **4**:39.49

Power Take-Off

Auxiliary Power Take-Off Drives for Agricultural Tractors—SAE J717 MAY80 ... **4**:39.31

Operating Requirements for Tractors and Power Take-Off Driven Implements—SAE J721 JUN80 ... **4**:39.30

Power Take-Off Definitions and Terminology for Agricultural Tractors—SAE J722 MAY80 ... **4**:39.32

Rear Power Take-Off for Agricultural Tractors—SAE J1170 JUN80 ... **4**:39.27

Safety

Lighting and Marking of Agricultural Equipment on Highways—SAE J137c ... **4**:39.39

Safety Alert Symbol for Agricultural, Construction and Industrial Equipment—SAE J284a ... **4**:39.43

Safety for Agricultural Equipment—SAE J208d ... **4**:39.44

Tires

Agricultural Tractor Tire Dynamic Indices—SAE J1261 FEB79 ... **4**:39.13

Agricultural Tractor Tire Loadings, Torque Factors, and Inflation Pressures—SAE J709d ... **4**:39.05

Lawn and Garden Tractors Load and Inflation Pressures and Tire Selection Table for Future Design—SAE J344 ... **4**:39.14

Liquid Ballast Table for Drive Tires of Agricultural Machines—SAE J884 MAY80 ... **4**:39.10

Tire Selection Tables for Agricultural and Light Industrial Machines of Future Design—SAE J711c ... **4**:39.12

Wheels

Industrial and Agricultural Disc Wheels—SAE J712a ... **4**:39.32

Wheel Mounting Elements for Industrial and Agricultural Disc Wheels—SAE J714b ... **4**:39.36

AIR CLEANERS

Air Cleaner Elements—SAE J1141 ... **3**:24.57

Air Cleaner Test Code—SAE J726 MAY81 ... **3**:24.58

AIR CONDITIONING

Automotive Air Conditioning Hose—SAE J51b ... **1**:11.139

Design Guidelines for Air Conditioning Systems for Construction and Industrial Equipment Cabs—SAE J169 APR80 ... **4**:40.301

NOTE: Page numbers shown include the volume number in bold followed by the section number and page number within that section.

Information Relating to Duty Cycles and Average Power Requirements of Truck and Bus Engine Accessories—SAE J1343 JUL81 . . . . **4**:36.32

Performance Test for Air Conditioned Agricultural Equipment—SAE J1006 MAR80 . . . . **4**:39.41

Safety Practices for Mechanical Vapor Compression Refrigeration Equipment or Systems Used to Cool Passenger Compartment of Motor Vehicles—SAE J639 OCT81 . . . . **4**:34.26

Test Method for Measuring Power Consumption of Air Conditioning and Air Brake Compressors for Trucks and Buses—SAE J1340 JUL81 . . . . . . **4**:36.29

ALARMS
Alarm—Back Up—Electric—Performance, Test, and Application—SAE J994 SEP80 . . . . **3**:26.32

ALLOYS
Eddy Current Testing by Electromagnetic Methods—SAE J425 MAR81 . . . . **1**:3.48
Infrared Testing—SAE J359 JUN81 . . . . **1**:3.47
Liquid Penetrant Test Methods—SAE J426c . . . **1**:3.52
Magnetic Particle Inspection—SAE J420 MAR81 **1**:3.47
Nondestructive Tests—SAE J358 JAN80 . . . . . **1**:3.45
Numbering Metals and Alloys—SAE J1086 . . . . **1**:1.01
Penetrating Radiation Inspection—SAE J427b . . **1**:3.53
Ultrasonic Inspection—SAE J428b **1**:3.55

Aluminum
Alloy and Temper Designation Systems for Aluminum—SAE J993b **1**:10.02
Aluminum Alloys—Fundamentals—SAE J451b . . **1**:10.01
Anodized Aluminum Automotive Parts—SAE J399a **1**:10.27
Chemical Compositions and Mechanical and Physical Properties of SAE Aluminum Casting Alloys—SAE J453c **1**:10.08
Chemical Compositions, Mechanical Property Limits, and Dimensional Tolerances of SAE Wrought Aluminum Alloys—SAE J457j **1**:10.26
General Data on Wrought Aluminum Alloys—SAE J454 JUL81 . . . . **1**:10.11
General Information on SAE Aluminum Casting Alloys—SAE J452c **1**:10.05

Copper
Cast Copper Alloys—SAE J462 SEP81 . . . . . . **1**:10.64
Wrought and Cast Copper Alloys—SAE J461 SEP81 . . . . **1**:10.30
Wrought Copper and Copper Alloys—SAE J463 SEP81 . . . . **1**:10.67

Magnesium
Magnesium Alloys—SAE J464c **1**:10.106
Magnesium Casting Alloys—SAE J465c **1**:10.106
Magnesium Wrought Alloys—SAE J466c **1**:10.111

Nickel
Wrought Nickel and Nickel-Related Alloys—SAE J470c **1**:10.127

Steel (See Also: STEEL)
Alloy Steel Machinability Ratings—SAE J770c . . **1**:2.24
Formerly Standard SAE Alloy Steels—SAE J778 OCT80 . . . . **1**:1.15
Hardenability Bands for Carbon and Alloy H Steels—SAE J1268 JUN81 . . . . **1**:1.26
High Strength Carbon and Alloy Die Drawn Steels—SAE J935 JUL81 . . . . **1**:2.04

Superalloys
Special Purpose Alloys ("Superalloys")—SAE J467b **1**:10.115

Zinc
Zinc Alloy Ingot and Die Casting Compositions—SAE J468b **1**:10.126
Zinc Die Casting Alloys—SAE J469a **1**:10.127

ALL-TERRAIN VEHICLES
Snowmobile and All-Terrain Vehicle Pulley Guards and Shields—SAE J93 . . . . **4**:38.15
Vehicle Identification Numbers—Snowmobile and All-Terrain Vehicles—SAE J64 FEB81 . . . . . **4**:38.03

ALUMINUM ALLOYS
See: ALLOYS

ANTHROPOMETRY
Bodyforms for Use in Motor Vehicle Passenger Compartment Impact Development—SAE J984 JUN80 . . . . **4**:34.149
Describing and Measuring the Driver's Field of View—SAE J1050a **4**:34.108
Devices for Use in Defining and Measuring Vehicle Seating Accommodation—SAE J826 APR80 . . **4**:34.27
Driver Hand Control Reach—SAE J287 FEB80 . . **4**:34.72
Film Analysis Guides for Dynamic Studies of Test Subjects—SAE J138 . . . . **4**:34.135
Motor Vehicle Dimensions—SAE J1100 JUL79 . **4**:34.49
Motor Vehicle Driver's Eye Range—SAE J941 MAR81 . . . . **4**:34.66
Steering Control System—Passenger Car—Laboratory Test Procedure—SAE J944 JUN80 . . . . . **4**:34.150
Synthetic Skins for Automotive Testing—SAE J202 **4**:34.124
Vision Factors Considerations in Rear View Mirror Design—SAE J985 . . . . **4**:34.44
Vision Glossary—SAE J264 . . . . **4**:34.119

ANTIFREEZE
Engine Coolant Concentrate—Ethylene-Glycol Type—SAE J1034 . . . . **1**:11.122
Engine Coolants—SAE J814c **1**:11.118

AUDIO CASSETTES
See: CASSETTES

AXLES
Axle and Manual Transmission Lubricant Viscosity Classification—SAE J306 MAY81 . . . . **3**:23.16
Axle and Manual Transmission Lubricants—SAE J308c **3**:23.15
Axle Efficiency Test Procedure—SAE J1266 . . . **4**:29.29
Axle Rating for Industrial Wheel Loaders and Loader-Backhoes—SAE J43 . . . . **4**:40.222
Axles—Nomenclature and Terminology—SAE J923 . . . . **4**:29.25
Brake Flange Mounting—On-Highway Vehicles—SAE J337 . . . . **4**:36.54
Trailer Axle Alignment—SAE J875 . . . . **4**:36.54

BACKHOES
See: CONSTRUCTION AND INDUSTRIAL MACHINERY

BACKUP ALARMS
See: ALARMS

BACKUP LAMPS
See: LAMPS

BALL JOINTS
Ball Joints—SAE J490 OCT81 . . . . **2**:14.08
Performance Test Procedure—Ball Joints and Spherical Rod Ends—SAE J1367 SEP81 . . . . **2**:14.16
Spherical Rod Ends—SAE J1120 SEP79 . . . . . **2**:14.12

BALL STUDS
Ball Stud and Socket Assembly Test Procedure—SAE J193 SEP79 . . . . **2**:14.06
Ball Studs and Ball Stud Socket Assemblies—SAE J491b **2**:14.01

BATTERIES
Battery Cable—SAE J1127 JUN80 . . . . **2**:20.48
Grounding of Storage Batteries—SAE J538a . . . **2**:20.12
Life Test for Automotive Storage Batteries—SAE J240 JUN82 . . . . **2**:20.11
Storage Batteries—SAE J537 JUN82 . . . . **2**:20.04
Storage Batteries for Construction and Industrial Machinery—SAE J930b **4**:40.314

BEARINGS
Bearing and Bushing Alloys (Information Report)—SAE J459c **1**:10.28
Bearing and Bushing Alloys (Standard)—SAE J460e **1**:10.28
Sleeve Type Half Bearings—SAE J506b **3**:24.38

BELTS
See Also: SEAT BELTS
Automotive Synchronous Belt Drives—SAE J1313 OCT80 . . . . **2**:16.12
Automotive V-Belt Drives—SAE J637b **2**:16.04
SI (Metric) Synchronous Belts and Pulleys—SAE J1278 OCT80 . . . . **2**:16.08

NOTE: Page numbers shown include the volume number in bold followed by the section number and page number within that section.

Tractor Belt Speed and Pulley Width—SAE J720
MAY80 .... 4:39.32
V-Belts and Pulleys—SAE J636c 2:16.01

BOATS
   See: MOTORBOATS
BOLTS
   See: FASTENERS
BOOMS
   Crane Boom Hoist Disengaging Device—SAE J999
   OCT80 .... 4:40.147
   Crane Boomstop—SAE J220 OCT80 .... 4:40.144
   Pipelayers and Side Booms, Tractor-Mounted—
   Specifications and Test—SAE J743 DEC80 .. 4:40.153
   Radius-of-Load and Boom Angle Measuring Sys-
   tem—SAE J375 OCT80 .... 4:40.145
   Telescopic Boom Length Indicating System—SAE
   J1180 OCT80 .... 4:40.144

BRAKES
   See Also: HYDRAULIC SYSTEMS
   Air Brake Gladhand Service (Control) and Emer-
   gency (Supply) Line Couplers—Trucks, Truck-
   Tractors, and Trailers—SAE J318 SEP80 .... 2:22.130
   Automotive Air Brake Reservoir Volume—SAE J813 2:22.129
   Automotive and Off-Highway Air Brake Reservoir
   Performance and Identification Requirements—
   SAE J10 SEP80 .... 2:22.131
   Automotive Brake Definitions and Nomenclature—
   SAE J656g 2:22.55
   Automotive Hydraulic Brake System—Metric Banjo
   Bolt Connections—SAE J1291 JUL80 ...... 2:22.146
   Automotive Hydraulic Brake System—Metric Tube
   Connections—SAE J1290 JUL80 .... 2:22.141
   Brake and Electrical Connection Locations—Truck-
   Tractor and Truck-Trailer—SAE J702b 4:36.55
   Brake Block Chamfer—SAE J662 .... 2:22.66
   Brake Diaphragm Maintenance—Tractor and Semi-
   trailer—SAE J666 .... 4:36.56
   Brake Disc and Drum Thermocouple Installation—
   SAE J79 .... 2:22.133
   Brake Flange Mounting—On-Highway Vehicles—
   SAE J337 .... 4:36.54
   Brake Master Cylinder Reservoir Diaphragm
   Gasket—SAE J1605 .... 2:22.17
   Brake Rating Horsepower Requirements—Commer-
   cial Vehicles—SAE J257 JUN80 .... 2:22.127
   Brake System Performance Requirements—Truck,
   Bus, and Combination of Vehicles—SAE J992b 2:22.113
   Braking Performance—In-Service Crawler Tractors
   and Crawler Loaders—SAE J1026 JUN82 ... 4:40.192
   Braking Performance—New Off-Highway Dump-
   ers—SAE J1224 JUN82 .... 4:40.199
   Braking Performance—Rollers and Compactors—
   SAE J1136 SEP79 .... 4:40.201
   Braking Performance—Rubber-Tired Construction
   Machines—SAE J1152 APR80 .... 4:40.193
   Emergency Air Brake Systems—Motor Vehicles and
   Vehicle Combinations—SAE J263 SEP80 .... 2:22.128
   Hydraulic Master Cylinders for Motor Vehicle
   Brakes—Performance Requirements—SAE
   J1154 .... 2:22.28
   Hydraulic Valves for Motor Vehicle Brake Systems—
   Performance Requirements—SAE J1137 .... 2:22.32
   Hydraulic Wheel Cylinders for Automotive Drum
   Brakes—SAE J101 MAR80 .... 2:22.21
   Information Relating to Duty Cycles and Average
   Power Requirements of Truck and Bus Engine Ac-
   cessories—SAE J1343 JUL81 .... 4:36.32
   Minimum Performance Criteria for Braking Systems
   for Rubber-Tired Skidders—SAE J1178 ..... 4:40.63
   Minimum Requirements for Wheel Slip Brake Con-
   trol System Malfunction Signals—SAE J1230
   OCT79 .... 2:22.138
   Rivets for Brake Linings and Bolts for Brake Blocks—
   SAE J663b 2:22.66
   Rubber Boots for Drum Type Hydraulic Brake Wheel
   Cylinders—SAE J1604 .... 2:22.19

Rubber Cups for Hydraulic Actuating Cylinders—
SAE J1601 .... **2**:22.148
Rubber Seals for Hydraulic Disc Brake Cylinders—
SAE J1603 .... **2**:22.15
Service Brake Structural Integrity Requirements—
Vehicles Over 10 000 lb (4500 KG) GVWR—SAE
J1404 .... **2**:22.74
Service Brake System Performance Requirements—
Passenger Car—SAE J937b **2**:22.88
Service Brake System Performance Requirements—
Light-Duty Truck—SAE J155 .... **2**:22.94
Service Brake System Performance Requirements—
Passenger Car—Trailer Combinations—SAE
J135a **2**:22.106
Service Brake System Performance Requirements—
Motorcycles and Motor-Driven Cycles—SAE
J109a **2**:22.118
Service Brake System Performance Requirements—
Snowmobiles—SAE J44 .... **4**:38.11
Snowmobile Brake Control Systems—SAE J1282
SEP80 .... **4**:38.10
Test Method for Measuring Power Consumption of
Air Conditioning and Air Brake Compressors for
Trucks and Buses—SAE J1340 JUL81 .... **4**:36.29
Tubing—Motor Vehicle Brake System Hydraulic—
SAE J1047 .... **2**:22.138
Vehicle Grade Parking Performance Requirements—
SAE J293 .... **2**:22.74

Brake Fluids
   Central Fluid Systems—SAE J71a **3**:23.23
   Determination of Brake Fluid Temperature—SAE
   J291 JUN80 .... **2**:22.133
   Handling and Dispensing of Motor Vehicle Brake
   Fluid—SAE J76 .... **2**:22.51
   Labeling of Motor Vehicle Brake Fluid Containers—
   SAE J988 .... **2**:22.50
   Motor Vehicle Brake Fluid—SAE J1703 JAN80 . **2**:22.41
   Motor Vehicle Brake Fluid Container Compatibil-
   ity—SAE J75 .... **2**:22.50
   Motor Vehicle Brake Fluid—Arctic—SAE J1702f . **2**:22.33
   Service Maintenance of Motor Vehicle Brake Fluid
   in Motor Vehicle Brake Actuating Systems—SAE
   J77 .... **2**:22.53

Brake Hoses
   Application of Hydraulic Brake Hose to Motor Vehi-
   cles—SAE J1406 MAR81 .... **2**:22.13
   Automotive Air Brake Hose and Hose Assemblies—
   SAE J1402 OCT80 .... **2**:22.07
   Road Vehicle—Hydraulic Brake Hose Assemblies for
   Use with Non-Petroleum Base Hydraulic Fluids—
   SAE J1401 JAN81 .... **2**:22.01
   Vacuum Brake Hose—SAE J1403a **2**:22.11

Brake Linings
   Brake Lining Quality Control Test Procedure—SAE
   J661a **2**:22.63
   Color Code for Location Identification of Combina-
   tion Linings of Two Different Materials or Two
   Shoe Brakes—SAE J659 .... **2**:22.66
   Friction Identification System for Brake Linings and
   Brake Blocks for Motor Vehicles—SAE J866a . **2**:22.62
   Gogan Hardness of Brake Lining—SAE J379a ... **2**:22.60
   Minimum Requirements for Motor Vehicle Brake Lin-
   ings—SAE J998 .... **2**:22.65
   Rivets for Brake Linings and Bolts for Brake Blocks—
   SAE J663b **2**:22.66
   Specific Gravity of Brake Lining—SAE J380 .... **2**:22.61
   Swell, Growth, and Dimensional Stability of Brake
   Linings—SAE J160 JUN80 .... **2**:22.62
   Test Procedures for Brake Shoe and Lining Adhe-
   sives and Bonds—SAE J840c **2**:22.67

Brake Shoes
   Color Code for Location Identification of Combina-
   tion Linings of Two Different Materials or Two
   Shoe Brakes—SAE J659 .... **2**:22.66
   Test Procedures for Brake Shoe and Lining Adhe-
   sives and Bonds—SAE J840c **2**:22.67

NOTE: Page numbers shown include the volume number in bold followed by the section number and page number within that section.

Brake Tests

Brake Rating Test Code—Commercial Vehicle Inertia Dynamometer—SAE J971 . . . . **2**:22.126

Brake System Dynamometer Test Procedure—Passenger Car—SAE J212 JUN80 . . . . **2**:22.90

Brake System Rating Test Code—Commercial Vehicles—SAE J880 MAY80 . . . . **2**:22.119

Brake System Road Test Code—Motorcycles—SAE J108a **2**:22.116

Brake System Road Test Code—Passenger Car and Light-Duty Truck—SAE J843d **2**:22.77

Brake System Road Test Code—Passenger Car and Light Duty Truck-Trailer Combinations—SAE J134 JUN79 . . . . **2**:22.97

Brake System Road Test Code—Truck, Bus, and Combination of Vehicles—SAE J786a **2**:22.107

Brake System Test Procedure—Snowmobiles—SAE J45 . . . . **4**:38.11

Brake System Torque Balance Test Code—Commercial Vehicles—SAE J225 JUN80 . . . . **2**:22.125

Brake Test Code—Inertia Dynamometer—SAE J667 . . . . **2**:22.75

Brake Test Procedure and Brake Performance Criteria for Agricultural Equipment—SAE J1041 . . . **4**:39.15

Displacement of Pneumatic Brake Actuators—SAE J1155 SEP80 . . . . **2**:22.132

Hydraulic Master Cylinders for Motor Vehicle Brakes—Test Procedure—SAE J1153 . . . . . . **2**:22.24

Hydraulic Valves for Motor Vehicle Brake Systems Test Procedure—SAE J1118 . . . . **2**:22.28

In-Service Brake Performance Test Procedure—Vehicles Over 4500 kg (10 000 lb)—SAE J1250 FEB80 . . . . **2**:22.59

In-Service Brake Performance Test Procedure Passenger Car and Light-Duty Truck—SAE J201 . . **2**:22.57

Motor Vehicle Grade Parking Performance Test Code—SAE J360 . . . . **2**:22.73

Service Brake Structural Integrity Test Procedure—Passenger Car—SAE J229 JUN80 . . . . . . **2**:22.96

Service Brake Structural Integrity Test Procedure—Vehicles Over 10 000 LB (4500 kg) GVWR—SAE J294 . . . . **2**:22.114

Simulated Mountain Brake Performance Test Procedure—SAE J1247 APR80 . . . . **2**:22.82

Stopping Distance Test Procedure—SAE J299 JAN80 . . . . **2**:22.132

Test Code—Truck, Truck-Tractor, and Trailer Air Service Brake System Pneumatic Pressure and Time Levels—SAE J982 SEP80 . . . . **2**:22.129

Wheel Slip Brake Control System Road Test Code—SAE J46 JUN80 . . . . **2**:22.134

BRAZING

Welding, Brazing, and Soldering—Materials and Practices—SAE J1147 . . . . **1**:9.07

BUCKETS

Capacity Rating—Loader Bucket—SAE J742 OCT79 . . . . **4**:40.217

Crane and Cable Excavator Basic Operating Control Arrangements—SAE J983 OCT80 . . . . **4**:40.150

Excavator Hoe Bucket Rating—SAE J296 OCT80 . . . . **4**:40.219

Shovel Dipper, Clam Bucket, and Dragline Bucket Rating—SAE J67 OCT80 . . . . **4**:40.216

BUMPERS

Approach, Departure, and Ramp Breakover Angles—Passenger Car and Light Duty Trucks—SAE J689 . . . . **4**:32.03

Bumper Evaluation Test Procedure—Passenger Cars—SAE J980a **4**:32.02

Bumper Jack Requirements—Motor Vehicles—SAE J979 . . . . **4**:32.01

Bumper Jacking Test Procedure—Motor Vehicles—SAE J978 . . . . **4**:32.01

BUSES

Automobile, Truck, Truck-Tractor, Trailer, and Motor Coach Wiring—SAE J1292 OCT81 . . . . . . **2**:20.39

Brake Rating Horsepower Requirements—Commercial Vehicles—SAE J257 JUN80 . . . . **2**:22.127

Brake Rating Test Code—Commercial Vehicle Inertia Dynamometer—SAE J971 . . . . **2**:22.126

Brake System Performance Requirements—Truck, Bus, and Combination of Vehicles—SAE J992b **2**:22.113

Brake System Road Test Code—Truck, Bus, and Combination of Vehicles—SAE J786a **2**:22.107

Brake System Torque Balance Test Code—Commercial Vehicles—SAE J225 JUN80 . . . . **2**:22.125

Exterior Sound Level for Heavy Trucks and Buses—SAE J366b **3**:26.18

Information Relating to Duty Cycles and Average Power Requirements of Truck and Bus Engine Accessories—SAE J1343 JUL81 . . . . **4**:36.32

Joint TMC/SAE Fuel Consumption Test Procedure—Type II—SAE J1321 OCT81 . . . . **4**:36.08

Nomenclature—Truck, Bus, Trailer—SAE J687c **4**:36.01

Rolling Resistance Measurement Procedure for Highway Truck and Bus Tires—SAE J1379 JUN82 . . . . **4**:30.08

SAE Wind Tunnel Test Procedure for Trucks and Buses—SAE J1252 JUL81 . . . . **4**:36.33

School Bus Red Signal Lamps—SAE J887 MAY82 **2**:21.69

School Bus Stop Arm—SAE J1133a **2**:21.70

Test Method for Measuring Power Consumption of Cooling Fans for Trucks and Buses—SAE J1339 JUL81 . . . . **4**:36.27

Test Method for Measuring Power Consumption of Hydraulic Pumps for Trucks and Buses—SAE J1341 JUL81 . . . . **4**:36.29

Test Method for Measuring Power Consumption of Air Conditioning and Air Brake Compressors for Trucks and Buses—SAE J1340 JUL81 . . . . . . **4**:36.29

Test Method for Measuring Power Consumption of Fan Drive Systems for Trucks and Buses—SAE J1342 JUL81 . . . . **4**:36.30

The Measurement of Highway Truck and Bus Tire Rolling Resistance—SAE J1380 JUN82 . . . . . **4**:30.10

Truck and Bus Tire Performance Requirements and Test Procedures—SAE J341a **4**:30.17

Windshield Defrosting Systems Performance Requirements—Trucks, Buses, and Multipurpose Vehicles—SAE J382 . . . . **4**:34.17

Windshield Defrosting Systems Test Procedure—Trucks, Buses, and Multipurpose Vehicles—SAE J381 . . . . **4**:34.15

Windshield Wiper Systems—Trucks, Buses, and Multipurpose Vehicles—SAE J198 . . . . **4**:34.09

BUSHINGS

Bearing and Bushing Alloys (Information Report)—SAE J459c **1**:10.28

Bearing and Bushing Alloys (Standard)—SAE J460e **1**:10.28

Split Type Bushings—Design and Application—SAE J835 DEC81 . . . . **3**:24.45

CABLES

Battery Cable—SAE J1127 JUN80 . . . . **2**:20.48

High Tension Ignition Cable—SAE J557 . . . . . **2**:20.46

High Tension Ignition Cable Assemblies—Marine—SAE J1191 . . . . **4**:41.19

Low Tension Primary Cable—SAE J1128 . . . . . **2**:20.50

Marine Control Cable Connection—Engine Clutch Lever—SAE J960 JUN80 . . . . **4**:41.03

Marine Control Cable Connection—Engine Throttle Lever—SAE J961 JUN80 . . . . **4**:41.04

Marine Push-Pull Control Cables—SAE J917 JUN80 . . . . **4**:41.02

Seven Conductor Jacketed Cable for Truck Trailer Connections—SAE J1067 . . . . **2**:20.61

Seven-Conductor Electrical Connector for Truck-Trailer Jumper Cable—SAE J560b **2**:20.60

CARBURETORS

Carburetor Airflow Reference Standards—SAE J228 JAN80 . . . . **3**:24.118

Marine Carburetors—SAE J1223 DEC80 . . . . . **4**:41.21

NOTE: Page numbers shown include the volume number in bold followed by the section number and page number within that section.

CASSETTES

Performance Requirements for the Automotive Audio Cassette—SAE J1274 JUN80 .... 2:20.71

Testing Methods for Audio Cassettes—SAE J1275 JUN80 .... 2:20.72

CHAINS

Passenger and Light Truck Tire Traction Device Profile Determination and Classification—SAE J1232 .... 4:36.57

Safety Chain of Full Trailers or Converter Dollies—SAE J697a 4:36.51

Tire Chain Clearance—Trucks, Buses, and Combinations of Vehicles—SAE J683a 4:36.56

Trailer Couplings, Hitches and Safety Chains—Automotive Type—SAE J684f 4:35.01

CAST IRON
See: IRON

CIRCUITS

Automotive Printed Circuits—SAE J771c 2:20.42

CIRCUIT BREAKERS

Circuit Breaker—Internal Mounted—Automatic Reset—SAE J258 .... 2:20.39

Circuit Breakers—SAE J553c 2:20.37

CLAM BUCKETS
See: BUCKETS

CLAMPS
See: FASTENERS

CLUTCHES

Clutch Friction Test Machine (SAE No. 2)—Test Procedure—SAE J286 .... 4:29.35

Flywheels for Single-Plate Spring-Loaded Clutches—SAE J618 JUN80 .... 3:24.70

Flywheels for Two-Plate Spring-Loaded Clutches—SAE J619 JUN80 .... 3:24.71

Housing Internal Dimensions for Single and Two Plate Spring Loaded Clutches—SAE J373a ... 3:24.72

Industrial Power Take-Offs with Driving Ring Type Overcenter Clutches—SAE J621d 4:40.164

Marine Control Cable Connection—Engine Clutch Lever—SAE J960 JUN80 .... 4:41.03

One-Way Clutches—Nomenclature and Terminology—SAE J1087 AUG81 .... 4:29.33

Overcenter Clutch Spin Test Procedure—SAE J1079 .... 4:40.163

SAE Nodal Mount—SAE J1134 .... 4:36.55

Spring-Loaded Clutch Spin Test Procedure—SAE J1073 JUN80 .... 3:24.72

COATINGS

Electroplating and Related Finishes—SAE J474b . 1:10.143

Florida Exposure of Automotive Finishes—SAE J951 FEB80 .... 1:11.67

Test for Chip Resistance of Surface Coatings—SAE J400 JUN80 .... 1:11.64

Vibration Damping Materials and Underbody Coatings—SAE J671 APR82 .... 1:11.56

COLLISIONS
See: IMPACT

COMPACTORS
See: CONSTRUCTION AND INDUSTRIAL MACHINERY

CONNECTORS
See: FASTENERS

CONSTRUCTION AND INDUSTRIAL MACHINERY

Bolt and Capscrew Sizes for Use in Construction and Industrial Machinery—SAE J370 .... 2:13.101

Categories of Off-Road Self-Propelled Work Machines—SAE J1116 JUN81 .... 4:40.01

Center of Gravity Test Code—SAE J874 MAR81 4:40.101

Classification and Nomenclature Towing Winch for Skidders and Crawler Tractors—SAE J1014 OCT79 .... 4:40.38

Classification, Nomenclature and Specification Definitions for Trenching Machines—SAE J1382 MAY82 .... 4:40.29

Countersunk Square Holes for Cutting Edges and End Bits—SAE J740b 4:40.163

Definitions for Machine Availability (Construction and Industrial)—SAE J1032 APR80 .... 4:40.64

Format for Commercial Literature Specifications—Off-Road Work Machines—SAE J1233 ..... 4:40.17

Gradeability Test Code—SAE J950 APR80 .... 4:40.105

Identification Terminology of Earthmoving Machines—SAE J1057 JUN81 .... 4:40.04

Industrial Power Take-Offs with Driving Ring Type Overcenter Clutches—SAE J621d 4:40.164

Machine Drag Test Code—SAE J873 APR80 ... 4:40.100

Machine Slope Operation Test Code—SAE J897 . 4:40.107

Measurement of Whole Body Vibration of the Seated Operator of Off-Highway Work Machines—SAE J1013 JAN80 .... 4:39.57

Off-Road Tire and Rim Selection and Application—SAE J1315 MAY81 .... 4:40.209

Product Identification Numbering System of Off-Road Work Machines—SAE J1360 JUN81 ... 4:40.03

Remote and Automatic Control Systems for Construction and Industrial Machinery—SAE J956 . 4:40.303

Reserve Tractive Ability Test Code—SAE J872 OCT80 .... 4:40.98

Sound Measurement—Construction Site—SAE J1075 SEP80 .... 3:26.51

Sound Measurement—Trenching Equipment—SAE J1262 SEP80 .... 3:26.60

Sound Power Determination—Earthmoving Machinery—Static Condition—SAE J1372 DEC81 ... 3:26.53

Specification Definitions—Off-Road Work Machines—SAE J1234 .... 4:40.12

Storage Batteries for Construction and Industrial Machinery—SAE J930b 4:40.314

Ton Mile Per Hour Application Practice—SAE J1098 APR80 .... 4:40.213

Unauthorized Starting or Movement of Machines—SAE J1083 FEB80 .... 4:40.63

Wiring Identification System for Industrial and Construction Equipment—SAE J210 .... 4:40.192

Backhoes

Axle Rating for Industrial Wheel Loaders and Loader-Backhoes—SAE J43 .... 4:40.222

Excavator Hoe Bucket Rating—SAE J296 OCT80 4:40.219

Hydraulic Backhoe Lift Capacity—SAE J31 .... 4:40.220

Nomenclature—Hydraulic Backhoes—SAE J326 SEP80 .... 4:40.218

Specification Definitions—Hydraulic Backhoes—SAE J49 APR80 .... 4:40.50

Brake Systems

Braking Performance—New Off-Highway Dumpers—SAE J1224 JUN82 .... 4:40.199

Braking Performance—Rubber-Tired Construction Machines—SAE J1152 APR80 .... 4:40.193

Compactors

Braking Performance—Rollers and Compactors—SAE J1136 SEP79 .... 4:40.201

Component Nomenclature—Rollers/Compactors—SAE J1017 .... 4:40.36

Cranes

Braking Performance—Rubber-Tired Construction Machines—SAE J1152 APR80 .... 4:40.193

Cantilevered Boom Crane Structures—Method of Test—SAE J1063 OCT80 .... 4:40.115

Crane and Cable Excavator Basic Operating Control Arrangements—SAE J983 OCT80 .... 4:40.150

Crane Boom Hoist Disengaging Device—SAE J999 OCT80 .... 4:40.147

Crane Boomstop—SAE J220 OCT80 .... 4:40.144

Crane Hoist Line Speed and Power Test Code—SAE J820 OCT80 .... 4:40.141

Crane Load Moment System—SAE J159 OCT80 4:40.147

Crane Load Stability Test Code—SAE J765 OCT80 .... 4:40.142

Crane Structures—Method of Test—SAE J987 OCT80 .... 4:40.110

Lifting Crane Sheave and Drum Sizes—SAE J881 OCT80 .... 4:40.158

NOTE: Page numbers shown include the volume number in bold followed by the section number and page number within that section.

Lifting Crane, Wire-Rope Strength Factors—SAE
J959 OCT80 .... **4**:40.148

Load Indicating Devices in Lifting Crane Service—
SAE J376 OCT80 .... **4**:40.146

Mobile Crane Stability Ratings—SAE J1289
APR81 .... **4**:40.153

Mobile Crane Working Area Definitions—SAE
J1028 OCT80 .... **4**:40.152

Nomenclature and Dimensions for Crane Shovels—
SAE J958 MAR81 .... **4**:40.40

Radius-of-Load and Boom Angle Measuring System—SAE J375 OCT80 .... **4**:40.145

Rating Chart for Cantilevered Boom Cranes—SAE
J1257 OCT80 .... **4**:40.121

Rope Drum Rotation Indicating Device—SAE
J1332 OCT81 .... **4**:40.157

Telescopic Boom Length Indicating System—SAE
J1180 OCT80 .... **4**:40.144

Design Dimensions

Access Systems for Off-Road Machines—SAE J185
JUN81 .... **4**:40.260

Control Locations for Construction and Industrial
Equipment Design—SAE J898 APR80 ...... **4**:40.269

Deflection of Seat Cushions for Off-Road Work Machines—SAE J1051 JAN80 .... **4**:40.264

Determining Operator Seat Location on Off-Road
Work Machines—SAE J1163 JAN80 ..... **4**:40.265

Instrument Face Design and Location for Construction and Industrial Equipment—SAE J209
APR80 .... **4**:40.272

Minimum Access Dimensions for Construction and
Industrial Machinery—SAE J925 .... **4**:40.258

Operator Controls on Industrial Equipment—SAE
J297 APR80 .... **4**:40.276

Operator Enclosures Human Factor Design Considerations—SAE J154a **4**:40.270

Operator's Seat Dimensions for Off-Road Self-Propelled Work Machines—SAE J899 OCT80 ... **4**:40.267

Universal Symbols for Operator Controls—SAE
J1500 JUN80 .... **INDEX** 102

USA Human Physical Dimensions—SAE J833
JAN80 .... **4**:40.255

Dozers

Dozer Capacity—SAE J1265 FEB80 ...... **4**:40.161

Hole Placement on Dozer End Bits—SAE J63
FEB80 .... **4**:40.158

Hole Spacing for Scraper and Bulldozer Cutting
Edges—SAE J737b **4**:40.158

Nomenclature—Dozer—SAE J729 MAY80 .... **4**:40.24

Scraper and Bulldozer Cutting Edge Cross Sections,
Rolled, Cast, Forged or Machined—SAE J738b ... **4**:40.160

Specification Definitions—Dozers—SAE J173
JAN80 .... **4**:40.26

Dumpers

Braking Performance—New Off-Highway Dumpers—SAE J1224 JUN82 .... **4**:40.199

Braking Performance—Rubber-Tired Construction
Machines—SAE J1152 APR80 .... **4**:40.193

Capacity Ratings—Scraper, Dumper Body and
Trailer Body—SAE J741b **4**:40.215

Component Nomenclature—Dumper Trailer—SAE
J734c **4**:40.34

Component Nomenclature—Dumpers—SAE J1016 **4**:40.35

Electrical Propulsion Rotating Equipment—Off-Road
Dumper—SAE J1317 JUN82 .... **4**:40.190

Minimum Performance Criteria for Emergency
Steering of Wheeled Earthmoving Construction
Machines—SAE J53 .... **4**:40.305

Electrical Systems

Electrical Charging Systems for Construction and
Industrial Machinery—SAE J180 APR80 ... **4**:40.186

Electrical Connector for Auxiliary Starting of Construction, Agricultural, and Off-Road Machinery—
SAE J1283 JUN80 .... **4**:40.175

Electrical Propulsion Rotating Equipment—Off-Road
Dumper—SAE J1317 JUN82 .... **4**:40.190

Electrical System for Construction and Industrial Machinery—SAE J821a **4**:40.184

Excavators

Braking Performance—Rubber-Tired Construction
Machines—SAE J1152 APR80 .... **4**:40.193

Excavator Hand Signals—SAE J1307 MAY81 .. **4**:40.229

Excavator Hoe Bucket Rating—SAE J296 OCT80 **4**:40.219

Hydraulic Excavator Digging Forces—SAE J1179
OCT80 .... **4**:40.226

Hydraulic Excavator Lift Capacity Rating—SAE
J1097 OCT80 .... **4**:40.222

Hydraulic Excavator Operator Controls—SAE
J1177 OCT80 .... **4**:40.227

Nomenclature and Dimensions for Hydraulic Excavators—SAE J1193 MAR81 .... **4**:40.42

Fuel Systems

Dry-Break Fueling Installation for Construction Machinery—SAE J176a **4**:40.69

Guidelines for Fluid Level Indicators—SAE J48 .. **4**:40.69

Graders

Braking Performance—Rubber-Tired Construction
Machines—SAE J1152 APR80 .... **4**:40.193

Component Nomenclature—Graders—SAE J870 . **4**:40.23

Grader Cutting Edge—SAE J739b **4**:40.160

Minimum Performance Criteria for Emergency
Steering of Wheeled Earthmoving Construction
Machines—SAE J53 .... **4**:40.305

Operator Controls for Graders—SAE J1071 .... **4**:40.277

Heating, Ventilating, and Air Conditioning

Design Guidelines for Air Conditioning Systems for
Construction and Industrial Equipment Cabs—
SAE J169 APR80 .... **4**:40.301

Fuel-Fired Heaters—Air Heating—for Construction
and Industrial Machinery—SAE J1024 APR80 . **4**:40.287

Operator Cab Environment for Heated, Ventilated,
and Air Conditioned Construction and Industrial
Equipment—SAE J1129 .... **4**:40.302

Hydraulic Systems

Assessing Cleanliness of Hydraulic Fluid Power
Components and Systems—SAE J1227 ..... **4**:40.70

External Leakage Classifications for Hydraulic Systems—SAE J1176 .... **4**:40.98

Hydraulic Cylinder Test Procedure—SAE J214
OCT80 .... **4**:40.94

Hydraulic Directional Control Valves, 3000 psi Maximum—SAE J748 OCT80 .... **4**:40.80

Hydraulic Motor Test Procedure—SAE J746
OCT80 .... **4**:40.87

Hydraulic Power Circuit Filtration—SAE J931a .. **4**:40.92

Hydraulic Power Pump Test Procedure—SAE J745
OCT80 .... **4**:40.76

Hydraulic Power Pumps—SAE J744 OCT80 ... **4**:40.78

Hydraulic Systems Diagnostic Port Sizes and Locations—SAE J1298 OCT80 .... **4**:40.76

Measuring and Reporting the Internal Leakage of
a Hydraulic Fluid Power Valve—SAE J1235
SEP80 .... **4**:40.84

Method of Measuring and Reporting the Pressure
Differential-Flow Characteristics of a Hydraulic
Fluid Power Valve—SAE J1117 SEP80 ..... **4**:40.81

Standardized Fluid for Hydraulic Component
Tests—SAE J1276 AUG79 .... **4**:40.85

Lighting Systems

Combination Tail and Floodlamp for Industrial
Equipment—SAE J94 APR80 .... **4**:40.182

Dimensional Specifications for Sealed Lighting Unit
for Construction and Industrial Machinery—SAE
J572a **4**:40.180

Flashing Warning Lamp for Industrial Equipment—
SAE J96 .... **4**:40.181

Headlamps for Industrial Equipment—SAE J95
APR80 .... **4**:40.182

Lighting and Marking of Construction and Industrial
Machinery—SAE J1029 APR80 .... **4**:40.182

Sealed Lighting Units for Construction and Industrial
Machinery—SAE J598 APR80 .... **4**:40.179

NOTE: Page numbers shown include the volume number in bold followed by the section number and page number within that section.

Loaders

Axle Rating for Industrial Wheel Loaders and Loader-Backhoes—SAE J43 . . . . **4**:40.222

Braking Performance—In-Service Crawler Tractors and Crawler Loaders—SAE J1026 JUN82 . . . **4**:40.192

Braking Performance—Rubber-Tired Construction Machines—SAE J1152 APR80 . . . . **4**:40.193

Capacity Rating—Loader Bucket—SAE J742 OCT79 . . . . **4**:40.217

Component Nomenclature—Loader—SAE J731d . **4**:40.27

Lift Arm Safety Device for Loaders—SAE J38 . . . **4**:40.234

Minimum Performance Criteria for Emergency Steering of Wheeled Earthmoving Construction Machines—SAE J53 . . . . **4**:40.305

Operating Load for Loaders—SAE J818b **4**:40.66

Specification Definitions—Loaders—SAE J732 FEB80 . . . . **4**:40.48

Steering Frame Lock for Articulated Loaders and Tractors—SAE J276 JUN81 . . . . **4**:40.234

Lubricants

Lubricant Types—Construction and Industrial Machinery—SAE J754a **4**:40.67

Lubrication Chart—Construction and Industrial Machinery—SAE J753 JUN82 . . . . **4**:40.67

Oil Change System for Quick Service of Off-Road Self-Propelled Work Machines—SAE J1069 JUN81 . . . . **4**:40.68

Maintenance

Engineering Design Serviceability Guide Lines—Construction and Industrial Machinery—SAE J817a **4**:40.307

Format for Construction Equipment Manuals—SAE J920a **4**:40.313

Maintenance Interval—Construction Equipment—SAE J752b **4**:40.68

Symbols and Color Codes for Maintenance Instructions, Container and Filler Identification—SAE J223 APR80 . . . . **4**:40.70

Mowers

Industrial Rotary Mowers—SAE J232 . . . . **4**:40.281

Nomenclature—Industrial Mowers—SAE J990 . . **4**:40.279

Safety for Industrial Flail Mowers—SAE J1001 DEC80 . . . . **4**:40.282

Operator Protective Structures

Deflection Limiting Volume—ROPS/FOPS Laboratory Evaluation—SAE J397b **4**:40.244

Identification Terminology—Pipelayers—SAE J1295 JUN80 . . . . **4**:40.42

Labeling of ROPS and FOPS—SAE J1164 . . . . . **4**:40.243

Lift Arm Safety Device for Loaders—SAE J38 . . . **4**:40.234

Minimum Performance Criteria for Falling Object Protective Structure (FOPS)—SAE J231 JAN81 . . . . **4**:40.245

Minimum Performance Criteria for Falling Object Protective Structure (FOPS) for Industrial Equipment—SAE J1043 APR80 . . . . **4**:40.246

Operator Protection for Industrial Equipment—SAE J1042 APR80 . . . . **4**:40.243

Performance Criteria for Rollover Protective Structures (ROPS) for Construction, Earthmoving, Forestry, and Mining Machines—SAE J1040c . . . **4**:40.235

Performance Prediction of Roll-Over Protective Structures (ROPS) Through Analytical Methods—SAE J1215 . . . . **4**:40.254

Safety for Industrial Wheeled Equipment—SAE J98 DEC80 . . . . **4**:40.278

Seat Belts for Construction Machines—SAE J386 APR80 . . . . **4**:40.283

Steel Products for Rollover Protective Structures (ROPS) and Falling Object Protective Structures (FOPS)—SAE J1119 APR80 . . . . **4**:40.248

Steering Frame Lock for Articulated Loaders and Tractors—SAE J276 JUN81 . . . . **4**:40.234

Rippers

Nomenclature—Rippers, Rooters, Scarifiers—SAE J733b **4**:40.33

Rollers

Braking Performance—Rollers and Compactors—SAE J1136 SEP79 . . . . **4**:40.201

Component Nomenclature—Rollers/Compactors—SAE J1017 . . . . **4**:40.36

Rooters

Nomenclature—Rippers, Rooters, Scarifiers—SAE J733b **4**:40.33

Safety

Horn—Forward Warning—Electric—Performance, Test, and Application—SAE J1105 SEP80 . . . **3**:26.34

Lighting and Marking of Industrial Equipment on Highways—SAE J99 APR80 . . . . **4**:40.183

Mobile Crane Stability Ratings—SAE J1289 APR81 . . . . **4**:40.153

Safety Considerations for the Operator—SAE J153 **4**:40.277

Safety for Industrial Wheeled Equipment—SAE J98 DEC80 . . . . **4**:40.278

Safety Signs—SAE J115 SEP79 . . . . **4**:40.285

Seat Belts for Construction Machines—SAE J386 APR80 . . . . **4**:40.283

Scarifiers

Nomenclature—Rippers, Rooters, Scarifiers—SAE J733b **4**:40.33

Scrapers

Capacity Ratings—Scraper, Dumper Body and Trailer Body—SAE J741b **4**:40.215

Component Nomenclature—Scrapers—SAE J728a **4**:40.21

Elevating Scrapers—Capacity Rating—SAE J957 . **4**:40.216

Hole Spacing for Scraper and Bulldozer Cutting Edges—SAE J737b **4**:40.158

Loading Ability Test Code—Scrapers—SAE J764 APR80 . . . . **4**:40.108

Minimum Performance Criteria for Emergency Steering of Wheeled Earthmoving Construction Machines—SAE J53 . . . . **4**:40.305

Scraper and Bulldozer Cutting Edge Cross Sections, Rolled, Cast, Forged or Machined—SAE J738b **4**:40.160

Sound Levels

Engine Sound Level Measurement Procedure—SAE J1074 . . . . **3**:26.64

Sound Measurement—Construction Site—SAE J1075 SEP80 . . . . **3**:26.51

Sound Measurement—Earthmoving Machinery—Operator—Singular Type—SAE J919 SEP80 . . **3**:26.37

Sound Measurement—Earthmoving Machinery—Operator—Work Cycle—SAE J1166 SEP80 . . **3**:26.39

Sound Measurement—Earthmoving Machinery—Exterior—SAE J88 SEP80 . . . . **3**:26.57

Tractors

Braking Performance—In-Service Crawler Tractors and Crawler Loaders—SAE J1026 JUN82 . . . **4**:40.192

Braking Performance—Rubber-Tired Construction Machines—SAE J1152 APR80 . . . . **4**:40.193

Classification and Nomenclature Towing Winch for Skidders and Crawler Tractors—SAE J1014 OCT79 . . . . **4**:40.38

Component Nomenclature—Crawler Tractor—SAE J727 MAY80 . . . . **4**:40.18

Component Nomenclature—Industrial Tractors (Wheel)—SAE J1092 . . . . **4**:40.19

Component Nomenclature—Two and Four-Wheel Tractors—SAE J869a **4**:40.19

Drawbars—Crawler Tractor—SAE J749a **4**:40.214

Minimum Performance Criteria for Emergency Steering of Wheeled Earthmoving Construction Machines—SAE J53 . . . . **4**:40.305

Pipelayers and Side Booms, Tractor-Mounted—Specifications and Test—SAE J743 DEC80 . . **4**:40.153

Specification Definitions—Winches for Crawler Tractors and Skidders—SAE J1158 . . . . **4**:40.59

Steering Frame Lock for Articulated Loaders and Tractors—SAE J276 JUN81 . . . . **4**:40.234

CONTROLS

Automatic Transmissions—Manual Control Sequence—SAE J915 . . . . **4**:29.14

NOTE: Page numbers shown include the volume number in bold followed by the section number and page number within that section.

Automatic Vehicle Speed Control—Motor Vehicles—SAE J195 .... **2**:18.12

Control Locations for Construction and Industrial Equipment Design—SAE J898 APR80 ...... **4**:40.269

Crane and Cable Excavator Basic Operating Control Arrangements—SAE J983 OCT80 .... **4**:40.150

Design Criteria—Driver Hand Controls Location for Passenger Cars, Multi-Purpose Passenger Vehicles, and Trucks (10 000 GVW and Under)—SAE J1138 .... **4**:34.105

Driver Hand Control Reach—SAE J287 FEB80 .. **4**:34.72

Hydraulic Excavator Operator Controls—SAE J1177 OCT80 .... **4**:40.227

Marine Control Cable Connection—Engine Clutch Lever—SAE J960 JUN80 .... **4**:41.03

Marine Control Cable Connection—Engine Throttle Lever—SAE J961 JUN80 .... **4**:41.04

Marine Push-Pull Control Cables—SAE J917 JUN80 .... **4**:41.02

Operator Controls and Displays on Motorcycles—SAE J107 APR80 .... **4**:37.01

Operator Controls for Graders—SAE J1071 .... **4**:40.277

Operator Controls on Agricultural Equipment—SAE J841 MAY80 .... **4**:39.46

Operator Controls on Industrial Equipment—SAE J297 APR80 .... **4**:40.276

Remote and Automatic Control Systems for Construction and Industrial Machinery—SAE J956 .... **4**:40.303

Snowmobile Brake Control Systems—SAE J1282 SEP80 .... **4**:38.10

Supplemental Information—Driver Hand Controls Location for Passenger Cars, Multi-Purpose Passenger Vehicles, and Trucks (10 000 GVW and Under)—SAE J1139 .... **4**:34.107

Symbols for Motor Vehicle Controls, Indicators and Tell-Tales—SAE J1048 MAR80 .... **4**:34.153

Universal Symbols for Operator Controls—SAE J1500 JUN80 .... **INDEX** 102

Universal Symbols for Operator Controls on Agricultural Equipment—SAE J389b **4**:39.47

Universal Symbols for Operator Controls on Industrial Equipment—SAE J298 .... **4**:40.274

COOLING SYSTEMS

Engine Coolant Concentrate—Ethylene-Glycol Type—SAE J1034 .... **1**:11.122

Engine Coolants—SAE J814c **1**:11.118

Engine Cooling System Field Test (Air-to-Boil)—SAE J819 MAR80 .... **4**:40.106

Fan Hub Bolt-Circles and Pilot Holes—SAE J635a **3**:24.141

Glossary of Engine Cooling System Terms—SAE J1004 SEP81 .... **3**:24.121

Guide to the Application and Use of Engine Coolant Pump Face Seals—SAE J1245 JUN82 ...... **3**:24.144

Oil Cooler Nomenclature and Glossary—SAE J1244 JUN81 .... **3**:24.133

Pressure Relief for Cooling System—SAE J151 .. **3**:24.102

COPPER ALLOYS

See: **ALLOYS**

CORROSION

Corrosion Test for Insulation Materials—SAE J1389 MAY82 .... **1**:11.93

Undervehicle Corrosion Test—SAE J1293 JAN80 **1**:3.34

COUPLERS

Air Brake Gladhand Service (Control) and Emergency (Supply) Line Couplers—Trucks, Truck-Tractors, and Trailers—SAE J318 SEP80 .... **2**:22.130

Connection and Accessory Locations for Towing Doubles Trailers and Multi-Axle Trailers—SAE J849b **4**:36.49

Dimensional Standard for Cylindrical Hydraulic Couplers for Agricultural Tractors—SAE J1036 ... **4**:39.26

Fifth Wheel Kingpin, Heavy Duty—Commercial Trailers and Semitrailers—SAE J848a **4**:36.49

Fifth Wheel Kingpin Performance—Commercial Trailers and Semitrailers—SAE J133 JAN82 .. **4**:36.46

Fifth Wheel Kingpin—Commercial Trailers and Semitrailers—SAE J700 JAN82 .... **4**:36.48

Marine Propeller-Shaft Couplings—SAE J756 AUG81 .... **4**:41.01

Three-Point Hitch, Implement Quick-Attaching Coupler, Agricultural Tractors—SAE J909 APR80 .... **4**:39.17

Trailer Couplings, Hitches and Safety Chains—Automotive Type—SAE J684f **4**:35.01

Truck Tractor Semitrailer Interchange Coupling Dimensions—SAE J701a **4**:36.43

CRANES

See: **CONSTRUCTION AND INDUSTRIAL MACHINERY**

CRASHWORTHINESS

See: **IMPACT**

CYLINDERS

Cylinder Rod Wiper Seal Ingression Test—SAE J1195 .... **4**:40.96

Engine Rotation and Cylinder Numbering—SAE J824 .... **3**:24.24

Hydraulic Cylinder Test Procedure—SAE J214 OCT80 .... **4**:40.94

Hydraulic Master Cylinders for Motor Vehicle Brakes—Test Procedure—SAE J1153 .... **2**:22.24

Hydraulic Master Cylinders for Motor Vehicle Brakes—Performance Requirements—SAE J1154 .... **2**:22.28

Hydraulic Wheel Cylinders for Automotive Drum Brakes—SAE J101 MAR80 .... **2**:22.21

Rubber Cups for Hydraulic Actuating Cylinders—SAE J1601 .... **2**:22.148

DEADENERS

Methods of Tests for Automotive-Type Sealers, Adhesives, and Deadeners—SAE J243 ...... **1**:11.46

Vibration Damping Materials and Underbody Coatings—SAE J671 APR82 .... **1**:11.56

DEFOGGING SYSTEMS

Passenger Car Backlight Defogging System—SAE J953 .... **4**:34.18

DEFROSTING SYSTEMS

Passenger Car Windshield Defrosting Systems—SAE J902b **4**:34.13

Windshield Defrosting Systems Performance Requirements—Trucks, Buses, and Multipurpose Vehicles—SAE J382 .... **4**:34.17

Windshield Defrosting Systems Test Procedure—Trucks, Buses, and Multipurpose Vehicles—SAE J381 .... **4**:34.15

DIESEL ENGINES

See: **ENGINES**

DIMENSIONS

Motor Vehicle Dimensions—SAE J1100 JUL79 . **4**:34.49

Motor Vehicle Fiducial Marks—SAE J182a **4**:34.121

DIPPERS

Shovel Dipper, Clam Bucket, and Dragline Bucket Rating—SAE J67 OCT80 .... **4**:40.216

DIPSTICKS

Engine and Transmission Dipstick Marking—SAE J614b **3**:24.68

DISC WHEELS

See: **WHEELS**

DISTRIBUTORS

Ignition Distributors—Marine—SAE J1294 APR80 .... **4**:41.15

DOORS

Passenger Car Door System Crush Test Procedure—SAE J367 JUN80 .... **4**:34.148

DOZERS

See: **CONSTRUCTION AND INDUSTRIAL MACHINERY**

DRAWBARS

Drawbars—Crawler Tractor—SAE J749a **4**:40.214

DRIVESHAFTS

Universal Joints and Driveshafts—Nomenclature and Terminology—SAE J901b **4**:29.17

NOTE: Page numbers shown include the volume number in bold followed by the section number and page number within that section.

DRIVETRAINS
Towed Vehicle Drivetrain Test Procedure—Passenger Cars and Light Duty Trucks—SAE J1144a . **4**:28.07

DUMPERS
See: **CONSTRUCTION AND INDUSTRIAL MACHINERY**

EARTHMOVING MACHINERY
See: **CONSTRUCTION AND INDUSTRIAL MACHINERY**

ELASTOMERIC MATERIALS
Automotive Plastic Parts Specification—SAE J1345 FEB82 . . . . **1**:11.71
Automotive Rubber Mats—SAE J80 MAY82 . . . **1**:11.104
Classification System for Rubber Materials for Automotive Applications—SAE J200 APR80 . . . . . **1**:11.01
Recommended Guidelines for Fatigue Testing of Elastomeric Materials and Components—SAE J1183 . . . . **1**:11.29
Sponge- and Expanded Cellular-Rubber Products—SAE J18 DEC79 . . . . **1**:11.40
Test for Dynamic Properties of Elastomeric Isolators—SAE J1085a **1**:11.34

ELECTRICAL SYSTEMS
Automobile, Truck, Truck-Tractor, Trailer, and Motor Coach Wiring—SAE J1292 OCT81 . . . . **2**:20.39
Blade Type Electric Fuses—SAE J1284 DEC79 . **2**:20.34
Cranking Motor Application Considerations—SAE J1375 MAR82 . . . . **2**:20.18
Electric Engine Preheaters and Battery Warmers for Diesel Engines—SAE J1310 APR81 . . . . . . **4**:40.291
Electrical Charging Systems for Construction and Industrial Machinery—SAE J180 APR80 . . . . **4**:40.186
Electrical Generating System (Alternator Type) Performance Curve and Test Procedure—SAE J56 **2**:20.18
Electrical Propulsion Rotating Equipment—Off-Road Dumper—SAE J1317 JUN82 . . . . **4**:40.190
Electrical System for Construction and Industrial Machinery—SAE J821a **4**:40.184
Low Temperature Cranking Load Requirements of an Engine—SAE J1253 . . . . **2**:20.17
Maintenance of Design Voltage—Snowmobile Electrical Systems—SAE J277 . . . . **4**:38.04
Motorcycle and Motor Driven Cycle Electrical System (Maintenance of Design Voltage)—SAE J392 **2**:21.41
Nomenclature—Automotive Electrical Systems—SAE J831 . . . . **2**:20.01
Voltage Drop for Starting Motor Circuits—SAE J541a **2**:20.12
Voltages for Diesel Electrical Systems—SAE J539a **2**:20.12

ELECTRIC VEHICLES
Electric Vehicle Test Procedure—SAE J227a . . . **4**:28.09

ELECTROMAGNETICS
Eddy Current Testing by Electromagnetic Methods—SAE J425 MAR81 . . . . **1**:3.48
Electromagnetic Susceptibility Procedures for Vehicle Components (Except Aircraft)—SAE J1113a **2**:20.80
Open Field Whole-Vehicle Radiated Susceptibility 10 kHz—18 GHz, Electric Field—SAE J1338 JUN81 . . . . **2**:20.109
Performance Levels and Methods of Measurement of Electromagnetic Radiation from Vehicles and Devices (20–1000 MHz)—SAE J551 JUN81 . . **2**:20.26

ELECTRONICS
Electromagnetic Susceptibility Procedures for Vehicle Components (Except Aircraft)—SAE J1113a **2**:20.80
Glossary of Automotive Electronic Terms—SAE J1213 . . . . **2**:20.120
Guide to Manifold Absolute Pressure Transducer Representative Test Method—SAE J1346 JUN81 . . . . **2**:20.125
Guide to Manifold Absolute Pressure Transducer Representative Specification—SAE J1347 JUN81 . . . . **2**:20.128
Open Field Whole-Vehicle Radiated Susceptibility 10 kHz—18 GHz, Electric Field—SAE J1338 JUN81 . . . . **2**:20.109

Recommended Environmental Practices for Electronic Equipment Design—SAE J1211 . . . . . . **2**:20.92

ELECTROPLATING
Electroplating and Related Finishes—SAE J474b . **1**:10.143
Electroplating of Nickel and Chromium on Metal Parts—Automotive Ornamentation and Hardware—SAE J207 . . . . **1**:10.137

EMISSIONS
Acoustic Emission Test Methods—SAE J1242 . . **1**:3.56
Constant Volume Sampler System for Exhaust Emissions Measurement—SAE J1094a **3**:25.102
Continuous Hydrocarbon Analysis of Diesel Emissions—SAE J215 JAN80 . . . . **3**:25.21
Crankcase Emission Control Test Code—SAE J900 NOV80 . . . . **3**:25.54
Determination of Emissions from Gas Turbine Powered Light Duty Surface Vehicles—SAE J1130 . **3**:25.133
Determination of Sulfur Compounds in Automotive Exhaust—SAE J1280 JAN80 . . . . **3**:25.60
Diesel Emission Production Audit Test Procedure—SAE J1243 AUG79 . . . . **3**:25.27
Diesel Engine Emission Measurement Procedure—SAE J1003 . . . . **3**:25.25
Diesel Engine Smoke Measurement—SAE J255a . **3**:25.32
Diesel Smoke Measurement Procedure—SAE J35 **3**:25.51
Emissions Terminology and Nomenclature—SAE J1145a **3**:25.143
Instrumentation and Techniques for Exhaust Gas Emissions Measurement—SAE J254 . . . . **3**:25.93
Instrumentation and Techniques for Vehicle Refueling Emissions Measurement—SAE J1045 . . . . **3**:25.124
Measurement of Carbon Dioxide, Carbon Monoxide, and Oxides of Nitrogen in Diesel Exhaust—SAE J177 APR82 . . . . **3**:25.01
Measurement of Fuel Evaporative Emissions from Gasoline Powered Passenger Cars and Light Trucks—SAE J170a **3**:25.78
Measurement of Fuel Evaporative Emissions from Gasoline Powered Passenger Cars and Light Trucks Using the Enclosure Technique—SAE J171 JUN82 . . . . **3**:25.84
Measurement Procedure for Evaluation of Full-Flow, Light Extinction Smokemeter Performance—SAE J1157 . . . . **3**:25.40
Methane Measurement Using Gas Chromatography—SAE J1151 NOV79 . . . . **3**:25.146
Test Procedure for Measurement of Small Utility Engine Exhaust Emissions—SAE J1088 . . . . . . **3**:25.128
Test Procedure for Measuring Carbon Monoxide Concentrations in Vehicle Passenger Compartments—SAE J989a **3**:25.58

ENGINES
Engine and Transmission Identification Numbers—SAE J129 DEC81 . . . . **4**:27.03
Engine Charge Air Cooler Nomenclature—SAE J1148 . . . . **3**:24.127
Engine Cooling System Field Test (Air-to-Boil)—SAE J819 MAR80 . . . . **4**:40.106
Engine Power Test Code—Spark Ignition and Diesel—SAE J1349 DEC80 . . . . **3**:24.09
Engine Preheaters—SAE J226a **3**:24.116
Engine Rotation and Cylinder Numbering—SAE J824 . . . . **3**:24.24
Engine Sound Level Measurement Procedure—SAE J1074 . . . . **3**:26.64
Engine Terminology and Nomenclature—General—SAE J604d **3**:24.01
Glossary of Engine Cooling System Terms—SAE J1004 SEP81 . . . . **3**:24.121
Information Relating to Duty Cycles and Average Power Requirements of Truck and Bus Engine Accessories—SAE J1343 JUL81 . . . . **4**:36.32
Low Temperature Cranking Load Requirements of an Engine—SAE J1253 . . . . **2**:20.17
Marine Engine Rating Code—SAE J1228 MAR80 . . . . **4**:41.11

NOTE: Page numbers shown include the volume number in bold followed by the section number and page number within that section.

Measurement Procedure for Determination of Silencer Effectiveness in Reducing Engine Intake or Exhaust Sound Level—SAE J1207 OCT81 . . .   **3**:26.65

Procedure for Measuring Basic Highway Vehicle Engine Performance and Fuel Consumption—Spark Ignition and Diesel—SAE J1312 SEP80 . . . . .   **3**:24.11

Rotary-Trochoidal Engine Nomenclature and Terminology—SAE J1220 . . . .   **3**:24.03

Diesel Engines

Continuous Hydrocarbon Analysis of Diesel Emissions—SAE J215 JAN80 . . . .   **3**:25.21

Diesel Emission Production Audit Test Procedure—SAE J1243 AUG79 . . . .   **3**:25.27

Diesel Engine Emission Measurement Procedure—SAE J1003 . . . .   **3**:25.25

Diesel Engine Smoke Measurement—SAE J255a   **3**:25.32

Diesel Smoke Measurement Procedure—SAE J35   **3**:25.51

Electric Engine Preheaters and Battery Warmers for Diesel Engines—SAE J1310 APR81 . . . .   **4**:40.291

Engine Power Test Code—Spark Ignition and Diesel—SAE J1349 DEC80 . . . .   **3**:24.09

Measurement of Intake Air or Exhaust Gas Flow of Diesel Engines—SAE J244 . . . .   **3**:25.11

Selection and Application Guidelines for Diesel, Gasoline, and Propane Fired Liquid Cooled Engine Pre-Heaters—SAE J1350 DEC81 . . . .   **4**:40.287

Testing Techniques for Diesel Fuel Injection Systems—SAE J969b **3**:24.92

Gas Turbine Engines

Gas Turbine Engine Nomenclature—SAE J828 JAN80 . . . .   **3**:24.02

Gas Turbine Engine Test Code—SAE J116a **3**:24.16

Small Engines

Bystander Sound Level Measurement Procedure for Small Engine Powered Equpiment—SAE J1175   **3**:26.49

Multiposition Small Engine Exhaust System Fire Ignition Suppression—SAE J335b **3**:24.102

Operator Ear Sound Level Measurement Procedure for Small Engine Powered Equipment—SAE J1174 . . . .   **3**:26.48

Small Spark Ignition Engine Test Code—SAE J607a   **3**:24.14

EXCAVATORS

See: CONSTRUCTION AND INDUSTRIAL MACHINERY

EXHAUST SYSTEMS

Nomenclature for Exhaust System Parts—SAE J97   **3**:24.117

FABRICS

See: MATERIALS

FALLING OBJECT PROTECTIVE STRUCTURES

See: OPERATOR PROTECTIVE STRUCTURES

FANS

Engine Cooling Fan Structural Analysis—SAE J1390 APR82 . . . .   **3**:24.130

Fan Hub Bolt-Circles and Pilot Holes—SAE J635a   **3**:24.141

Information Relating to Duty Cycles and Average Power Requirements of Truck and Bus Engine Accessories—SAE J1343 JUL81 . . . .   **4**:36.32

Test Method for Measuring Power Consumption of Cooling Fans for Trucks and Buses—SAE J1339 JUL81 . . . .   **4**:36.27

Test Method for Measuring Power Consumption of Fan Drive Systems for Trucks and Buses—SAE J1342 JUL81 . . . .   **4**:36.30

FASTENERS

See Also: PINS

Decarburization in Hardened and Tempered Threaded Fasteners—SAE J121a **1**:4.44

Mechanical and Material Requirements for Externally Threaded Fasteners—SAE J429 JAN80 . .   **1**:4.01

Mechanical and Material Requirements for Metric Externally Threaded Steel Fasteners—SAE J1199 . . . .   **1**:4.06

Test Methods for Metric Threaded Fasteners—SAE J1216 . . . .   **1**:4.11

Torque-Tension Test Procedure for Steel Threaded Fasteners—SAE J174 . . . .   **2**:13.76

Bolts

Automotive Hydraulic Brake System—Metric Banjo Bolt Connections—SAE J1291 JUL80 . . . . .   **2**:22.146

Bolt and Capscrew Sizes for Use in Construction and Industrial Machinery—SAE J370 . . . . . .   **2**:13.101

Hex Bolts—SAE J105 . . . .   **2**:13.01

Hi-Head Finished Hex Bolts—SAE J871a **2**:13.04

Holes in Bolt and Capscrew Shanks and Slots in Nuts for Cotter Pins—SAE J485 . . . .   **2**:13.79

Mechanical and Material Requirements for Wheel Bolts—SAE J1102 . . . .   **1**:4.18

Rivets for Brake Linings and Bolts for Brake Blocks—SAE J663b **2**:22.66

Round Head Bolts—SAE J481 . . . .   **2**:13.04

Surface Discontinuities on Bolts, Screws, and Studs—SAE J123c **1**:4.37

Surface Discontinuities on General Application Bolts, Screws, and Studs—SAE J1061a **1**:4.33

Clamps

Hose Clamps—SAE J536b **2**:13.101

Connectors

Automotive Hydraulic Brake System—Metric Tube Connections—SAE J1290 JUL80 . . . .   **2**:22.141

Brake and Electrical Connection Locations—Truck-Tractor and Truck-Trailer—SAE J702b **4**:36.55

Connection and Accessory Locations for Towing Doubles Trailers and Multi-Axle Trailers—SAE J849b **4**:36.49

Connectors and Plugs—SAE J856 . . . .   **2**:21.09

Electrical Connector for Auxiliary Starting of Construction, Agricultural, and Off-Road Machinery—SAE J1283 JUN80 . . . .   **4**:40.175

Five Conductor Electrical Connectors for Automotive Type Trailers—SAE J895 . . . .   **2**:20.55

Four- and Eight-Conductor Rectangular Electrical Connectors for Automotive Type Trailers—SAE J1239 . . . .   **2**:20.57

Fuel Injection Tubing Connections—SAE J521b .   **3**:24.94

Hydraulic Flanged Tube, Pipe, and Hose Connections, 4-Bolt Split Flange Type—SAE J518c **2**:19.107

Metric Thread Fuel Injection Tubing Connections—SAE J242a **3**:24.93

Selection, Installation, and Maintenance of Hose and Hose Assemblies—SAE J1273 SEP79 . . . . . .   **2**:19.104

Seven Conductor Jacketed Cable for Truck Trailer Connections—SAE J1067 . . . .   **2**:20.61

Seven-Conductor Electrical Connector for Truck-Trailer Jumper Cable—SAE J560b **2**:20.60

Nuts

Alignment of Nut Slots—SAE J484 . . . .   **2**:13.54

Crown (Blind, Acorn) Nuts—SAE J483a **2**:13.54

Hexagon High Nuts—SAE J482a **2**:13.53

Holes in Bolt and Capscrew Shanks and Slots in Nuts for Cotter Pins—SAE J485 . . . .   **2**:13.79

Mechanical and Material Requirements for Steel Nuts—SAE J995 JUN79 . . . .   **1**:4.15

Nut and Conical Spring Washer Assemblies—SAE J238 . . . .   **2**:13.74

Push-On Spring Nuts—SAE J892a **2**:13.63

Spring Nuts—SAE J891a **2**:13.55

Square and Hex Nuts—SAE J104 . . . .   **2**:13.47

Steel Stamped Nuts of One Pitch Thread Design—SAE J1053 . . . .   **2**:13.64

Surface Discontinuities on Nuts—SAE J122a . . .   **1**:4.40

Rivets

Blind Rivets—Break Mandrel Type—SAE J1200 .   **2**:13.95

Mechanical and Chemical Requirements for Non-threaded Fasteners—SAE J430 . . . .   **1**:4.18

Rivets and Riveting—SAE J492 . . . .   **2**:13.85

Rivets for Brake Linings and Bolts for Brake Blocks—SAE J663b **2**:22.66

Screws

Bolt and Capscrew Sizes for Use in Construction and Industrial Machinery—SAE J370 . . . . . .   **2**:13.101

Flanged 12-Point Screws—SAE J58 . . . .   **2**:13.42

NOTE: Page numbers shown include the volume number in bold followed by the section number and page number within that section.

Holes in Bolt and Capscrew Shanks and Slots in Nuts
for Cotter Pins—SAE J485 . . . . **2**:13.79
Lag Screws—SAE J103 . . . . **2**:13.46
Mechanical and Quality Requirements for Machine
Screws—SAE J82 JUN79 . . . . **1**:4.14
Mechanical and Quality Requirements for Tapping
Screws—SAE J933 JUN79 . . . . **1**:4.19
Metric Thread Rolling Screws—SAE J1237 . . . . **1**:4.29
Screw Threads—SAE J475a **2**:12.01
Slotted and Recessed Head Screws—SAE
J478a **2**:13.07
Slotted Headless Setscrews—SAE J479a **2**:13.40
Square Head Setscrews—SAE J102 . . . . . . **2**:13.41
Steel Self-Drilling Tapping Screws—SAE J78
JUN79 . . . . **1**:4.21
Surface Discontinuities on Bolts, Screws, and
Studs—SAE J123c **1**:4.37
Surface Discontinuities on General Application
Bolts, Screws, and Studs—SAE J1061a **1**:4.33
Thread Rolling Screws—SAE J81 JUN79 . . . . . **1**:4.26

Studs
Surface Discontinuities on Bolts, Screws, and
Studs—SAE J123c **1**:4.37
Surface Discontinuities on General Application
Bolts, Screws, and Studs—SAE J1061a **1**:4.33

Washers
Conical Spring Washers—SAE J773b **2**:13.73
Lock Washers—SAE J489b **2**:13.68
Nut and Conical Spring Washer Assemblies—SAE
J238 . . . . **2**:13.74
Plain Washers—SAE J488 . . . . **2**:13.68
Thrust Washers—Design and Application—SAE
J924 JAN81 . . . . **3**:24.50

FATIGUE
Recommended Guidelines for Fatigue Testing of
Elastomeric Materials and Components—SAE
J1183 . . . . **1**:11.29
Technical Report on Fatigue Properties—SAE
J1099 . . . . **1**:3.57

FIBERBOARDS
  See: MATERIALS

FILTERS
Air Cleaner Elements—SAE J1141 . . . . **3**:24.57
Air Cleaner Test Code—SAE J726 MAY81 . . . . **3**:24.58
Glossary of Terms Related to Fluid Filters and Filter
Testing—SAE J1124 . . . . **3**:24.98

FINISHES
  See: COATINGS

FITTINGS
Automotive Pipe Fittings—SAE J530 JAN81 . . . **2**:19.128
Automotive Tube Fittings—SAE J512 OCT80 . . **2**:19.04
Coding Systems for Identification of Fluid Conduc-
tors and Connectors—SAE J846 FEB82 . . . . . **2**:19.01
Hose Push-On Fittings—SAE J1231 . . . . **2**:19.89
Hydraulic Hose Fittings—SAE J516 MAR81 . . . **2**:19.72
Hydraulic Tube Fittings—SAE J514 APR80 . . . . **2**:19.46
Lubrication Fittings—SAE J534 JAN81 . . . . . . **2**:19.143
Performance Requirements for SAE J844d Nonme-
tallic Tubing and Fitting Assemblies Used in Auto-
motive Air Brake Systems—SAE J1131 . . . . . **2**:19.126
Pressure Ratings for Hydraulic Tubing and Fittings—
SAE J1065 . . . . **2**:19.119
Refrigeration Tube Fittings—SAE J513f **2**:19.26
Spherical and Flanged Sleeve (Compression) Tube
Fittings—SAE J246 MAR81 . . . . **2**:19.18

FLANGES
Airflow or Vacuum Governor Flanges—SAE J622
JAN80 . . . . **3**:24.75
Brake Flange Mounting—On-Highway Vehicles—
SAE J337 . . . . **4**:36.54
Exhaust Flanges—Industrial Engines—SAE
J624a **4**:40.170
Hydraulic Flanged Tube, Pipe, and Hose Connec-
tions, 4-Bolt Split Flange Type—SAE J518c . . **2**:19.107
Mounting Flanges and Power Take-Off Shafts for
Small Engines—SAE J609a **3**:24.18

Mounting Flanges for Engine Accessory Drives—
SAE J896 . . . . **4**:40.168
Water Connection Flanges—SAE J535 JAN80 . . **3**:24.74

FLASHERS
Flasher Test Equipment—SAE J823c **2**:21.77
Flashing Warning Lamp for Industrial Equipment—
SAE J96 . . . . **4**:40.181
Service Performance Requirements for Turn Signal
Flashers—SAE J1055 . . . . **2**:21.56
Service Performance Requirements for Vehicular
Hazard Warning Flashers—SAE J1056 . . . . . **2**:21.59
Service Performance Requirements for Warning
Lamp Alternating Flashers—SAE J1104 . . . . **2**:21.60
Turn Signal Flashers—SAE J590e **2**:21.55
Vehicular Hazard Warning Signal Flasher—SAE
J945b **2**:21.58
Warning Lamp Alternating Flashers—SAE J1054 . **2**:21.60

FLYWHEELS
Engine Flywheel Housings—SAE J617c **4**:40.166
Engine Flywheel Housings with Sealed Flanges—
SAE J1172 . . . . **3**:24.72
Flywheel Spin Test Procedure—SAE J1240 . . . . **3**:24.73
Flywheels for Engine Mounted Torque Converters—
SAE J927b **4**:40.169
Flywheels for Industrial Engines Used with Industrial
Power Take-Offs Equipped with Driving-Ring Type
Overcenter Clutches and Engine Mounted Marine
Gears—SAE J620d **4**:40.172
Flywheels for Single Bearing Engine Mounted Power
Generators—SAE J162a **4**:40.170
Flywheels for Single-Plate Spring-Loaded Clutches—
SAE J618 JUN80 . . . . **3**:24.70
Flywheels for Two-Plate Spring-Loaded Clutches—
SAE J619 JUN80 . . . . **3**:24.71
Procedure for Measuring Bore Eccentricity and Face
Deviation of Flywheels, Flywheel Housings, and
Flywheel Housing Adapters—SAE J1033 . . . . **4**:40.165

FOG LAMPS
  See: LAMPS

FOPS
  See: OPERATOR PROTECTIVE STRUCTURES

FORESTRY MACHINES
Categories of Off-Road Self-Propelled Work Ma-
chines—SAE J1116 JUN81 . . . . **4**:40.01
Fire Prevention on Forestry Equipment—SAE
J1212 . . . . **4**:40.62
Format for Commercial Literature Specifications—
Off-Road Work Machines—SAE J1233 . . . . . **4**:40.17
Identification Terminology of Mobile Forestry Ma-
chines—SAE J1209 . . . . **4**:40.14
Labeling of ROPS and FOPS—SAE J1164 . . . . **4**:40.243
Minimum Performance Criteria for Falling Object
Protective Structure (FOPS)—SAE J231 JAN81 **4**:40.245
Operator Protective Structure Performance Criteria
for Certain Forestry Equipment—SAE J1084
APR80 . . . . **4**:40.247
Performance Criteria for Rollover Protective Struc-
tures (ROPS) for Construction, Earthmoving, For-
estry, and Mining Machines—SAE J1040c . . . **4**:40.235
Product Identification Numbering System of Off-
Road Work Machines—SAE J1360 JUN81 . . . **4**:40.03
Specification Definitions—Off-Road Work Ma-
chines—SAE J1234 . . . . **4**:40.12
Unauthorized Starting or Movement of Machines—
SAE J1083 FEB80 . . . . **4**:40.63

Feller Buncher
Component Nomenclature—Feller Buncher—SAE
J1254 . . . . **4**:40.45
Felling Head Terminology and Nomenclature—SAE
J1272 OCT79 . . . . **4**:40.57
Specification Definitions—Feller/Buncher—SAE
J1255 . . . . **4**:40.60

Skidders
Classification and Nomenclature Towing Winch for
Skidders and Crawler Tractors—SAE J1014
OCT79 . . . . **4**:40.38

NOTE: Page numbers shown include the volume number in bold followed by the section number and page number within that section.

Component Nomenclature—Articulated Log Skidder, Rubber-Tired—SAE J1109 APR80 . . . . . **4**:40.45

Component Nomenclature—Skidder-Grapple—SAE J1111 MAR81 . . . . **4**:40.47

Minimum Performance Criteria for Braking Systems for Rubber-Tired Skidders—SAE J1178 . . . . . **4**:40.63

Specification Definitions—Articulated, Rubber-Tired Log Skidder—SAE J1110 APR80 . . . . **4**:40.53

Specification Definitions—Skidder-Grapple—SAE J1112 APR80 . . . . **4**:40.55

Specification Definitions—Winches for Crawler Tractors and Skidders—SAE J1158 . . . . **4**:40.59

FUEL

Alternative Automotive Fuels—SAE J1297 APR82 **3**:23.39

Automotive Gasolines—SAE J312 JUN82 . . . . . **3**:23.25

Diesel Fuels—SAE J313 APR82 . . . . **3**:23.34

Effective Dates of Revisions—SAE J301 . . . . . . **3**:23.01

FUEL ECONOMY

Fuel Economy Measurement—Road Test Procedure—SAE J1082 SEP80 . . . . **3**:24.156

Fuel Economy Measurement—Road Test Procedure—Cold Start and Warm-Up Fuel Economy—SAE J1256 JUN80 . . . . **3**:24.188

Information Relating to Duty Cycles and Average Power Requirements of Truck and Bus Engine Accessories—SAE J1343 JUL81 . . . . **4**:36.32

Joint RCCC/SAE Fuel Consumption Test Procedure (Short Term-In-Service Vehicle) Type I—SAE J1264 . . . . **4**:36.05

Joint TMC/SAE Fuel Consumption Test Procedure—Type II—SAE J1321 OCT81 . . . . **4**:36.08

Procedure for Measuring Basic Highway Vehicle Engine Performance and Fuel Consumption—Spark Ignition and Diesel—SAE J1312 SEP80 . . . . . **3**:24.11

Road Load Measurement and Dynamometer Simulation Using Coastdown Techniques—SAE J1263 **3**:24.165

Test Method for Measuring Power Consumption of Cooling Fans for Trucks and Buses—SAE J1339 JUL81 . . . . **4**:36.27

Test Method for Measuring Power Consumption of Hydraulic Pumps for Trucks and Buses—SAE J1341 JUL81 . . . . **4**:36.29

Test Method for Measuring Power Consumption of Air Conditioning and Air Brake Compressors for Trucks and Buses—SAE J1340 JUL81 . . . . . . **4**:36.29

Test Method for Measuring Power Consumption of Fan Drive Systems for Trucks and Buses—SAE J1342 JUL81 . . . . **4**:36.30

The Measurement of Highway Truck and Bus Tire Rolling Resistance—SAE J1380 JUN82 . . . . . **4**:30.10

FUEL INJECTION

Calibrating Nozzle and Holder Assembly for Diesel Fuel Injection Systems—SAE J968c **3**:24.90

Calibration Fluid for Diesel Injection Equipment—SAE J967d **3**:24.98

Diesel Fuel Injection Nozzle and Holder Assembly (17 mm Nominal Diameter)—SAE J265 . . . . . **3**:24.88

Diesel Fuel Injection Nozzle Holder Assembly (9.5 mm)—SAE J347a **3**:24.87

Diesel Fuel Injection Pump Mountings—SAE J626b **3**:24.80

Fuel Injection Equipment Nomenclature—SAE J830b **3**:24.78

Fuel Injection Nozzle Gaskets—SAE J59 . . . . . **3**:24.88

Fuel Injection Tubing—SAE J529b **2**:19.127

Fuel Injection Tubing Connections—SAE J521b . **3**:24.94

Master Calibrating Fuel Injection Pump—SAE J981 . . . . **3**:24.89

Metric Thread Fuel Injection Tubing Connections—SAE J242a **3**:24.93

Test Stands for Diesel Fuel Injection Systems—SAE J970a **3**:24.92

Testing Techniques for Diesel Fuel Injection Systems—SAE J969b **3**:24.92

FUEL SYSTEMS

Dry-Break Fueling Installation for Construction Machinery—SAE J176a **4**:40.69

Filler Pipes and Openings of Motor Vehicle Fuel Tanks—SAE J1140 MAR80 . . . . **3**:24.152

Fuel and Lubricant Tanks for Motorcycles—SAE J1241 . . . . **4**:37.05

Fuel Pump Mountings for Diaphragm Type Pumps—SAE J625 JUL80 . . . . **3**:24.77

Fuel Tank Filler Cap and Cap Retainer—SAE J829c **3**:24.151

Fuel Tank Filler Cap and Cap Retainer—Threaded Pressure-Vacuum Type—SAE J1114 . . . . . . **3**:24.150

Fuel Tank Filler Conditions—Passenger Car, Multi-Purpose Passenger Vehicles, and Light Duty Trucks—SAE J398b **3**:24.155

Gasoline Dispenser Nozzle Spouts—SAE J285 JUL81 . . . . **3**:24.156

LP-Gas Fuel Systems Components—SAE J372a . . **3**:24.101

Metallic and Nonmetallic Nonpressure Integral Fuel Tank—Snowmobile—SAE J288a **4**:38.17

FUSES

Blade Type Electric Fuses—SAE J1284 DEC79 . **2**:20.34

Electric Fuses (Cartridge Type)—SAE J554b . . . **2**:20.32

Fusible Links—SAE J156a **2**:20.55

GAS TURBINE ENGINES

See: ENGINES

GASKETS

Brake Master Cylinder Reservoir Diaphragm Gasket—SAE J1605 . . . . **2**:22.17

Fuel Injection Nozzle Gaskets—SAE J59 . . . . . **3**:24.88

Nonmetallic Automotive Gasket Materials—SAE J90b **1**:11.105

GASOLINE

See: FUEL

GEARS

Planetary Gear(s)—Terminology—SAE J646 JUL81 **4**:29.07

Starting Motor Pinions and Ring Gears—SAE J543c **2**:20.14

GENERATORS

Electric Starting Motor Test Procedure—SAE J544 MAY82 . . . . **2**:20.16

Electrical Charging Systems for Construction and Industrial Machinery—SAE J180 APR80 . . . . **4**:40.186

Electrical Generating System (Alternator Type) Performance Curve and Test Procedure—SAE J56 **2**:20.18

Flywheels for Single Bearing Engine Mounted Power Generators—SAE J162a **4**:40.170

Generator Mountings—SAE J545b **2**:20.14

GLASS

See: MATERIALS

GLAZING

Automotive Safety Glazing—SAE J673b **4**:34.36

Drop Test for Evaluating Laminated Safety Glass for Use in Automotive Windshields—SAE J938a . . **4**:34.41

Light Transmittance of Automotive Windshields Safety Glazing Materials—SAE J1203 . . . . . **4**:34.38

Passenger Car Glazing Shade Bands—SAE J100 . **4**:34.40

Passenger Car Glazing—Electrical Circuits—SAE J216 . . . . **4**:34.40

Safety Glazing Materials—Motor Vehicles—SAE J674a **4**:34.39

GRADERS

See: CONSTRUCTION AND INDUSTRIAL MACHINERY

GRIT

Cast Shot and Grit Size Specifications for Peening and Cleaning—SAE J444a **1**:8.09

Metallic Shot and Grit Mechanical Testing—SAE J445a **1**:8.10

HARDENABILITY BANDS

Hardenability Bands for Carbon and Alloy H Steels—SAE J1268 JUN81 . . . . **1**:1.26

HEADLAMPS

See: LAMPS

HEATERS

Fuel-Fired Heaters—Air Heating—for Construction and Industrial Machinery—SAE J1024 APR80 . **4**:40.287

Motor Vehicle Heater Test Procedure—SAE J638 JUN82 . . . . **4**:34.20

NOTE: Page numbers shown include the volume number in bold followed by the section number and page number within that section.

Selection and Application Guidelines for Diesel, Gasoline, and Propane Fired Liquid Cooled Engine Pre-Heaters—SAE J1350 DEC81 . . . . **4**:40.287

HINGES
Vehicle Passenger Door Hinge Systems—SAE J934 JUL82 . . . . **4**:34.01

HITCHES
Test Procedure for Measuring Hydraulic Lift Force Capacity on Agricultural Tractors Equipped with Three-Point Hitch—SAE J283 . . . . **4**:39.22
Three-Point Free-Link Hitch Attachment of Implements to Agricultural Wheeled Tractors—SAE J715 MAY80 . . . . **4**:39.19
Three-Point Hitch, Implement Quick-Attaching Coupler, Agricultural Tractors—SAE J909 APR80 . **4**:39.17
Trailer Couplings, Hitches and Safety Chains—Automotive Type—SAE J684f **4**:35.01

HORNS
Horn—Forward Warning—Electric—Performance, Test, and Application—SAE J1105 SEP80 . . . **3**:26.34
Performance of Vehicle Traffic Horns—SAE J377 **3**:26.24

HOSES
Application of Hydraulic Brake Hose to Motor Vehicles—SAE J1406 MAR81 . . . . **2**:22.13
Automotive Air Brake Hose and Hose Assemblies—SAE J1402 OCT80 . . . . **2**:22.07
Automotive Air Conditioning Hose—SAE J51b . . **1**:11.139
Coding Systems for Identification of Fluid Conductors and Connectors—SAE J846 FEB82 . . . . . **2**:19.01
Coolant System Hoses—SAE J20e **1**:11.123
Flex-Impulse Test Procedure for Hydraulic Hose Assemblies—SAE J1405 . . . . **2**:19.106
Fuel and Oil Hoses—SAE J30 JUN82 . . . . **1**:11.127
Hose Clamps—SAE J536b **2**:13.101
Hose Push-On Fittings—SAE J1231 . . . . **2**:19.89
Hydraulic Flanged Tube, Pipe, and Hose Connections, 4-Bolt Split Flange Type—SAE J518c . . **2**:19.107
Hydraulic Hose—SAE J517 JUN82 . . . . **2**:19.92
Hydraulic Hose Fittings—SAE J516 MAR81 . . . **2**:19.72
Power Steering Pressure Hose—High Volumetric Expansion Type—SAE J188 . . . . **1**:11.134
Power Steering Pressure Hose—Low Volumetric Expansion Type—SAE J191 . . . . **1**:11.137
Power Steering Pressure Hose—Wire Braid—SAE J190 . . . . **1**:11.138
Power Steering Return Hose—Low Pressure—SAE J189 . . . . **1**:11.135
Road Vehicle—Hydraulic Brake Hose Assemblies for Use with Non-Petroleum Base Hydraulic Fluids—SAE J1401 JAN81 . . . . **2**:22.01
Selection, Installation, and Maintenance of Hose and Hose Assemblies—SAE J1273 SEP79 . . . . . . **2**:19.104
Tests and Procedures for High-Temperature Transmission Oil Hose, Lubricating Oil Hose and Hose Assemblies—SAE J1019 . . . . **2**:19.107
Tests and Procedures for SAE 100R Series Hydraulic Hose and Hose Assemblies—SAE J343 JUN80 . . . . **2**:19.105
Vacuum Brake Hose—SAE J1403a **2**:22.11
Windshield Wiper Hose—SAE J50a **1**:11.139

HOUSINGS
Engine Flywheel Housings—SAE J617c **4**:40.166
Engine Flywheel Housings with Sealed Flanges—SAE J1172 . . . . **3**:24.72
Housing Internal Dimensions for Single and Two Plate Spring Loaded Clutches—SAE J373a . . . **3**:24.72

HYDRAULIC SYSTEMS
See Also: BRAKES
Application of Hydraulic Brake Hose to Motor Vehicles—SAE J1406 MAR81 . . . . **2**:22.13
Assessing Cleanliness of Hydraulic Fluid Power Components and Systems—SAE J1227 . . . . . **4**:40.70
Automatic Transmission Hydraulic Control Systems—Terminology—SAE J648a **4**:29.09
Automotive Hydraulic Brake System—Metric Banjo Bolt Connections—SAE J1291 JUL80 . . . . . . **2**:22.146

Automotive Hydraulic Brake System—Metric Tube Connections—SAE J1290 JUL80 . . . . **2**:22.141
Central Fluid Systems—SAE J71a **3**:23.23
External Leakage Classifications for Hydraulic Systems—SAE J1176 . . . . **4**:40.98
Flex-Impulse Test Procedure for Hydraulic Hose Assemblies—SAE J1405 . . . . **2**:19.106
Fluid for Passenger Car Type Automatic Transmissions—SAE J311b **3**:23.20
Hydraulic Control Valve Test Procedure—SAE J747 OCT80 . . . . **4**:40.89
Hydraulic Cylinder Test Procedure—SAE J214 OCT80 . . . . **4**:40.94
Hydraulic Directional Control Valves, 3000 psi Maximum—SAE J748 OCT80 . . . . **4**:40.80
Hydraulic Hose—SAE J517 JUN82 . . . . **2**:19.92
Hydraulic Master Cylinders for Motor Vehicle Brakes—Test Procedure—SAE J1153 . . . . . **2**:22.24
Hydraulic Master Cylinders for Motor Vehicle Brakes—Performance Requirements—SAE J1154 . . . . **2**:22.28
Hydraulic Motor Test Procedure—SAE J746 OCT80 . . . . **4**:40.87
Hydraulic "O" Ring—SAE J515a **2**:19.112
Hydraulic Power Circuit Filtration—SAE J931a . . **4**:40.92
Hydraulic Power Pump Test Procedure—SAE J745 OCT80 . . . . **4**:40.76
Hydraulic Power Pumps—SAE J744 OCT80 . . . **4**:40.78
Hydraulic Systems Diagnostic Port Sizes and Locations—SAE J1298 OCT80 . . . . **4**:40.76
Hydraulic Valves for Motor Vehicle Brake Systems—Performance Requirements—SAE J1137 . . . . **2**:22.32
Hydraulic Valves for Motor Vehicle Brake Systems Test Procedure—SAE J1118 . . . . **2**:22.28
Hydraulic Wheel Cylinders for Automotive Drum Brakes—SAE J101 MAR80 . . . . **2**:22.21
Hydrodynamic Drive Test Code—SAE J643b . . . **4**:29.04
Hydrodynamic Drives Terminology—SAE J641b . **4**:29.02
Measuring and Reporting the Internal Leakage of a Hydraulic Fluid Power Valve—SAE J1235 SEP80 . . . . **4**:40.84
Method for Assessing the Cleanliness Level of New Hydraulic Fluid—SAE J1277 MAY82 . . . . . . **4**:40.86
Method of Measuring and Reporting the Pressure Differential-Flow Characteristics of a Hydraulic Fluid Power Valve—SAE J1117 SEP80 . . . . . **4**:40.81
Pressure Ratings for Hydraulic Tubing and Fittings—SAE J1065 . . . . **2**:19.119
Reporting Cleanliness Levels of Hydraulic Fluids—SAE J1165 OCT80 . . . . **4**:40.85
Road Vehicle—Hydraulic Brake Hose Assemblies for Use with Non-Petroleum Base Hydraulic Fluids—SAE J1401 JAN81 . . . . **2**:22.01
Rubber Cups for Hydraulic Actuating Cylinders—SAE J1601 . . . . **2**:22.148
Standardized Fluid for Hydraulic Component Tests—SAE J1276 AUG79 . . . . **4**:40.85
Symbols for Hydrodynamic Drives—SAE J640 DEC81 . . . . **4**:29.01
Test Method for Measuring Power Consumption of Hydraulic Pumps for Trucks and Buses—SAE J1341 JUL81 . . . . **4**:36.29
Tubing—Motor Vehicle Brake System Hydraulic—SAE J1047 . . . . **2**:22.138

IGNITION SYSTEMS
Electrical Generating System (Alternator Type) Performance Curve and Test Procedure—SAE J56 **2**:20.18
High Tension Ignition Cable—SAE J557 . . . . . . **2**:20.46
High Tension Ignition Cable Assemblies—Marine—SAE J1191 . . . . **4**:41.19
Ignition Switch—SAE J259 . . . . **2**:20.39
Ignition System Measurements Procedure—SAE J973a **2**:20.02
Ignition System Nomenclature and Terminology—SAE J139 . . . . **2**:20.01
Ignition Timing—SAE J327 . . . . **3**:24.23

NOTE: Page numbers shown include the volume number in bold followed by the section number and page number within that section.

IMPACT

Barrier Collision Tests—SAE J850 JUN80 . . . . . 4:34.142

Bodyforms for Use in Motor Vehicle Passenger Compartment Impact Development—SAE J984 JUN80 . . . . 4:34.149

Collision Deformation Classification—SAE J224 MAR80 . . . . 4:34.125

Instrumentation for Impact Tests—SAE J211 JUN80 . . . . 4:34.137

Moving Barrier Collision Tests—SAE J972 JUN80 4:34.138

Passenger Car Door System Crush Test Procedure—SAE J367 JUN80 . . . . 4:34.148

Passenger Car Roof Crush Test Procedure—SAE J374 JUN80 . . . . 4:34.147

Steering Control System—Passenger Car—Laboratory Test Procedure—SAE J944 JUN80 . . . . 4:34.150

Wheels—Passenger Cars—Impact Performance Requirements and Test Procedures—SAE J175 . . 4:31.02

INDUSTRIAL MACHINERY
See: CONSTRUCTION AND INDUSTRIAL MACHINERY

INSTRUMENT PANELS

Instrument Face Design and Location for Construction and Industrial Equipment—SAE J209 APR80 4:40.272

Location and Operation of Instruments and Controls in Motor Truck Cabs—SAE J680 JUN82 . . . . 4:36.60

INSULATIONS

Compression and Recovery of Insulation Paddings—SAE J1352 MAY81 . . . . 1:11.92

Corrosion Test for Insulation Materials—SAE J1389 MAY82 . . . . 1:11.93

Heat Insulation Materials Test Procedure—SAE J1324 DEC81 . . . . 1:11.56

Hot Odor Test for Insulation Materials—SAE J1351 JUL81 . . . . 1:11.92

Hot Plate Method for Evaluating Heat Resistance and Thermal Insulation Properties of Materials—SAE J1361 APR81 . . . . 1:11.91

Nonmetallic Loom—SAE J562a 2:20.68

Test Method for Measuring the Relative Drapeability of Flexible Insulation Materials—SAE J1325 SEP80 . . . . 1:11.89

Test Method for Measuring Thickness of Resilient Insulating Paddings—SAE J1355 MAR81 . . . . 1:11.90

IRON

Automotive Ductile (Nodular) Iron Castings—SAE J434c 1:6.06

Automotive Gray Iron Castings—SAE J431 AUG79 1:6.01

Automotive Malleable Iron Castings—SAE J158a 1:6.04

Eddy Current Testing by Electromagnetic Methods—SAE J425 MAR81 . . . . 1:3.48

Elevated Temperature Properties of Cast Irons—SAE J125 . . . . 1:6.08

Magnetic Particle Inspection—SAE J420 MAR81 1:3.47

Nondestructive Tests—SAE J358 JAN80 . . . . . 1:3.45

Numbering System for Designating Grades of Cast Ferrous Materials—SAE J859 . . . . 1:6.01

Penetrating Radiation Inspection—SAE J427b . . 1:3.53

JACKS

Bumper Jack Requirements—Motor Vehicles—SAE J979 . . . . 4:32.01

JOINTS
See: UNIVERSAL JOINTS

KEYS

Woodruff Key Slots and Keyways—SAE J503 . . . 2:15.06

Woodruff Keys—SAE J502 . . . . 2:15.05

KINGPINS

Fifth Wheel Kingpin, Heavy Duty—Commercial Trailers and Semitrailers—SAE J848a 4:36.49

Fifth Wheel Kingpin Performance—Commercial Trailers and Semitrailers—SAE J133 JAN82 . . 4:36.46

Fifth Wheel Kingpin—Commercial Trailers and Semitrailers—SAE J700 JAN82 . . . . 4:36.48

LAMPS

Auxiliary Driving Lamps—SAE J581a 2:21.37

Auxiliary Low Beam Lamp—SAE J582 SEP81 . . 2:21.38

Clearance, Side Marker, and Identification Lamps—SAE J592f **2**:21.63

Connectors and Plugs—SAE J856 . . . . **2**:21.09

Cornering Lamps—SAE J852b **2**:21.54

Lamp Bulb Retention System—SAE J567c **2**:21.06

Lamp Bulbs and Sealed Beam Headlamp Units—SAE J573g **2**:21.22

Lighting Inspection Code—SAE J599 MAY81 . . **2**:21.71

Motorcycle Auxiliary Front Lamps—SAE J1306 JUN80 . . . . **2**:21.41

School Bus Red Signal Lamps—SAE J887 MAY82 **2**:21.69

Service Performance Requirements and Test Procedures for Motor Vehicle Lamp Bulbs—SAE J1049 AUG79 . . . . **2**:21.25

Snowmobile and Snowmobile Cutter Lamps, Reflective Devices, and Associated Equipment—SAE J292 . . . . **4**:38.07

Spot Lamps—SAE J591b **2**:21.62

Backup Lamps

Backup Lamp Switches—SAE J1076 . . . . **2**:21.64

Backup Lamps (Reversing Lamps)—SAE J593 AUG81 . . . . **2**:21.64

Rear Cornering Lamp—SAE J1373 JUN82 . . . . **2**:21.55

Fog Lamps

Front Fog Lamps—SAE J583 MAY81 . . . . **2**:21.38

Headlamps

Dimensional Specifications for General Service Sealed Lighting Units—SAE J760a **2**:21.20

Dimensional Specifications for Sealed Beam Headlamp Units—SAE J571 FEB81 . . . . **2**:21.11

Dimensional Specifications for Sealed Lighting Unit for Construction and Industrial Machinery—SAE J572a **4**:40.180

Headlamp Aiming Device for Mechanically Aimable Sealed Beam Headlamp Units—SAE J602 OCT80 . . . . **2**:21.74

Headlamp Beam Switching—SAE J564c **2**:21.04

Headlamp Switch—SAE J253 . . . . **2**:21.65

Headlamp Testing Machines—SAE J600 MAY81 **2**:21.73

Headlamps for Agricultural Equipment—SAE J975 MAY80 . . . . **4**:39.38

Headlamps for Industrial Equipment—SAE J95 APR80 . . . . **4**:40.182

Headlamp-Turn Signal Spacing—SAE J1221 . . . **2**:21.48

Lamp Bulbs and Sealed Beam Headlamp Units—SAE J573g **2**:21.22

Motorcycle Headlamps—SAE J584b **2**:21.39

Sealed Beam Headlamp Assembly—SAE J580 AUG79 . . . . **2**:21.34

Sealed Beam Headlamp Units for Motor Vehicles—SAE J579c **2**:21.32

Sealed Lighting Units for Construction and Industrial Machinery—SAE J598 APR80 . . . . **4**:40.179

Semiautomatic Headlamp Beam Switching Devices—SAE J565 JUN82 . . . . **2**:21.04

Service Performance Requirements for Sealed Beam Headlamp Units for Motor Vehicles—SAE J32a **2**:21.33

Snowmobile Headlamps—SAE J280 . . . . **4**:38.04

142 mm × 200 mm Sealed Beam Headlamp Unit—SAE J1132 . . . . **2**:21.18

License Plate Lamps

License Plate Lamps (Rear Registration Plate Lamps)—SAE J587 OCT81 . . . . **2**:21.45

Parking Lamps

Parking Lamps (Front Position Lamps)—SAE J222a **2**:21.62

Stop Lamps

Mechanical Stop Lamp Switch—SAE J249 . . . . . **2**:21.44

Motorcycle Stop Lamp Switch—SAE J1167 . . . . **4**:37.03

Snowmobile Stop Lamp—SAE J278 . . . . **4**:38.05

Stop Lamps—SAE J586d **2**:21.43

Supplemental High Mounted Stop and Rear Turn Signal Lamps—SAE J186a **2**:21.52

Tail Lamps

Combination Tail and Floodlamp for Agricultural Equipment—SAE J976 MAY80 . . . . **4**:39.39

NOTE: Page numbers shown include the volume number in bold followed by the section number and page number within that section.

Combination Tail and Floodlamp for Industrial
Equipment—SAE J94 APR80 . . . . 4:40.182
Snowmobile Tail Lamp (Rear Position Lamp)—SAE
J279 . . . . 4:38.06
Tail Lamps (Rear Position Lamps)—SAE J585e . . 2:21.42

Turn Signal Lamps
Headlamp-Turn Signal Spacing—SAE J1221 . . . 2:21.48
Motorcycle Turn Signal Lamps—SAE J131a 2:21.42
Service Performance Requirements for Turn Signal
Flashers—SAE J1055 . . . . 2:21.56
Side Turn Signal Lamps—SAE J914b 2:21.53
Supplemental High Mounted Stop and Rear Turn
Signal Lamps—SAE J186a 2:21.52
Turn Signal Lamps—SAE J588f 2:21.46
Turn Signal Switch—SAE J589b 2:21.53

Warning Lamps
Flashing Warning Lamp for Agricultural Equip-
ment—SAE J974 MAY80 . . . . 4:39.38
Flashing Warning Lamp for Industrial Equipment—
SAE J96 . . . . 4:40.181
Flashing Warning Lamps for Authorized Emergency,
Maintenance and Service Vehicles—SAE J595b 2:21.67
School Bus Red Signal Lamps—SAE J887 MAY82 2:21.69
Vehicular Hazard Warning Signal Flasher—SAE
J945b 2:21.58
Warning Lamp Alternating Flashers—SAE J1054 . 2:21.60
360 Deg Emergency Warning Lamp—SAE J845 . 2:21.68

LATCHES
Passenger Car Side Door Latch Systems—SAE J839
JUL82 . . . . 4:34.02
Vehicle Hood Latch Systems—SAE J362 JUL82 . 4:34.05

LATEX
See Also: ELASTOMERIC MATERIALS
Latex Dipped Goods and Coatings for Automotive
Applications—SAE J19 NOV80 . . . . 1:11.45
Latex Foam Rubbers—SAE J17 OCT79 . . . . . . 1:11.37
Nondestructive Tests—SAE J358 JAN80 . . . . . 1:3.45
Penetrating Radiation Inspection—SAE J427b . . 1:3.53
Ultrasonic Inspection—SAE J428b 1:3.55

LEAKAGE
Leakage Testing—SAE J1267 . . . . 1:3.50

LICENSE PLATE LAMPS
See: LAMPS

LICENSE PLATES
Motor Vehicle License Plates—SAE J686 JUL81 . 4:27.06

LIGHTERS
Six- and Twelve-Volt Cigar Lighter Receptacles—
SAE J563b 2:20.70

LIGHTING
See Also: LAMPS
Color Specification for Electric Signal Lighting De-
vices—SAE J578d 2:21.30
Connectors and Plugs—SAE J856 . . . . 2:21.09
Dimensional Specifications for General Service
Sealed Lighting Units—SAE J760a 2:21.20
Dimensional Specifications for Sealed Lighting Unit
for Construction and Industrial Machinery—SAE
J572a 4:40.180
Lighting and Marking of Agricultural Equipment on
Highways—SAE J137c 4:39.39
Lighting and Marking of Construction and Industrial
Machinery—SAE J1029 APR80 . . . . 4:40.182
Lighting and Marking of Industrial Equipment on
Highways—SAE J99 APR80 . . . . 4:40.183
Lighting Identification Code—SAE J759 MAR82 . 2:21.03
Lighting Inspection Code—SAE J599 MAY81 . . 2:21.71
Plastic Materials for Use in Optical Parts Such as
Lenses and Reflectors of Motor Vehicle Lighting
Devices—SAE J576 NOV81 . . . . 2:21.30
Preferred Conversion Values for Dimensions in
Lighting—Inch-Pound Units/SI—SAE J1322
MAY81 . . . . 2:21.01
Rear Cornering Lamp—SAE J1373 JUN82 . . . . 2:21.55
Reflex Reflectors—SAE J594f 2:21.65
Sealed Lighting Units for Construction and Industrial
Machinery—SAE J598 APR80 . . . . 4:40.179

Service Performance Requirements for Motor Vehi-
cle Lighting Devices and Components—SAE
J256b 2:21.28
Terminology—Motor Vehicle Lighting—SAE J387 2:21.01
Tests for Motor Vehicle Lighting Devices and Com-
ponents—SAE J575 JUN80 . . . . 2:21.26

LOADERS
**See: CONSTRUCTION AND INDUSTRIAL
MACHINERY**

LOOMS
Nonmetallic Loom—SAE J562a 2:20.68

LUBRICANTS
See Also: OILS
Automotive Lubricating Greases—SAE J310
MAR80 . . . . 3:23.17
Axle and Manual Transmission Lubricant Viscosity
Classification—SAE J306 MAY81 . . . . 3:23.16
Axle and Manual Transmission Lubricants—SAE
J308c 3:23.15
Effective Dates of Revisions—SAE J301 . . . . . . 3:23.01
Lubricant Types—Construction and Industrial Ma-
chinery—SAE J754a 4:40.67
Lubrication Chart—Construction and Industrial Ma-
chinery—SAE J753 JUN82 . . . . 4:40.67
Maintenance Interval—Construction Equipment—
SAE J752b 4:40.68
Powershift Transmission Fluid Classification—SAE
J1285 FEB80 . . . . 3:23.22
Standardized Fluid for Hydraulic Component
Tests—SAE J1276 AUG79 . . . . 4:40.85

MAGNESIUM ALLOYS
See: ALLOYS

MARINE EQUIPMENT
External Ignition Protection of Marine Electrical De-
vices—SAE J1171 . . . . 4:41.08
High Tension Ignition Cable Assemblies—Marine—
SAE J1191 . . . . 4:41.19
Ignition Distributors—Marine—SAE J1294 APR80 4:41.15
Marine Carburetors—SAE J1223 DEC80 . . . . . 4:41.21
Marine Control Cable Connection—Engine Clutch
Lever—SAE J960 JUN80 . . . . 4:41.03
Marine Control Cable Connection—Engine Throttle
Lever—SAE J961 JUN80 . . . . 4:41.04
Marine Electrical Switches—SAE J1320 JUN81 . 4:41.22
Marine Engine Mountings Direct Drive Transmis-
sion—SAE J233 JUN80 . . . . 4:41.08
Marine Engine Rating Code—SAE J1228
MAR80 . . . . 4:41.11
Marine Engine Wiring—SAE J378c 4:41.16
Marine Propeller-Shaft Couplings—SAE J756
AUG81 . . . . 4:41.01
Marine Propeller-Shaft Ends and Hubs—SAE J755
JUN80 . . . . 4:41.05
Marine Push-Pull Control Cables—SAE J917
JUN80 . . . . 4:41.02
Static Electric Outboard Thrust—SAE J1286
NOV81 . . . . 4:41.04

MASTER CYLINDERS
See Also: BRAKES
Hydraulic Master Cylinders for Motor Vehicle
Brakes—Test Procedure—SAE J1153 . . . . . . 2:22.24
Hydraulic Master Cylinders for Motor Vehicle
Brakes—Performance Requirements—SAE
J1154 . . . . 2:22.28

MATERIALS
Compression and Recovery of Insulation Paddings—
SAE J1352 MAY81 . . . . 1:11.92
Flammability of Automotive Interior Materials—
Horizontal Test Method—SAE J369a 1:11.96
Heat Insulation Materials Test Procedure—SAE
J1324 DEC81 . . . . 1:11.56
Hot Odor Test for Insulation Materials—SAE J1351
JUL81 . . . . 1:11.92
Nondestructive Tests—SAE J358 JAN80 . . . . . 1:3.45
Test Method for Determining Dimensional Stability
of Automotive Textile Materials—SAE J883 . . 1:11.59

NOTE: Page numbers shown include the volume number in bold followed by the section number and page number within that section.

Test Method for Determining Resistance to Snagging and Abrasion of Automotive Bodycloth—SAE J948a **1**:11.98

Test Method for Measuring the Relative Drapeability of Flexible Insulation Materials—SAE J1325 SEP80 .... **1**:11.89

Test Method for Measuring Thickness of Automotive Textiles and Plastics—SAE J882 .... **1**:11.60

Test Method for Measuring Thickness of Resilient Insulating Paddings—SAE J1355 MAR81 .... **1**:11.90

Test Method for Measuring Wet Color Transfer Characteristics—SAE J1326 AUG80 .... **1**:11.89

Test Method for Wicking of Automotive Fabrics and Fibrous Materials—SAE J913a **1**:11.83

Test Method of Stretch and Set of Textiles and Plastics—SAE J855 AUG80 .... **1**:11.100

Felts

Felts—Wool and Part Wool—SAE J314 MAY81 . **1**:11.102

Fiberboards

Fiberboard Crease Bending Test—SAE J119 JAN82 .... **1**:11.86

Fiberboard Test Procedure—SAE J315 SEP80 .. **1**:11.78

Glossary of Fiberboard Terminology—SAE J947 JUL80 .... **1**:11.76

Standard Classification System for Fiberboards—SAE J1323 AUG80 .... **1**:11.81

Test Method for Determining Stiffness (Modulus of Bending) of Fiberboards—SAE J949 AUG81 .. **1**:11.98

Test Method for Determining Visual Color Match to Master Specimen for Fabrics, Vinyls, Coated Fiberboards, and Other Automotive Trim Materials—SAE J361a **1**:11.99

Glass

Automotive Safety Glazing—SAE J673b **4**:34.36

Drop Test for Evaluating Laminated Safety Glass for Use in Automotive Windshields—SAE J938a .. **4**:34.41

Light Transmittance of Automotive Windshields Safety Glazing Materials—SAE J1203 ..... **4**:34.38

Passenger Car Glazing Shade Bands—SAE J100 . **4**:34.40

Passenger Car Glazing—Electrical Circuits—SAE J216 .... **4**:34.40

Safety Glazing Materials—Motor Vehicles—SAE J674a **4**:34.39

Plastics

Liquid Penetrant Test Methods—SAE J426c ... **1**:3.52

Marking of Plastic Parts—SAE J1344 OCT80 ... **1**:11.68

Plastic Materials for Use in Optical Parts Such as Lenses and Reflectors of Motor Vehicle Lighting Devices—SAE J576 NOV81 .... **2**:21.30

Test Method for Determining Cold Cracking of Flexible Plastic Materials—SAE J323 .... **1**:11.60

Ultrasonic Inspection—SAE J428b **1**:3.55

Trim Materials

Anodized Aluminum Automotive Parts—SAE J399a **1**:10.27

Electroplating of Nickel and Chromium on Metal Parts—Automotive Ornamentation and Hardware—SAE J207 .... **1**:10.137

Hot Plate Method for Evaluating Heat Resistance and Thermal Insulation Properties of Materials—SAE J1361 APR81 .... **1**:11.91

Method of Testing Resistance to Crocking of Organic Trim Materials—SAE J861 .... **1**:11.59

Method of Testing Resistance to Scuffing of Trim Materials—SAE J365a **1**:11.83

Nonmetallic Trim Materials—Test Method for Determining the Staining Resistance to Hydrogen Sulfide Gas—SAE J322 .... **1**:11.61

Test Method for Determining Blocking Resistance and Associated Characteristics of Automotive Trim Materials—SAE J912a **1**:11.85

Test Method for Determining Visual Color Match to Master Specimen for Fabrics, Vinyls, Coated Fiberboards, and Other Automotive Trim Materials—SAE J361a **1**:11.99

Test Method for Determining Window Fogging Resistance of Interior Trim Materials—SAE J275 . **1**:11.62

Test Method for Measuring Weight of Organic Trim Materials—SAE J860 .... **1**:11.59

METALS

See Also: ALLOYS

Numbering Metals and Alloys—SAE J1086 .... **1**:1.01

Preferred Thicknesses for Uncoated Flat Metals (Thru 12 mm)—SAE J446a **1**:9.07

Sintered Powder Metal Parts: Ferrous—SAE J471d **1**:8.01

Steel, High Strength, Hot Rolled Sheet and Strip, Cold Rolled Sheet, and Coated Sheet—SAE J1392 MAY82 .... **1**:1.76

Surface Texture—SAE J448a **1**:9.03

Surface Texture Control—SAE J449a **1**:9.05

METRIC SYSTEM

Preferred Conversion Values for Dimensions in Lighting—Inch-Pound Units/SI—SAE J1322 MAY81 .... **2**:21.01

Rules for SAE Use of SI (Metric) Units—SAE J916 JUN82 .... **INDEX** 89

MINING MACHINERY

Minimum Performance Criteria for Falling Object Protective Structure (FOPS)—SAE J231 JAN81 **4**:40.245

Performance Criteria for Rollover Protective Structures (ROPS) for Construction, Earthmoving, Forestry, and Mining Machines—SAE J1040c **4**:40.235

Product Identification Numbering System of Off-Road Work Machines—SAE J1360 JUN81 ... **4**:40.03

Unauthorized Starting or Movement of Machines—SAE J1083 FEB80 .... **4**:40.63

MIRRORS

Measuring the Radius of Curvature of Convex Mirrors—SAE J1246 MAY82 .... **4**:34.42

Passenger Car Rear Vision—SAE J834a **4**:34.45

Rear View Mirrors—Motorcycles—SAE J268 MAY82 .... **4**:37.03

Test Procedure for Determining Reflectivity of Rear View Mirrors—SAE J964a **4**:34.41

Vision Factors Considerations in Rear View Mirror Design—SAE J985 .... **4**:34.44

MOTORBOATS

Blade Type Electric Fuses—SAE J1284 DEC79 . **2**:20.34

Operator Sound Level Exposure Assessment Procedure for Pleasure Motorboats—SAE J1281 NOV79 .... **3**:26.30

Static Electric Outboard Thrust—SAE J1286 NOV81 .... **4**:41.04

MOTORCYCLES

Brake System Road Test Code—Motorcycles—SAE J108a **2**:22.116

Definitions—Motorcycles—SAE J213a **4**:37.01

Fuel and Lubricant Tanks for Motorcycles—SAE J1241 .... **4**:37.05

Maximum Sound Level Potential for Motorcycles—SAE J47 .... **3**:26.01

Measurement of Exhaust Sound Levels of Stationary Motorcycles—SAE J1287 MAR82 .... **3**:26.04

Motorcycle and Motor Driven Cycle Electrical System (Maintenance of Design Voltage)—SAE J392 .... **2**:21.41

Motorcycle Auxiliary Front Lamps—SAE J1306 JUN80 .... **2**:21.41

Motorcycle Bank Angle Measurement Procedure—SAE J1168 .... **4**:37.04

Motorcycle Headlamps—SAE J584b **2**:21.39

Motorcycle Stop Lamp Switch—SAE J1167 .... **4**:37.03

Motorcycle Turn Signal Lamps—SAE J131a **2**:21.42

Operator Controls and Displays on Motorcycles—SAE J107 APR80 .... **4**:37.01

Rear View Mirrors—Motorcycles—SAE J268 MAY82 .... **4**:37.03

Service Brake System Performance Requirements—Motorcycles and Motor-Driven Cycles—SAE J109a **2**:22.118

Sound Levels for Motorcycles—SAE J331a ... **3**:26.02

Universal Symbols for Operator Controls—SAE J1500 JUN80 .... **INDEX** 102

NOTE: Page numbers shown include the volume number in bold followed by the section number and page number within that section.

Vehicle Identification Numbers—Motorcycles—SAE J364a **4**:27.03

MOUNTINGS
Brake Flange Mounting—On-Highway Vehicles— SAE J337 . . . . **4**:36.54
Diesel Fuel Injection Pump Mountings—SAE J626b **3**:24.80
Engine Foot Mounting (Front and Rear)—SAE J616c **4**:40.168
Engine Mountings—SAE J615b **3**:24.69
Extra Wide Single Tire Rim and Wheel Mounting for Rear Axles—SAE J876a **4**:36.53
Filter Base Mounting—SAE J363 FEB80 . . . . . . **3**:24.73
Fuel Pump Mountings for Diaphragm Type Pumps— SAE J625 JUL80 . . . . **3**:24.77
Generator Mountings—SAE J545b **2**:20.14
Locating Ledge for Flat Pad Engine Mountings— SAE J832 . . . . **3**:24.69
Magneto Mountings—SAE J546 . . . . **2**:20.19
Marine Engine Mountings Direct Drive Transmission—SAE J233 JUN80 . . . . **4**:41.08
Mounting Brackets and Socket for Warning Lamp and Slow-Moving Vehicle (SMV) Identification Emblem—SAE J725 MAY80 . . . . **4**:39.41
Starting Motor Mountings—SAE J542c **2**:20.13
Wheel Mounting Elements for Industrial and Agricultural Disc Wheels—SAE J714b **4**:39.36

MOWERS
See: CONSTRUCTION AND INDUSTRIAL MACHINERY

MUFFLERS
Muffler Parts Nomenclature—SAE J261 . . . . . . **3**:24.115
Nomenclature for Exhaust System Parts—SAE J97 **3**:24.117

NICKEL ALLOYS
See: ALLOYS

NOISE
See: SOUND

NOZZLES
Calibrating Nozzle and Holder Assembly for Diesel Fuel Injection Systems—SAE J968c **3**:24.90
Diesel Fuel Injection Nozzle and Holder Assembly (17 mm Nominal Diameter)—SAE J265 . . . . . **3**:24.88
Diesel Fuel Injection Nozzle Holder Assemblies— SAE J629b **3**:24.85
Diesel Fuel Injection Nozzle Holder Assembly (9.5 mm)—SAE J347a **3**:24.87
Fuel Injection Nozzle Gaskets—SAE J59 . . . . . **3**:24.88
Gasoline Dispenser Nozzle Spouts—SAE J285 JUL81 . . . . **3**:24.156

NUTS
See: FASTENERS

O-RINGS
Hydraulic "O" Ring—SAE J515a **2**:19.112
Hydraulic Tube Fittings—SAE J514 APR80 . . . . **2**:19.46
Rubber Rings for Automotive Applications—SAE J120a **1**:11.112

OCCUPANT PROTECTION
See: RESTRAINT SYSTEMS AND SEAT BELTS

ODOMETERS
Factors Affecting Accuracy of Mechanically Driven Automotive Speedometer-Odometers—SAE J862 JUN81 . . . . **2**:18.01

OILS
Engine Oil Performance and Engine Service Classification—SAE J183 FEB80 . . . . **3**:23.01
Engine Oil Tests—SAE J304 JUN82 . . . . **3**:23.09
Engine Oil Viscosity Classification—SAE J300 SEP80 . . . . **3**:23.05
Oil Cooler Nomenclature and Glossary—SAE J1244 JUN81 . . . . **3**:24.133
Physical and Chemical Properties of Engine Oils— SAE J357a **3**:23.11
The Lubricant Performance and Service Classification Maintenance Procedure—SAE J1146 NOV80 . . . . **3**:23.41

OPERATOR PROTECTIVE STRUCTURES
Deflection Limiting Volume—ROPS/FOPS Laboratory Evaluation—SAE J397b **4**:40.244

Inverted Vehicle Drop Test Procedure—SAE J996 JUN80 . . . . **4**:34.146
Labeling of ROPS and FOPS—SAE J1164 . . . . . **4**:40.243
Lift Arm Safety Device for Loaders—SAE J38 . . . **4**:40.234
Minimum Performance Criteria for Falling Object Protective Structure (FOPS)—SAE J231 JAN81 . . . . **4**:40.245
Minimum Performance Criteria for Falling Object Protective Structure (FOPS) for Industrial Equipment—SAE J1043 APR80 . . . . **4**:40.246
Operator Protection for Industrial Equipment—SAE J1042 APR80 . . . . **4**:40.243
Operator Protective Structure Performance Criteria for Certain Forestry Equipment—SAE J1084 APR80 . . . . **4**:40.247
Overhead Protection for Agricultural Tractors—Test Procedures and Performance Requirements— SAE J167 JUN81 . . . . **4**:39.56
Performance Criteria for Rollover Protective Structures (ROPS) for Construction, Earthmoving, Forestry, and Mining Machines—SAE J1040c . . . **4**:40.235
Performance Prediction of Roll-Over Protective Structures (ROPS) Through Analytical Methods— SAE J1215 . . . . **4**:40.254
Roll-Over Protective Structures (ROPS) for Wheeled Agricultural Tractors—SAE J1194 . . . . **4**:39.49
Roll-Over Tests without Collision—SAE J857 JUN80 . . . . **4**:34.143
Steel Products for Rollover Protective Structures (ROPS) and Falling Object Protective Structures (FOPS)—SAE J1119 APR80 . . . . **4**:40.248
Steering Frame Lock for Articulated Loaders and Tractors—SAE J276 JUN81 . . . . **4**:40.234
Tire Guards for Protection of Operator of Earthmoving Haulage Machines—SAE J321b **4**:40.233

PARKING LAMPS
See: LAMPS

PARTICLE SIZES
Definition for Particle Size—SAE J391 JUL81 . . **1**:3.56

PIN
See: PRODUCT IDENTIFICATION NUMBER

PINS
Clevis Pins
Rod Ends and Clevis Pins—SAE J493 . . . . **2**:13.84
Cotter Pins
Cotter Pins—SAE J487a **2**:13.77
Holes in Bolt and Capscrew Shanks and Slots in Nuts for Cotter Pins—SAE J485 . . . . **2**:13.79
Dowel Pins
Unhardened Ground Dowel Pins—SAE J497 . . . **2**:13.84
Straight Pins
Grooved Straight Pins—SAE J494 . . . . **2**:13.80
Spring Type Straight Pins—SAE J496 . . . . **2**:13.82
Straight Pins (Solid)—SAE J495 . . . . **2**:13.79

PILOT HOLES
Fan Hub Bolt-Circles and Pilot Holes—SAE J635a **3**:24.141

PIPES
Automotive Pipe, Filler, and Drain Plugs—SAE J531 JAN81 . . . . **2**:19.134
Coding Systems for Identification of Fluid Conductors and Connectors—SAE J846 FEB82 . . . . . **2**:19.01
Dryseal Pipe Threads—SAE J476a **2**:12.01

PISTON RINGS
Piston Rings and Grooves (Metric)—SAE J1201 . **3**:24.31
Piston Rings and Pistons—SAE J929a **3**:24.24

PLASTICS
See: MATERIALS

PLUGS
Automotive Pipe, Filler, and Drain Plugs—SAE J531 JAN81 . . . . **2**:19.134
Automotive Straight Thread Filler and Drain Plugs— SAE J532 JAN81 . . . . **2**:19.138
Connectors and Plugs—SAE J856 . . . . **2**:21.09
Drain, Fill, and Level Plugs for Earthmoving Machinery—SAE J371a **4**:40.173

NOTE: Page numbers shown include the volume number in bold followed by the section number and page number within that section.

POWER TAKE-OFF (continued)
Preignition Rating of Spark Plugs—SAE J549 JUN82 ... **2**:20.26
Spark Plugs—SAE J548d ... **2**:20.20

POWER TAKE-OFF
Auxiliary Power Take-Off Drives for Agricultural Tractors—SAE J717 MAY80 ... **4**:39.31
Clearance Envelopes for Six- and Eight-Bolt Truck Transmission Mounted Power Take-Offs—SAE J772a ... **4**:29.15
Flywheels for Industrial Engines Used with Industrial Power Take-Offs Equipped with Driving-Ring Type Overcenter Clutches and Engine Mounted Marine Gears—SAE J620d ... **4**:40.172
Industrial Power Take-Offs with Driving Ring Type Overcenter Clutches—SAE J621d ... **4**:40.164
Mounting Flanges and Power Take-Off Shafts for Small Engines—SAE J609a ... **3**:24.18
Openings for Six- and Eight-Bolt Truck Transmission Mounted Power Take-Offs—SAE J704b ... **4**:29.16
Operating Requirements for Tractors and Power Take-Off Driven Implements—SAE J721 JUN80 ... **4**:39.30
Power Take-Off Definitions and Terminology for Agricultural Tractors—SAE J722 MAY80 ... **4**:39.32
Rating of Truck Power Take-Offs—SAE J705b ... **4**:36.59
Rear Power Take-Off for Agricultural Tractors—SAE J1170 JUN80 ... **4**:39.27

PRODUCT IDENTIFICATION NUMBER
Product Identification Numbering System of Off-Road Work Machines—SAE J1360 JUN81 ... **4**:40.03

PROPELLERS
Marine Propeller-Shaft Couplings—SAE J756 AUG81 ... **4**:41.01
Marine Propeller-Shaft Ends and Hubs—SAE J755 JUN80 ... **4**:41.05

PULLEYS
Automotive Synchronous Belt Drives—SAE J1313 OCT80 ... **2**:16.12
Automotive V-Belt Drives—SAE J637b ... **2**:16.04
SI (Metric) Synchronous Belts and Pulleys—SAE J1278 OCT80 ... **2**:16.08
Snowmobile and All-Terrain Vehicle Pulley Guards and Shields—SAE J93 ... **4**:38.15
Tractor Belt Speed and Pulley Width—SAE J720 MAY80 ... **4**:39.32
V-Belts and Pulleys—SAE J636c ... **2**:16.01

PUMPS
Diesel Fuel Injection Pump Mountings—SAE J626b ... **3**:24.80
Engine Coolant Pump Seals—SAE J780a ... **3**:24.142
Fuel Pump Mountings for Diaphragm Type Pumps—SAE J625 JUL80 ... **3**:24.77
Guide to the Application and Use of Engine Coolant Pump Face Seals—SAE J1245 JUN82 ... **3**:24.144
Hydraulic Power Pump Test Procedure—SAE J745 OCT80 ... **4**:40.76
Hydraulic Power Pumps—SAE J744 OCT80 ... **4**:40.78
Information Relating to Duty Cycles and Average Power Requirements of Truck and Bus Engine Accessories—SAE J1343 JUL81 ... **4**:36.32
Master Calibrating Fuel Injection Pump—SAE J981 ... **3**:24.89
Test Method for Measuring Power Consumption of Hydraulic Pumps for Trucks and Buses—SAE J1341 JUL81 ... **4**:36.29

RADIATORS
Large Size Radiator Filler Necks—SAE J868 ... **3**:24.121
Radiator Caps and Filler Necks—SAE J164 MAR82 ... **3**:24.120
Radiator Nomenclature—SAE J631 FEB82 ... **3**:24.123

RADIOS
Performance Levels and Methods of Measurement of Electromagnetic Radiation from Vehicles and Devices (20–1000 MHz)—SAE J551 JUN81 ... **2**:20.26

RECREATIONAL VEHICLES
Tire to Body Clearance Check for Recreational Vehicles—SAE J1214 ... **4**:35.03

REFLECTORS
Emergency Warning Device—SAE J774c ... **2**:21.66
Plastic Materials for Use in Optical Parts Such as Lenses and Reflectors of Motor Vehicle Lighting Devices—SAE J576 NOV81 ... **2**:21.30
Reflex Reflectors—SAE J594f ... **2**:21.65
Snowmobile and Snowmobile Cutter Lamps, Reflective Devices, and Associated Equipment—SAE J292 ... **4**:38.07

RESONATORS
Resonator Parts Nomenclature—SAE J262 ... **3**:24.115

RESTRAINT SYSTEMS
See Also: SEAT BELTS
Occupant Restraint System Evaluation—Passenger Cars—SAE J128 ... **4**:33.12

RIMS
Extra Wide Single Tire Rim and Wheel Mounting for Rear Axles—SAE J876a ... **4**:36.53
Labeling—Disc Wheels and Demountable Rims—Trucks—SAE J179a ... **4**:31.12
Nomenclature—Wheels and Rims—Trucks—SAE J393 ... **4**:31.13
Off-Highway Tire and Rim Classification—SAE J751 APR80 ... **4**:40.203
Off-Road Tire and Rim Selection and Application—SAE J1315 MAY81 ... **4**:40.209
Recommended Tolerances for Spoke-Type Wheels, Demountable Rims, and Rim Spacers—Trucks and Trailers—SAE J851 ... **4**:36.52
Wheels/Rims—Trucks—Test Procedures and Performance Requirements—SAE J267a ... **4**:31.05

RIPPERS
See: CONSTRUCTION AND INDUSTRIAL MACHINERY

RIVETS
See: FASTENERS

ROD ENDS
Metric Spherical Rod Ends—SAE J1259 APR80 ... **2**:14.15
Performance Test Procedure—Ball Joints and Spherical Rod Ends—SAE J1367 SEP81 ... **2**:14.16
Spherical Rod Ends—SAE J1120 SEP79 ... **2**:14.12

ROLLERS
See: CONSTRUCTION AND INDUSTRIAL MACHINERY

ROLLOVER PROTECTIVE STRUCTURES
See: OPERATOR PROTECTIVE STRUCTURES

ROOTERS
See: CONSTRUCTION AND INDUSTRIAL MACHINERY

ROPS
See: OPERATOR PROTECTIVE STRUCTURES

RUBBER
See: ELASTOMERIC MATERIALS AND LATEX

SAFETY
See Also: OPERATOR PROTECTIVE STRUCTURES AND RESTRAINT SYSTEMS
Access Systems for Off-Road Machines—SAE J185 JUN81 ... **4**:40.260
Barrier Collision Tests—SAE J850 JUN80 ... **4**:34.142
Bodyforms for Use in Motor Vehicle Passenger Compartment Impact Development—SAE J984 JUN80 ... **4**:34.149
Collision Deformation Classification—SAE J224 MAR80 ... **4**:34.125
Crane Load Moment System—SAE J159 OCT80 ... **4**:40.147
Instrumentation for Impact Tests—SAE J211 JUN80 ... **4**:34.137
Lift Arm Safety Device for Loaders—SAE J38 ... **4**:40.234
Moving Barrier Collision Tests—SAE J972 JUN80 ... **4**:34.138
Rear Underride Guard Test Procedure—SAE J260 JUN80 ... **4**:34.152
Recommendations for Children's Snowmobile—SAE J1038 FEB80 ... **4**:38.20
Safety Alert Symbol for Agricultural, Construction and Industrial Equipment—SAE J284a ... **4**:39.43
Safety Chain of Full Trailers or Converter Dollies—SAE J697a ... **4**:36.51
Safety for Agricultural Equipment—SAE J208d ... **4**:39.44

NOTE: Page numbers shown include the volume number in bold followed by the section number and page number within that section.

Safety for Industrial Flail Mowers—SAE J1001
DEC80 . . . . 4:40.282
Safety for Industrial Wheeled Equipment—SAE J98
DEC80 . . . . 4:40.278
Safety Glazing Materials—Motor Vehicles—SAE
J674a 4:34.39
Safety Practices for Mechanical Vapor Compression
Refrigeration Equipment or Systems Used to Cool
Passenger Compartment of Motor Vehicles—SAE
J639 OCT81 . . . . 4:34.26
Safety Signs—SAE J115 SEP79 . . . . 4:40.285
School Bus Stop Arm—SAE J1133a 2:21.70
Slow-Moving Vehicle Identification Emblem—SAE
J943a 4:39.40
Steering Control System—Passenger Car—Labora-
tory Test Procedure—SAE J944 JUN80 . . . . . 4:34.150
Steering Frame Lock for Articulated Loaders and
Tractors—SAE J276 JUN81 . . . . 4:40.234

SCARIFIERS
See: CONSTRUCTION AND INDUSTRIAL
MACHINERY
SCHOOL BUSES
See: BUSES
SCRAPERS
See: CONSTRUCTION AND INDUSTRIAL
MACHINERY
SCREWS
See: FASTENERS
SEALERS
Methods of Tests for Automotive-Type Sealers, Ad-
hesives, and Deadeners—SAE J243 . . . . 1:11.46
Synthetic Resin Plastic Sealers, Nondrying Type—
SAE J250 . . . . 1:11.45
SEALS
Cast Iron Sealing Rings—SAE J281 SEP80 . . . . 4:29.61
Cast Iron Sealing Rings (Metric)—SAE J1236
SEP80 . . . . 4:29.63
Cylinder Rod Wiper Seal Ingression Test—SAE
J1195 . . . . 4:40.96
Engine Coolant Pump Seals—SAE J780a 3:24.142
Guide to the Application and Use of Engine Coolant
Pump Face Seals—SAE J1245 JUN82 . . . . . . 3:24.144
Rubber Seals for Hydraulic Disc Brake Cylinders—
SAE J1603 . . . . 2:22.15
Seals—Application Guide to Radial Lip—SAE
J946d 4:29.43
Seals—Evaluation of Elastohydrodynamic—SAE
J1002 . . . . 4:29.54
Seals—Lathe Cut—SAE J654 . . . . 4:29.60
Seals—Terminology of Radial Lip—SAE J111c . . 4:29.38
Seals—Testing of Radial Lip—SAE J110c 4:29.57
SEAT BELTS
Dynamic Test Procedure—Type 1 and Type 2 Seat
Belt Assemblies—SAE J117 . . . . 4:33.04
Motor Vehicle Seat Belt Anchorages Test Proce-
dure—SAE J384 . . . . 4:33.08
Motor Vehicle Seat Belt Anchorages—Design Rec-
ommendations—SAE J383 . . . . 4:33.06
Motor Vehicle Seat Belt Anchorages—Performance
Requirements—SAE J385 . . . . 4:33.09
Motor Vehicle Seat Belt Assembly Installations—
SAE J800c 4:33.10
Seat Belt Assembly Webbing Abrasion Test Proce-
dure—SAE J339a 4:33.12
Seat Belt Assembly Webbing Abrasion Test Require-
ments—SAE J114 . . . . 4:33.12
Seat Belt Hardware Performance Requirements—
SAE J141 . . . . 4:33.03
Seat Belt Hardware Test Procedure—SAE J140a . 4:33.01
Seat Belts for Construction Machines—SAE J386
APR80 . . . . 4:40.283
SEATING
Deflection of Seat Cushions for Off-Road Work Ma-
chines—SAE J1051 JAN80 . . . . 4:40.264
Determining Operator Seat Location on Off-Road
Work Machines—SAE J1163 JAN80 . . . . . . 4:40.265

Devices for Use in Defining and Measuring Vehicle
Seating Accommodation—SAE J826 APR80 . . 4:34.27
Dynamic Cushioning Performance Criteria for Snow-
mobile Seats—SAE J89a 4:38.13
Dynamic Flex Fatigue Test for Slab Polyurethane
Foam—SAE J388 . . . . 4:34.34
Load Deflection Testing of Urethane Foams for Au-
tomotive Seating—SAE J815 MAY81 . . . . . . 4:34.36
Motor Vehicle Driver and Passenger Head Posi-
tion—SAE J1052 . . . . 4:34.122
Motor Vehicle Seating Systems—SAE J879b . . . 4:34.31
Operator's Seat Dimensions for Off-Road Self-Pro-
pelled Work Machines—SAE J899 OCT80 . . . 4:40.267
Urethane for Automotive Seating—SAE J954 . . . 4:34.35
SHOT PEENING
Cast Shot and Grit Size Specifications for Peening
and Cleaning—SAE J444a 1:8.09
Cast Steel Shot—SAE J827 . . . . 1:8.08
Cut Steel Wire Shot—SAE J441 . . . . 1:8.05
Metallic Shot and Grit Mechanical Testing—SAE
J445a 1:8.10
Procedures for Using Standard Shot Peening Test
Strip—SAE J443 . . . . 1:8.07
Size Classification and Characteristics of Glass
Beads for Peening—SAE J1173 . . . . 1:8.11
Test Strip, Holder and Gage for Shot Peening—SAE
J442 AUG79 . . . . 1:8.05
SKIDDERS
See: FORESTRY MACHINES
SKINS
Synthetic Skins for Automotive Testing—SAE
J202 . . . . 4:34.124
SMALL ENGINES
See: ENGINES
SMOKEMETERS
Measurement Procedure for Evaluation of Full-Flow,
Light Extinction Smokemeter Performance—SAE
J1157 . . . . 3:25.40
SNOWMOBILES
Brake System Test Procedure—Snowmobiles—SAE
J45 . . . . 4:38.11
Dynamic Cushioning Performance Criteria for Snow-
mobile Seats—SAE J89a 4:38.13
Exterior Sound Level for Snowmobiles—SAE J192
APR80 . . . . 3:26.25
Maintenance of Design Voltage—Snowmobile Elec-
trical Systems—SAE J277 . . . . 4:38.04
Metallic and Nonmetallic Nonpressure Integral Fuel
Tank—Snowmobile—SAE J288a 4:38.17
Operational Sound Level Measurement Procedure
for Snow Vehicles—SAE J1161 APR80 . . . . . 3:26.28
Operator Ear Sound Level Measurement Procedure
for Snow Vehicles—SAE J1160 . . . . 3:26.26
Recommendations for Children's Snowmobile—SAE
J1038 FEB80 . . . . 4:38.20
Service Brake System Performance Requirements—
Snowmobiles—SAE J44 . . . . 4:38.11
Snowmobile and All-Terrain Vehicle Pulley Guards
and Shields—SAE J93 . . . . 4:38.15
Snowmobile and Snowmobile Cutter Lamps, Reflec-
tive Devices, and Associated Equipment—SAE
J292 . . . . 4:38.07
Snowmobile Brake Control Systems—SAE J1282
SEP80 . . . . 4:38.10
Snowmobile Definitions and Nomenclature—Gen-
eral—SAE J33a 4:38.01
Snowmobile Headlamps—SAE J280 . . . . 4:38.04
Snowmobile Passenger Handgrips—SAE J1062 . 4:38.09
Snowmobile Stop Lamp—SAE J278 . . . . 4:38.05
Snowmobile Tail Lamp (Rear Position Lamp)—SAE
J279 . . . . 4:38.06
Snowmobile Throttle Control Systems—SAE J92 . 4:38.18
Speed Control Assurance for Snowmobiles—SAE
J1222 FEB81 . . . . 4:38.19
Tests for Snowmobile Switching Devices and Com-
ponents—SAE J68 OCT79 . . . . 4:38.08

NOTE: Page numbers shown include the volume number in bold followed by the section number and page number within that section.

Vehicle Identification Numbers—Snowmobile and
All-Terrain Vehicles—SAE J64 FEB81 . . . . .   **4**:38.03

SOLDERS
Solders—SAE J473a **1**:10.142
Welding, Brazing, and Soldering—Materials and
Practices—SAE J1147 . . . .   **1**:9.07

SOUND
See Also: ACOUSTICS
Bystander Sound Level Measurement Procedure for
Small Engine Powered Equpiment—SAE J1175   **3**:26.49
Engine Sound Level Measurement Procedure—SAE
J1074 . . . .   **3**:26.64
Exterior Sound Level for Heavy Trucks and Buses—
SAE J366b **3**:26.18
Exterior Sound Level for Snowmobiles—SAE J192
APR80 . . . .   **3**:26.25
Exterior Sound Level Measurement Procedure for
Pleasure Motorboats—SAE J34a **3**:26.29
Laboratory Measurement of the Airborne Noise Re-
duction of Acoustical Materials—SAE J1400
MAY82 . . . .   **1**:11.94
Maximum Sound Level for Passenger Cars and Light
Trucks—SAE J1030 . . . .   **3**:26.14
Maximum Sound Level Potential for Motorcycles—
SAE J47 . . . .   **3**:26.01
Measurement of Exhaust Sound Levels of Stationary
Motorcycles—SAE J1287 MAR82 . . . .   **3**:26.04
Measurement of Exterior Sound Level of Trucks with
Auxiliary Equipment—SAE J1077 . . . .   **3**:26.23
Measurement of Exterior Sound Levels for Heavy
Trucks Under Stationary Conditions—SAE J1096   **3**:26.20
Measurement of Light Vehicle Exhaust Sound Level
Under Stationary Conditions—SAE J1169 . . . .   **3**:26.16
Measurement Procedure for Determination of Si-
lencer Effectiveness in Reducing Engine Intake or
Exhaust Sound Level—SAE J1207 OCT81 . . .   **3**:26.65
Operational Sound Level Measurement Procedure
for Snow Vehicles—SAE J1161 APR80 . . . . .   **3**:26.28
Operator Ear Sound Level Measurement Procedure
for Snow Vehicles—SAE J1160 . . . .   **3**:26.26
Operator Ear Sound Level Measurement Procedure
for Small Engine Powered Equipment—SAE
J1174 . . . .   **3**:26.48
Operator Sound Level Exposure Assessment Proce-
dure for Pleasure Motorboats—SAE J1281
NOV79 . . . .   **3**:26.30
Qualifying a Sound Data Acquisition System—SAE
J184a **3**:26.07
Sound Level for Passenger Cars and Light Trucks—
SAE J986 NOV81 . . . .   **3**:26.12
Sound Level for Truck Cab Interior—SAE J336a .   **3**:26.19
Sound Level of Highway Truck Tires—SAE J57
JUL81 . . . .   **3**:26.21
Sound Levels for Motorcycles—SAE J331a **3**:26.02
Sound Measurement—Construction Site—SAE
J1075 SEP80 . . . .   **3**:26.51
Sound Measurement—Earthmoving Machinery—
Operator—Singular Type—SAE J919 SEP80 . .   **3**:26.37
Sound Measurement—Earthmoving Machinery—
Operator—Work Cycle—SAE J1166 SEP80 . .   **3**:26.39
Sound Measurement—Earthmoving Machinery—Ex-
terior—SAE J88 SEP80 . . . .   **3**:26.57
Sound Measurement—Self-Propelled Agricultural
Equipment—Exterior—SAE J1008 SEP80 . . . .   **3**:26.63
Sound Measurement—Trenching Equipment—SAE
J1262 SEP80 . . . .   **3**:26.60
Sound Power Determination—Earthmoving Machin-
ery—Static Condition—SAE J1372 DEC81 . . .   **3**:26.53

SPARK ARRESTERS
Multiposition Small Engine Exhaust System Fire Igni-
tion Suppression—SAE J335b **3**:24.102
Spark Arrester Test Carbon—SAE J997 JAN80 .   **3**:24.112
Spark Arrester Test Procedure for Large Size En-
gines—SAE J342 NOV80 . . . .   **3**:24.105
Spark Arrester Test Procedure for Medium Size En-
gines—SAE J350 JAN80 . . . .   **3**:24.109

SPARK PLUGS
Preignition Rating of Spark Plugs—SAE J549
JUN82 . . . .   **2**:20.26
Spark Plugs—SAE J548d **2**:20.20

SPEEDOMETERS
Automatic Vehicle Speed Control—Motor Vehi-
cles—SAE J195 . . . .   **2**:18.12
Factors Affecting Accuracy of Mechanically Driven
Automotive Speedometer-Odometers—SAE
J862 JUN81 . . . .   **2**:18.01
Speed Control Assurance for Snowmobiles—SAE
J1222 FEB81 . . . .   **4**:38.19
Speedometer Test Procedure—SAE J1059 . . . .   **2**:18.07
Speedometers and Tachometers—Automotive—
SAE J678e **2**:18.03

SPLINES
Involute Splines and Inspections—SAE J498c . . .   **2**:15.01
Parallel Side Splines for Soft Broached Holes in Fit-
tings—SAE J499a **2**:15.01
Serrated Shaft Ends—SAE J500 . . . .   **2**:15.03
Shaft Ends—SAE J501 . . . .   **2**:15.04

SPRINGS
Hard Drawn Carbon Steel Valve Spring Quality Wire
and Springs—SAE J172 . . . .   **1**:5.06
Hard Drawn Mechanical Spring Wire and Springs—
SAE J113 . . . .   **1**:5.04
Music Steel Spring Wire and Springs—SAE J178   **1**:5.09
Oil Tempered Carbon Steel Spring Wire and
Springs—SAE J316 . . . .   **1**:5.01
Oil Tempered Carbon Steel Valve Spring Quality
Wire and Springs—SAE J351 . . . .   **1**:5.02
Oil Tempered Chromium–Silicon Alloy Steel Wire
and Springs—SAE J157 . . . .   **1**:5.05
Oil Tempered Chromium-Vanadium Valve Spring
Quality Wire and Springs—SAE J132 . . . . . .   **1**:5.03
Rated Spring Capacity—SAE J274 . . . .   **2**:17.15
Special Quality High Tensile, Hard Drawn Mechani-
cal Spring Wire and Springs—SAE J271 . . . .   **1**:5.04
Stainless Steel, SAE 30302, Spring Wire and
Springs—SAE J230 . . . .   **1**:5.08
Stainless Steel 17-7 PH Spring Wire and Springs—
SAE J217 . . . .   **1**:5.07
Helical Springs
Helical Compression and Extension Spring Terminol-
ogy—SAE J1121 . . . .   **2**:17.09
Helical Springs: Specification Check Lists—SAE
J1122 . . . .   **2**:17.14
Leaf Springs
Leaf Springs for Motor Vehicle Suspension—SAE
J510c **2**:17.01
Leaf Springs for Motor Vehicle Suspension—Metric
Bar Sizes—SAE J1123a **2**:17.01
Pneumatic Springs
Pneumatic Spring Terminology—SAE J511a **2**:17.08

STEELS
Aging of Carbon Steel Sheet and Strip—SAE J763
JAN82 . . . .   **1**:2.20
Alloy Steel Machinability Ratings—SAE J770c . .   **1**:2.24
Automotive Steel Castings—SAE J435c **1**:6.12
Carbon and Alloy Steels—SAE J411 JUN81 . . .   **1**:2.01
Chemical Compositions of SAE Alloy Steels—SAE
J404 OCT80 . . . .   **1**:1.11
Chemical Compositions of SAE Carbon Steels—SAE
J403 SEP80 . . . .   **1**:1.08
Chemical Compositions of SAE Experimental
Steels—SAE J1081 JUN81 . . . .   **1**:1.14
Chemical Compositions of SAE Wrought Stainless
Steels—SAE J405d **1**:1.13
Classification of Common Imperfections in Sheet
Steel—SAE J810 JUN80 . . . .   **1**:3.24
Cleanliness Rating of Steels by the Magnetic Particle
Method—SAE J421 APR82 . . . .   **1**:3.37
Definitions for Macrostrain and Microstrain—SAE
J932 . . . .   **1**:3.57
Definitions of Heat Treating Terms—SAE J415
JUN82 . . . .   **1**:2.21

NOTE: Page numbers shown include the volume number in bold followed by the section number and page number within that section.

Detection of Surface Imperfections in Ferrous Rods, Bars, Tubes, and Wires—SAE J349 JUN80 . . .   **1**:3.42

Estimated Mechanical Properties and Machinability of Hot Rolled and Cold Drawn Carbon Steel Bars—SAE J414a   **1**:2.15

Formerly Standard SAE Alloy Steels—SAE J778 OCT80 . . . .   **1**:1.15

Formerly Standard SAE Carbon Steels—SAE J118a   **1**:1.16

General Characteristics and Heat Treatments of Steels—SAE J412h **1**:2.05

Glossary of Carbon Steel Sheet and Strip Terms—SAE J940 JAN82 . . . .   **1**:2.18

Grain Size Determination of Steels—SAE J418a   **1**:3.07

Hardenability Bands for Carbon and Alloy H Steels—SAE J1268 JUN81 . . . .   **1**:1.26

Hardness Tests and Hardness Number Conversions—SAE J417b **1**:3.03

High Strength Carbon and Alloy Die Drawn Steels—SAE J935 JUL81 . . . .   **1**:2.04

High Strength, Low Alloy Steel—SAE J410c . . .   **1**:1.74

High Strength, Quenched, and Tempered Structural Steels—SAE J368a **1**:1.79

Infrared Testing—SAE J359 JUN81 . . . . . .   **1**:3.47

Liquid Penetrant Test Methods—SAE J426c . . .   **1**:3.52

Magnetic Particle Inspection—SAE J420 MAR81   **1**:3.47

Mechanical Properties of Heat Treated Wrought Steels—SAE J413b **1**:2.13

Method for Determining Breakage Allowances for Sheet Steel—SAE J424 OCT81 . . . . . .   **1**:3.45

Methods of Determining Hardenability of Steels—SAE J406c **1**:1.17

Methods of Determining Plastic Deformation in Sheet Metal Stampings—SAE J863 DEC81 . . .   **1**:3.14

Methods of Measuring Case Depth—SAE J423a .   **1**:3.43

Methods of Measuring Decarburization—SAE J419   **1**:3.10

Methods of Sampling Steel for Chemical Analysis—SAE J408 JUN79 . . . .   **1**:1.71

Microscopic Determination of Inclusions in Steels—SAE J422 JUN79 . . . .   **1**:3.39

Numbering Metals and Alloys—SAE J1086 . . . .   **1**:1.01

Penetrating Radiation Inspection—SAE J427b . .   **1**:3.53

Permissible Variations from Specified Ladle Chemical Ranges and Limits for Steels—SAE J409c .   **1**:1.72

Preferred Thicknesses for Uncoated Flat Metals (Thru 12 mm)—SAE J446a **1**:9.07

Properties of Low Carbon Steel Sheets and Strip and Their Relationship to Formability—SAE J877   **1**:3.17

SAE Numbering System for Wrought or Rolled Steel—SAE J402 JUN81 . . . .   **1**:1.07

Selecting and Specifying Hot and Cold Rolled Steel Sheet and Strip—SAE J126 JUN81 . . . . . .   **1**:3.19

Selection and Heat Treatment of Tool and Die Steels—SAE J437a **1**:7.02

Selection and Use of Steels—SAE J401 APR81 .   **1**:1.05

Sheet Steel Thickness and Profile—SAE J1058 . .   **1**:3.16

Steel, High Strength, Hot Rolled Sheet and Strip, Cold Rolled Sheet, and Coated Sheet—SAE J1392 MAY82 . . . .   **1**:1.76

Surface Hardness Testing with Files—SAE J864 JUN79 . . . .   **1**:3.02

Surface Texture Measurement of Cold Rolled Sheet Steel—SAE J911 OCT81 . . . .   **1**:9.01

Technical Report on Fatigue Properties—SAE J1099 . . . .   **1**:3.57

Tensile Test Specimens—SAE J416 JUN79 . . . .   **1**:3.01

Tool and Die Steels—SAE J438b **1**:7.01

Ultrasonic Inspection—SAE J428b **1**:3.55

STEERING

Information Relating to Duty Cycles and Average Power Requirements of Truck and Bus Engine Accessories—SAE J1343 JUL81 . . . .   **4**:36.32

Minimum Performance Criteria for Emergency Steering of Wheeled Earthmoving Construction Machines—SAE J53 . . . .   **4**:40.305

Power Steering Pressure Hose—Low Volumetric Expansion Type—SAE J191 . . . .   **1**:11.137

Power Steering Pressure Hose—Wire Braid—SAE J190 . . . .   **1**:11.138

Power Steering Return Hose—Low Pressure—SAE J189 . . . .   **1**:11.135

Steering Control System—Passenger Car—Laboratory Test Procedure—SAE J944 JUN80 . . . . .   **4**:34.150

Steering Frame Lock for Articulated Loaders and Tractors—SAE J276 JUN81 . . . .   **4**:40.234

STOP LAMPS
  See: LAMPS

STUDS
  See: FASTENERS

SUPERALLOYS
  See: ALLOYS

SWITCHES

Backup Lamp Switches—SAE J1076 . . . .   **2**:21.64

Electric Blower Motor Switch—SAE J235 . . . . .   **2**:20.70

Electric Windshield Washer Switch—SAE J234 . .   **2**:20.69

Electric Windshield Wiper Switch—SAE J112a . .   **2**:20.69

Hazard Warning Signal Switch—SAE J910b **2**:21.68

Headlamp Beam Switching—SAE J564c **2**:21.04

Headlamp Switch—SAE J253 . . . .   **2**:21.65

Ignition Switch—SAE J259 . . . .   **2**:20.39

Marine Electrical Switches—SAE J1320 JUN81 .   **4**:41.22

Mechanical Stop Lamp Switch—SAE J249 . . . .   **2**:21.44

Semiautomatic Headlamp Beam Switching Devices—SAE J565 JUN82 . . . .   **2**:21.04

Tests for Snowmobile Switching Devices and Components—SAE J68 OCT79 . . . .   **4**:38.08

Turn Signal Switch—SAE J589b **2**:21.53

TACHOMETERS

Electric Tachometer Specification—Off Road—SAE J197 . . . .   **2**:18.10

Electric Tachometer Specification—On Road—SAE J196 JUN80 . . . .   **2**:18.08

Speedometers and Tachometers—Automotive—SAE J678e **2**:18.03

TAIL LAMPS
  See: LAMPS

TECHNICAL REPORTS

Guidelines for Developing and Revising SAE Nomenclature and Definitions—SAE J1115 . . . .   **INDEX** 101

Preparation of SAE Technical Reports—Surface Vehicles and Machines: Standards, Recommended Practices, Information Reports—SAE J1159 AUG79 . . . .   **INDEX** 86

Technical Committee Guideposts—SAE J1271 AUG79 . . . .   **INDEX** 81

TERMINALS

Electrical Terminals—Blade Type—SAE J858a . .   **2**:20.62

Electrical Terminals—Eyelet and Spade Type—SAE J561 JUN80 . . . .   **2**:20.64

Electrical Terminals—Pin and Receptacle Type—SAE J928 JUN80 . . . .   **2**:20.63

Low Tension Wiring and Cable Terminals and Splice Clips—SAE J163 . . . .   **2**:20.48

TEST SUBJECTS
  See: ANTHROPOMETRY

TEXTILES
  See: MATERIALS

THERMOCOUPLE

Brake Disc and Drum Thermocouple Installation—SAE J79 . . . .   **2**:22.133

THERMOSTATS

THROTTLES

Marine Control Cable Connection—Engine Throttle Lever—SAE J961 JUN80 . . . .   **4**:41.04

Snowmobile Throttle Control Systems—SAE J92 .   **4**:38.18

TIRE RIMS
  See: RIMS

TIRES

Agricultural Tractor Tire Dynamic Indices—SAE J1261 FEB79 . . . .   **4**:39.13

Agricultural Tractor Tire Loadings, Torque Factors, and Inflation Pressures—SAE J709d **4**:39.05

NOTE: Page numbers shown include the volume number in bold followed by the section number and page number within that section.

Lawn and Garden Tractors Load and Inflation Pressures and Tire Selection Table for Future Design—SAE J344 . . . . **4**:39.14
Liquid Ballast Table for Drive Tires of Agricultural Machines—SAE J884 MAY80 . . . . **4**:39.10
Methods for Testing Snap-In Tubeless Tire Valves—SAE J1206 . . . . **4**:30.21
Off-Highway Tire and Rim Classification—SAE J751 APR80 . . . . **4**:40.203
Off-Road Tire and Rim Selection and Application—SAE J1315 MAY81 . . . . **4**:40.209
Passenger and Light Truck Tire Traction Device Profile Determination and Classification—SAE J1232 . . . . **4**:36.57
Passenger Car Tire Performance Requirements and Test Procedures—SAE J918c **4**:30.01
Performance Requirements for Snap-In Tubeless Tire Valves—SAE J1205 . . . . **4**:30.23
Rolling Resistance Measurement Procedure for Passenger Car Tires—SAE J1269 JUL81 . . . . . . **4**:30.04
Rolling Resistance Measurement Procedure for Highway Truck and Bus Tires—SAE J1379 JUN82 . . . . **4**:30.08
Selection of Tires for Multipurpose Passenger Vehicles, Light-, Medium-, and Heavy-Duty Trucks, Buses, Trailers, and Semitrailers for Normal Highway Service—SAE J161a **4**:30.16
Sound Level of Highway Truck Tires—SAE J57 JUL81 . . . . **3**:26.21
Subjective Rating Scale for Evaluation of Noise and Ride Comfort Characteristics Related to Motor Vehicle Tires—SAE J1060 . . . . **4**:30.20
Test Procedure for Measuring Passenger Car Tire Revolutions per Mile—SAE J966 . . . . **4**:30.19
Test Procedures for Measuring Truck Tire Revolutions per Mile—SAE J1025 . . . . **4**:30.19
Testing Machines for Measuring the Uniformity of Passenger Car and Light Truck Tires—SAE J332 AUG81 . . . . **4**:30.14
The Measurement of Highway Truck and Bus Tire Rolling Resistance—SAE J1380 JUN82 . . . . . **4**:30.10
The Measurement of Passenger Car Tire Rolling Resistance—SAE J1270 OCT79 . . . . . . **4**:30.06
Tire Selection Tables for Agricultural and Light Industrial Machines of Future Design—SAE J711c **4**:39.12
Tire to Body Clearance Check for Recreational Vehicles—SAE J1214 . . . . **4**:35.03
Ton Mile Per Hour Application Practice—SAE J1098 APR80 . . . . **4**:40.213
Ton-Mile Per Hour Test Procedure—SAE J1015 . **4**:40.210
Truck and Bus Tire Performance Requirements and Test Procedures—SAE J341a **4**:30.17
Truck Overall Widths Across Dual Tires—SAE J693a **4**:36.53
Wet or Dry Pavement Passenger Car Tire Peak and Locked Wheel Braking Traction—SAE J345a . . **4**:30.12

TOOL MATERIALS
Selection and Heat Treatment of Tool and Die Steels—SAE J437a **1**:7.02
Sintered Carbide Tools—SAE J439a **1**:7.07
Sintered Tool Materials—SAE J1072 . . . . . . **1**:7.12
Tool and Die Steels—SAE J438b **1**:7.01

TOW BARS
Full Trailer Tow Bar Eye—SAE J847 . . . . . . **4**:36.51

TOWING
Towability Design Criteria—Passenger Cars and Light Duty Trucks—SAE J1142a **4**:28.01
Towed Vehicle Drivetrain Test Procedure—Passenger Cars and Light Duty Trucks—SAE J1144a . **4**:28.07
Towed Vehicle/Wrecker Attachment Test Procedure—Passenger Cars and Light Duty Trucks—SAE J1143a **4**:28.05

TRACTORS
See: AGRICULTURAL MACHINERY AND CONSTRUCTION AND INDUSTRIAL MACHINERY

TRAILERS
Automobile, Truck, Truck-Tractor, Trailer, and Motor Coach Wiring—SAE J1292 OCT81 . . . . **2**:20.39
Blade Type Electric Fuses—SAE J1284 DEC79 . **2**:20.34
Brake System Road Test Code—Passenger Car and Light Duty Truck-Trailer Combinations—SAE J134 JUN79 . . . . **2**:22.97
Capacity Ratings—Scraper, Dumper Body and Trailer Body—SAE J741b **4**:40.215
Connection and Accessory Locations for Towing Doubles Trailers and Multi-Axle Trailers—SAE J849b **4**:36.49
Fifth Wheel Kingpin, Heavy Duty—Commercial Trailers and Semitrailers—SAE J848a **4**:36.49
Fifth Wheel Kingpin Performance—Commercial Trailers and Semitrailers—SAE J133 JAN82 . . **4**:36.46
Fifth Wheel Kingpin—Commercial Trailers and Semitrailers—SAE J700 JAN82 . . . . **4**:36.48
Five Conductor Electrical Connectors for Automotive Type Trailers—SAE J895 . . . . **2**:20.55
Full Trailer Tow Bar Eye—SAE J847 . . . . . . **4**:36.51
Nomenclature—Truck, Bus, Trailer—SAE J687c . **4**:36.01
Rear Underride Guard Test Procedure—SAE J260 JUN80 . . . . **4**:34.152
Service Brake System Performance Requirements—Passenger Car—Trailer Combinations—SAE J135a **2**:22.106
Seven-Conductor Electrical Connector for Truck-Trailer Jumper Cable—SAE J560b **2**:20.60
Trailer Axle Alignment—SAE J875 . . . . **4**:36.54
Trailer Couplings, Hitches and Safety Chains—Automotive Type—SAE J684f **4**:35.01
Truck Tractor Semitrailer Interchange Coupling Dimensions—SAE J701a **4**:36.43

TRANSDUCERS
Guide to Manifold Absolute Pressure Transducer Representative Test Method—SAE J1346 JUN81 . . . . **2**:20.125
Guide to Manifold Absolute Pressure Transducer Representative Specification—SAE J1347 JUN81 . . . . **2**:20.128

TRANSMISSIONS
Automatic Transmission Functions—Terminology—SAE J649b **4**:29.09
Automatic Transmission Hydraulic Control Systems—Terminology—SAE J648a **4**:29.09
Automatic Transmissions—Manual Control Sequence—SAE J915 . . . . **4**:29.14
Automotive Transmission Terminology—SAE J645c **4**:29.07
Axle and Manual Transmission Lubricant Viscosity Classification—SAE J306 MAY81 . . . . **3**:23.16
Axle and Manual Transmission Lubricants—SAE J308c **3**:23.15
Clearance Envelopes for Six- and Eight-Bolt Truck Transmission Mounted Power Take-Offs—SAE J772a **4**:29.15
Engine and Transmission Identification Numbers—SAE J129 DEC81 . . . . **4**:27.03
Fluid for Passenger Car Type Automatic Transmissions—SAE J311b **3**:23.20
Openings for Six- and Eight-Bolt Truck Transmission Mounted Power Take-Offs—SAE J704b **4**:29.16
Passenger Car and Truck Automatic Transmission Test Code—SAE J651c **4**:29.10
Powershift Transmission Fluid Classification—SAE J1285 FEB80 . . . . **3**:23.22
Transmissions—Schematic Diagrams—SAE J647 JUL81 . . . . **4**:29.08

TRUCKS
Approach, Departure, and Ramp Breakover Angles—Passenger Car and Light Duty Trucks—SAE J689 . . . . **4**:32.03
Average Vehicle Dimensions for Use in Designing Docking Facilities for Motor Vehicles—SAE J699a **4**:36.39

NOTE: Page numbers shown include the volume number in bold followed by the section number and page number within that section.

Brake and Electrical Connection Locations—Truck-Tractor and Truck-Trailer—SAE J702b 4:36.55
Certificates of Maximum Net Horsepower for Motor Trucks and Truck Tractors—SAE J690 . . . . . . 4:36.37
Information Relating to Duty Cycles and Average Power Requirements of Truck and Bus Engine Accessories—SAE J1343 JUL81 . . . . 4:36.32
Joint RCCC/SAE Fuel Consumption Test Procedure (Short Term-In-Service Vehicle) Type I—SAE J1264 . . . . 4:36.05
Joint TMC/SAE Fuel Consumption Test Procedure—Type II—SAE J1321 OCT81 . . . . 4:36.08
Location and Operation of Instruments and Controls in Motor Truck Cabs—SAE J680 JUN82 . . . . . 4:36.60
Motor Truck CA Dimensions—SAE J691 . . . . . . 4:36.38
Nomenclature—Truck, Bus, Trailer—SAE J687c . 4:36.01
Passenger and Light Truck Tire Traction Device Profile Determination and Classification—SAE J1232 . . . . 4:36.57
Rating of Truck Power Take-Offs—SAE J705b . . 4:36.59
Rear Underride Guard Test Procedure—SAE J260 JUN80 . . . . 4:34.152
Rolling Resistance Measurement Procedure for Highway Truck and Bus Tires—SAE J1379 JUN82 . . . . 4:30.08
SAE Nodal Mount—SAE J1134 . . . . 4:36.55
SAE Wind Tunnel Test Procedure for Trucks and Buses—SAE J1252 JUL81 . . . . 4:36.33
Test Method for Measuring Power Consumption of Cooling Fans for Trucks and Buses—SAE J1339 JUL81 . . . . 4:36.27
Test Method for Measuring Power Consumption of Hydraulic Pumps for Trucks and Buses—SAE J1341 JUL81 . . . . 4:36.29
Test Method for Measuring Power Consumption of Air Conditioning and Air Brake Compressors for Trucks and Buses—SAE J1340 JUL81 . . . . . . 4:36.29
Test Method for Measuring Power Consumption of Fan Drive Systems for Trucks and Buses—SAE J1342 JUL81 . . . . 4:36.30
The Measurement of Highway Truck and Bus Tire Rolling Resistance—SAE J1380 JUN82 . . . . . 4:30.10
Truck Ability Prediction Procedure—SAE J688 . . 4:36.02
Truck Overall Widths Across Dual Tires—SAE J693a 4:36.53
Turning Ability and Off Tracking—Motor Vehicles—SAE J695b 4:36.39

Brake Systems
Brake Diaphragm Maintenance—Tractor and Semi-trailer—SAE J666 . . . . 4:36.56
Brake Flange Mounting—On-Highway Vehicles—SAE J337 . . . . 4:36.54
Brake System Performance Requirements—Truck, Bus, and Combination of Vehicles—SAE J992b 2:22.113
Brake System Road Test Code—Truck, Bus, and Combination of Vehicles—SAE J786a 2:22.107
Service Brake System Performance Requirements—Light-Duty Truck—SAE J155 . . . . . 2:22.94
Test Code—Truck, Truck-Tractor, and Trailer Air Service Brake System Pneumatic Pressure and Time Levels—SAE J982 SEP80 . . . . 2:22.129

Emissions
Measurement of Fuel Evaporative Emissions from Gasoline Powered Passenger Cars and Light Trucks—SAE J170a 3:25.78
Measurement of Fuel Evaporative Emissions from Gasoline Powered Passenger Cars and Light Trucks Using the Enclosure Technique—SAE J171 JUN82 . . . . 3:25.84

Sound Levels
Exterior Sound Level for Heavy Trucks and Buses—SAE J366b 3:26.18
Maximum Sound Level for Passenger Cars and Light Trucks—SAE J1030 . . . . 3:26.14
Measurement of Exterior Sound Level of Trucks with Auxiliary Equipment—SAE J1077 . . . . 3:26.23

Measurement of Exterior Sound Levels for Heavy Trucks Under Stationary Conditions—SAE J1096 **3**:26.20
Sound Level for Passenger Cars and Light Trucks—SAE J986 NOV81 . . . . **3**:26.12
Sound Level for Truck Cab Interior—SAE J336a . **3**:26.19

Vehicle Identification Numbers
Truck and Truck Tractor Vehicle Identification Number Systems—SAE J1108 DEC81 . . . . **4**:27.07
Truck Identification Terminology—SAE J1229 DEC81 . . . . **4**:27.04
Truck Vehicle Identification Numbers—SAE J187 **4**:27.05

Wheels
Commercial Vehicle Disc Wheels—SAE J694a . . **4**:36.52
Extra Wide Single Tire Rim and Wheel Mounting for Rear Axles—SAE J876a **4**:36.53
Hub Fatigue Test Procedures—SAE J1095 JUN82 **4**:31.09
Labeling—Disc Wheels and Demountable Rims—Trucks—SAE J179a **4**:31.12
Nomenclature—Wheels and Rims—Trucks—SAE J393 . . . . **4**:31.13
Recommended Tolerances for Spoke-Type Wheels, Demountable Rims, and Rim Spacers—Trucks and Trailers—SAE J851 . . . . **4**:36.52
Wheels/Rims—Trucks—Test Procedures and Performance Requirements—SAE J267a **4**:31.05

Windshields
Windshield Defrosting Systems Performance Requirements—Trucks, Buses, and Multipurpose Vehicles—SAE J382 . . . . **4**:34.17
Windshield Defrosting Systems Test Procedure—Trucks, Buses, and Multipurpose Vehicles—SAE J381 . . . . **4**:34.15
Windshield Wiper Systems—Trucks, Buses, and Multipurpose Vehicles—SAE J198 . . . . **4**:34.09

Wiring
Automobile, Truck, Truck-Tractor, Trailer, and Motor Coach Wiring—SAE J1292 OCT81 . . . . **2**:20.39

TUBES AND TUBINGS
Automotive Hydraulic Brake System—Metric Tube Connections—SAE J1290 JUL80 . . . . **2**:22.141
Brazed Double Wall Low Carbon Steel Tubing—SAE J527 JAN80 . . . . **2**:19.117
Detection of Surface Imperfections in Ferrous Rods, Bars, Tubes, and Wires—SAE J349 JUN80 . . . **1**:3.42
Flares for Tubing—SAE J533b **2**:19.113
Formed Tube Ends for Hose Connections—SAE J962b **2**:19.112
Fuel Injection Tubing—SAE J529b **2**:19.127
Fuel Injection Tubing Connections—SAE J521b . **3**:24.94
Metallic Air Brake System Tubing and Pipe—SAE J1149 . . . . **2**:19.122
Metric Thread Fuel Injection Tubing Connections—SAE J242a **3**:24.93
Nonmetallic Air Brake System Tubing—SAE J844 OCT80 . . . . **2**:19.124
Performance Requirements for SAE J844d Nonmetallic Tubing and Fitting Assemblies Used in Automotive Air Brake Systems—SAE J1131 . . . . . **2**:19.126
Pressure Ratings for Hydraulic Tubing and Fittings—SAE J1065 . . . . **2**:19.119
Seamless Copper Tube—SAE J528 JAN80 . . . . **2**:19.121
Seamless Low Carbon Steel Tubing Annealed for Bending and Flaring—SAE J524 JAN80 . . . . . **2**:19.115
Tubing—Motor Vehicle Brake System Hydraulic—SAE J1047 . . . . **2**:22.138
Welded and Cold Drawn Low Carbon Steel Tubing Annealed for Bending and Flaring—SAE J525 JAN80 . . . . **2**:19.115
Welded Flash Controlled Low Carbon Steel Tubing Normalized for Bending, Double Flaring, and Beading—SAE J356 JAN80 . . . . **2**:19.118
Welded Low Carbon Steel Tubing—SAE J526 JAN80 . . . . **2**:19.116
Windshield Washer Tubing—SAE J1037 . . . . . . **1**:11.141

TURBOCHARGERS
Turbocharger Connections—SAE J1135 . . . . . . **3**:24.22

NOTE: Page numbers shown include the volume number in bold followed by the section number and page number within that section.

Turbocharger Nomenclature and Terminology—
SAE J922 NOV79 . . . . 3:24.07

TURN SIGNAL LAMPS
See: LAMPS
UNIVERSAL JOINTS
Universal Joints and Driveshafts—Nomenclature
and Terminology—SAE J901b 4:29.17
VALVES
Engine Poppet Valve Materials—SAE J775 JUL80 1:1.80
Hydraulic Control Valve Test Procedure—SAE J747
OCT80 . . . . 4:40.89
Hydraulic Directional Control Valves, 3000 psi Max-
imum—SAE J748 OCT80 . . . . 4:40.80
Hydraulic Valves for Motor Vehicle Brake Systems—
Performance Requirements—SAE J1137 . . . . 2:22.32
Hydraulic Valves for Motor Vehicle Brake Systems
Test Procedure—SAE J1118 . . . . 2:22.28
Measuring and Reporting the Internal Leakage of
a Hydraulic Fluid Power Valve—SAE J1235
SEP80 . . . . 4:40.84
Method of Measuring and Reporting the Pressure
Differential-Flow Characteristics of a Hydraulic
Fluid Power Valve—SAE J1117 SEP80 . . . . . 4:40.81
Methods for Testing Snap-In Tubeless Tire Valves—
SAE J1206 . . . . 4:30.21
Performance Requirements for Snap-In Tubeless
Tire Valves—SAE J1205 . . . . 4:30.23
Valve Seat Inserts—Engine—SAE J610b 3:24.20
V-BELTS
See: BELTS
VEHICLE IDENTIFICATION NUMBERS
Passenger Car Identification Terminology—SAE
J218 DEC81 . . . . 4:27.02
Passenger Car Vehicle Identification Number Sys-
tem—SAE J273 DEC81 . . . . 4:27.02
Truck and Truck Tractor Vehicle Identification Num-
ber Systems—SAE J1108 DEC81 . . . . 4:27.07
Truck Vehicle Identification Numbers—SAE J187 4:27.05
Vehicle Identification Number Systems—SAE J272
DEC81 . . . . 4:27.01
Vehicle Identification Numbers—SAE J853 DEC81 4:27.03
Vehicle Identification Numbers—Motorcycles—SAE
J364a 4:27.03
Vehicle Identification Numbers—Snowmobile and
All-Terrain Vehicles—SAE J64 FEB81 . . . . . . 4:38.03
World Manufacturer Identifier—SAE J1044 DEC81 4:27.05
VIN
See: VEHICLE IDENTIFICATION NUMBERS
VISCOSITY
Axle and Manual Transmission Lubricant Viscosity
Classification—SAE J306 MAY81 . . . . 3:23.16
Axle and Manual Transmission Lubricants—SAE
J308c 3:23.15
Engine Oil Viscosity Classification—SAE J300
SEP80 . . . . 3:23.05
VISION
Describing and Measuring the Driver's Field of
View—SAE J1050a 4:34.108
Motor Vehicle Driver's Eye Range—SAE J941
MAR81 . . . . 4:34.66
Passenger Car Rear Vision—SAE J834a 4:34.45
Rear View Mirrors—Motorcycles—SAE J268
MAY82 . . . . 4:37.03
Vision Factors Considerations in Rear View Mirror
Design—SAE J985 . . . . 4:34.44
Vision Glossary—SAE J264 . . . . 4:34.119
WARNING DEVICES
Alarm—Back Up—Electric—Performance, Test, and
Application—SAE J994 SEP80 . . . . 3:26.32
Emergency Warning Device—SAE J774c 2:21.66
Flashing Warning Lamp for Agricultural Equip-
ment—SAE J974 MAY80 . . . . 4:39.38
Flashing Warning Lamp for Industrial Equipment—
SAE J96 . . . . 4:40.181
Flashing Warning Lamps for Authorized Emergency,
Maintenance and Service Vehicles—SAE J595b 2:21.67

Hazard Warning Signal Switch—SAE J910b 2:21.68
Safety Signs—SAE J115 SEP79 . . . . 4:40.285
School Bus Red Signal Lamps—SAE J887 MAY82 2:21.69
Vehicular Hazard Warning Signal Flasher—SAE
J945b 2:21.58
Warning Lamp Alternating Flashers—SAE J1054 . 2:21.60
360 Deg Emergency Warning Lamp—SAE J845 . 2:21.68
WARNING LAMPS
See: LAMPS
WASHERS
See: FASTENERS
WEAR
See Also: ABRASION
Method of Testing Resistance to Crocking of Or-
ganic Trim Materials—SAE J861 . . . . 1:11.59
Method of Testing Resistance to Scuffing of Trim
Materials—SAE J365a 1:11.83
Test Method for Determining Dimensional Stability
of Automotive Textile Materials—SAE J883 . . 1:11.59
Test Method for Determining Resistance to Snag-
ging and Abrasion of Automotive Bodycloth—SAE
J948a 1:11.98
Test Method for Wicking of Automotive Fabrics and
Fibrous Materials—SAE J913a 1:11.83
WELDING
Welding, Brazing, and Soldering—Materials and
Practices—SAE J1147 . . . . 1:9.07
WHEEL RIMS
See: RIMS
WHEELS
Extra Wide Single Tire Rim and Wheel Mounting
for Rear Axles—SAE J876a 4:36.53
Hub Fatigue Test Procedures—SAE J1095
JUN82 . . . . 4:31.09
Mechanical and Material Requirements for Wheel
Bolts—SAE J1102 . . . . 1:4.18
Nomenclature—Wheels and Rims—Trucks—SAE
J393 . . . . 4:31.13
Rear Wheel Splash and Stone Throw Protection—
SAE J682 . . . . 4:36.60
Recommended Tolerances for Spoke-Type Wheels,
Demountable Rims, and Rim Spacers—Trucks and
Trailers—SAE J851 . . . . 4:36.52
Wheel Chocks—SAE J348 . . . . 4:36.62
Wheels—Passenger Cars—Impact Performance Re-
quirements and Test Procedures—SAE J175 . . 4:31.02
Wheels—Passenger Cars—Performance Require-
ments and Test Procedures—SAE J328a 4:31.01
Wheels—Recreational and Utility Trailer Test Proce-
dures—SAE J1204 . . . . 4:31.03
Wheels/Rims—Trucks—Test Procedures and Per-
formance Requirements—SAE J267a 4:31.05
Disc Wheels
Commercial Vehicle Disc Wheels—SAE J694a . . 4:36.52
Industrial and Agricultural Disc Wheels—SAE
J712a 4:39.32
Labeling—Disc Wheels and Demountable Rims—
Trucks—SAE J179a 4:31.12
Wheel Mounting Elements for Industrial and Agricul-
tural Disc Wheels—SAE J714b 4:39.36
WINCHES
Classification and Nomenclature Towing Winch for
Skidders and Crawler Tractors—SAE J1014
OCT79 . . . . 4:40.38
Rating of Winches—SAE J706a 4:36.58
Specification Definitions—Winches for Crawler
Tractors and Skidders—SAE J1158 . . . . 4:40.59
WINDSHIELDS
Automotive Safety Glazing—SAE J673b 4:34.36
Drop Test for Evaluating Laminated Safety Glass for
Use in Automotive Windshields—SAE J938a . . 4:34.41
Light Transmittance of Automotive Windshields
Safety Glazing Materials—SAE J1203 . . . . . . 4:34.38
Passenger Car Glazing Shade Bands—SAE J100 . 4:34.40
Passenger Car Glazing—Electrical Circuits—SAE
J216 . . . . 4:34.40

NOTE: Page numbers shown include the volume number in bold followed by the section number and page number within that section.

Safety Glazing Materials—Motor Vehicles—SAE
J674a **4**:34.39

Defogging System
Passenger Car Backlight Defogging System—SAE
J953 . . . . **4**:34.18

Defrosting System
Passenger Car Windshield Defrosting Systems—
SAE J902b **4**:34.13
Windshield Defrosting Systems Performance Re-
quirements—Trucks, Buses, and Multipurpose Ve-
hicles—SAE J382 . . . . **4**:34.17
Windshield Defrosting Systems Test Procedure—
Trucks, Buses, and Multipurpose Vehicles—SAE
J381 . . . . **4**:34.15

Washers
Electric Windshield Washer Switch—SAE J234 . . **2**:20.69
Passenger Car Windshield Washer Systems—SAE
J942b **4**:34.11
Windshield Washer Tubing—SAE J1037 . . . . . . **1**:11.141

Wipers
Electric Windshield Wiper Switch—SAE J112a . . **2**:20.69
Passenger Car Windshield Wiper Systems—SAE
J903c **4**:34.06
Windshield Wiper Hose—SAE J50a **1**:11.139
Windshield Wiper Systems—Trucks, Buses, and
Multipurpose Vehicles—SAE J198 . . . . **4**:34.09

WIRE/WIRING
Automobile, Truck, Truck-Tractor, Trailer, and Motor
Coach Wiring—SAE J1292 OCT81 . . . . **2**:20.39
Detection of Surface Imperfections in Ferrous Rods,
Bars, Tubes, and Wires—SAE J349 JUN80 . . . **1**:3.42
Electrical System for Construction and Industrial Ma-
chinery—SAE J821a **4**:40.184
Five Conductor Electrical Connectors for Automo-
tive Type Trailers—SAE J895 . . . . **2**:20.55
Hard Drawn Carbon Steel Valve Spring Quality Wire
and Springs—SAE J172 . . . . **1**:5.06
Hard Drawn Mechanical Spring Wire and Springs—
SAE J113 . . . . **1**:5.04

High Tension Ignition Cable—SAE J557 . . . . . . **2**:20.46
High Tension Ignition Cable Assemblies—Marine—
SAE J1191 . . . . **4**:41.19
Lifting Crane, Wire-Rope Strength Factors—SAE
J959 OCT80 . . . . **4**:40.148
Low Tension Primary Cable—SAE J1128 . . . . . **2**:20.50
Low Tension Wiring and Cable Terminals and Splice
Clips—SAE J163 . . . . **2**:20.48
Marine Engine Wiring—SAE J378c **4**:41.16
Music Steel Spring Wire and Springs—SAE J178 **1**:5.09
Oil Tempered Carbon Steel Spring Wire and
Springs—SAE J316 . . . . **1**:5.01
Oil Tempered Carbon Steel Valve Spring Quality
Wire and Springs—SAE J351 . . . . **1**:5.02
Oil Tempered Chromium–Silicon Alloy Steel Wire
and Springs—SAE J157 . . . . **1**:5.05
Oil Tempered Chromium-Vanadium Valve Spring
Quality Wire and Springs—SAE J132 . . . . . **1**:5.03
Seven Conductor Jacketed Cable for Truck Trailer
Connections—SAE J1067 . . . . **2**:20.61
Special Quality High Tensile, Hard Drawn Mechani-
cal Spring Wire and Springs—SAE J271 . . . . . **1**:5.04
Stainless Steel, SAE 30302, Spring Wire and
Springs—SAE J230 . . . . **1**:5.08
Stainless Steel 17-7 PH Spring Wire and Springs—
SAE J217 . . . . **1**:5.07
Wiring Identification System for Industrial and Con-
struction Equipment—SAE J210 . . . . **4**:40.192

WOODRUFF KEYS
See: KEYS

WORLD MANUFACTURER IDENTIFIER (WMI)
World Manufacturer Identifier—SAE J1044 DEC81 **4**:27.05

YIELD STRENGTH
Use of the Terms Yield Point and Yield Strength—
SAE J450 . . . . **1**:9.01

ZINC ALLOYS
See: ALLOYS

NOTE: Page numbers shown include the volume number in bold followed by the section number and page number within that section.

SAE TECHNICAL
REPORTS REFERENCED
IN GOVERNMENT
REGULATIONS

SAE TECHNICAL REPORTS REFERENCED
IN GOVERNMENT REGULATIONS

It is known that the documents listed below are referenced or used in the Government regulatory system. Some of these documents have been revised and reissued since the original Government reference usage. However, the specific issue of the document referenced by regulation is still available through the SAE Publications Division, Society of Automotive Engineers, 400 Commonwealth Drive, Warrendale, PA 15096.

CALIFORNIA AIR RESOURCE BOARD (CARB)

Specifications for Fuel Pipes and Openings of Motor Vehicle Fuel Tanks

CARB Fuel Tank Filler Cap and Cap Retainer . . . . SAE J829b
CARB Fuel Tank Filler Cap and Cap Retainer—Threaded
Pressure—Vacuum Type. . . . . SAE J1114
CARB Engine Rating Code-Spark Ignition. . . . . SAE J245

ENVIRONMENTAL PROTECTION AGENCY

Title 40 CFR (40 CFR 85) Published Part J. Gaseous Emissions, Diesel Heavy Duty Engines—Paragraph 85.974–13, (a), (b), (c).

Measurement of CO_2, CO, NO_x, and Diesel Exhaust . . . . SAE J177
Continuous HC Analysis of Diesel Exhaust. . . . . SAE J215
Measurement of In-Take of Exhaust Flow of Diesel Engines . . . . SAE J244

NATIONAL HIGHWAY TRAFFIC SAFETY ADMINISTRATION

Federal Motor Vehicle Safety Standards

FMVSS-103 Passenger Car Windshield Defrosting Systems—
  August 1964 . . . . SAE J902
FMVSS-103 Passenger Car Windshield Defrosting Systems—
  March 1967 . . . . SAE J902a
FMVSS-104 Passenger Car Driver's Eye Range—November
  1965 . . . . SAE J941
FMVSS-104 Passenger Car Windshield Washer Systems—
  November 1965 . . . . SAE J942
FMVSS-104 Passenger Car Windshield Wiper Systems—May
  1966 . . . . SAE J903a
FMVSS-105-75 Moving Barrier Collision Tests—November
  1966 . . . . SAE J972
FMVSS-107 Passenger Car Driver's Eye Range—November
  1965 . . . . SAE J941
FMVSS-108 Automotive Turn Signal Flashers—October 1965 . . SAE J590b
FMVSS-108 Back Up Lamps—February 1968 . . . . SAE J593c
FMVSS-108 Clearance, Side Marker, Identification, and Parking
  Lamps—July 1972 . . . . SAE J592e
FMVSS-108 Color Specifications for Electric Signal Lighting
  Devices—February 1977 . . . . SAE J578c
FMVSS-108 Dimensional Specifications for Sealed Beam
  Headlamp Units—April 1965 . . . . SAE J571d
FMVSS-108 Headlamp Aiming Device for Mechanically Aimable
  Sealed Beam Units—August 1963 . . . . SAE J602
FMVSS-108 Headlamp Beam Switching—April 1964 . . . . SAE J564a
FMVSS-108 Headlamp Mountings—January 1960; Deleted
  1972 . . . . SAE J566
FMVSS-108 Lamp Bulbs and Sealed Beam Headlamp Units . . . . SAE J573d
FMVSS-108 License Plate Lamps—March 1969 . . . . SAE J587d
FMVSS-108 Lighting Inspection Code—March 1973 . . . . SAE J599e
FMVSS-108 Motorcycle and Motor Driven Cycle Headlamps—
  January 1949 . . . . SAE J584
FMVSS-108 Parking Lamps (Position Lamps)—December 1970 . SAE J222
FMVSS-108 Plastic Materials for Use in Optical Parts, Such as
  Lenses and Reflectors, of Motor Vehicle Lighting
  Devices—August 1966 . . . . SAE J576b
FMVSS-108 Plastic Materials for Use in Optical Parts, Such as
  Lenses and Reflectors, of Motor Vehicle Lighting
  Devices—May 1970 . . . . SAE J576c

FMVSS-108 Reflex Reflectors—March 1970 . . . . SAE J594e
FMVSS-108 Sealed Beam Headlamp—June 1966 . . . . SAE J580a
FMVSS-108 Sealed Beam Headlamp Units for Motor Vehicles—
  August 1965 . . . . SAE J579a
FMVSS-108 Sealed Beam Headlamp Units for Motor Vehicles—
  December 1974 . . . . SAE J579c
FMVSS-108 Semi-Automatic Headlamp Beam Switching
  Devices—February 1969 . . . . SAE J565b
FMVSS-108 Stop Lamps—August 1970. . . . . SAE J586b
FMVSS-108 Tail Lamps—August 1970 . . . . SAE J585d
FMVSS-108 Test for Motor Vehicle Lighting Devices and
  Components—August 1967 . . . . SAE J575d
FMVSS-108 Test for Motor Vehicle Lighting Devices and
  Components—August 1970 . . . . SAE J575e
FMVSS-108 Test for Motor Vehicle Lighting Devices and
  Components—April 1975 . . . . SAE J575f
FMVSS-108 Turn Signal Lamps—June 1966 . . . . SAE J588d
FMVSS-108 Turn Signal Lamps—August 1970; Edit. Change—
  September 1970. . . . . SAE J588e
FMVSS-108 Turn Signal Operating Units—April 1964 . . . . . SAE J589
FMVSS-108 School Bus Red Signal Lamps—July 1964 . . . . . SAE J887
FMVSS-108 Vehicular Hazard Signal Operating Unit—January
  1966 . . . . SAE J910
FMVSS-108 Vehicular Hazard Warning Signal Flasher—February
  1966 . . . . SAE J945
FMVSS-108 142 mm x 200 mm Sealed Beam Headlamp Unit—
  January 1975 . . . . SAE J1132
FMVSS-111 Test Procedure for Determining Reflectivity of
  Rearview Mirrors—August 1974 . . . . SAE J964a
FMVSS-116 Brazed Double Wall Low Carbon Steel Tubing—
  January 1955 . . . . SAE J527
FMVSS-116 Motor Vehicle Brake Fluid—April 1968 . . . . . . SAE J1703b
FMVSS-201 Instrument Panel Laboratory Impact Test
  Procedure—June 1965 . . . . SAE J921
FMVSS-201 Instrumentation for Laboratory Impact Tests—
  November 1966 . . . . SAE J977
FMVSS-201 Passenger Car Side Door Latch Systems—May
  1965; Edit. Change—January 1972 . . . . SAE J839b
FMVSS-202 Manikins for Use in Defining Vehicle Seating
  Accommodation—November 1962. . . . . SAE J826
FMVSS-203 Steering Wheel Assembly Laboratory Test
  Procedure—December 1965 . . . . SAE J944
FMVSS-205 Automotive Glazing—August 1967 . . . . SAE J673a
FMVSS-206 Passenger Car Side Door Latch Systems—May
  1965; Edit. Change—January 1972 . . . . SAE J839b
FMVSS-206 Vehicular Passenger Door Hinge System—July
  1965 . . . . SAE J934
FMVSS-208 Human Tolerance to Impact Conditions as Related
  to Motor Vehicle Design—October 1966 . . . . SAE J885a
FMVSS-209 Air Cleaner Test Code—June 1962. . . . . SAE J726a
FMVSS-209 Motor Vehicle Seat Belt Assembly Installations—
  September 1965 . . . . SAE J800b
FMVSS-210 Manikins for Use in Defining Vehicle Seating
  Accommodation—November 1962. . . . . SAE J826
FMVSS-213 Instrumentation for Impact Tests—December
  1971. . . . . SAE J211a
FMVSS-215 Lighting Inspection Code—July 1970 . . . . SAE J599b
FMVSS-215 Headlamp Aiming Device for Mechanically Aimable
  Sealed Beam Headlamp Units—July 1970 . . . . SAE J602
FMVSS-222 Instrumentation for Barrier Collision Tests—
  December 1971 . . . . SAE J211a

71

FMVSS-PART 572 Instrumentation for Barrier Collision Tests—
December 1971 . . . . SAE J211a
FMVSS-PART 581 Headlamp Aiming Device for
Mechanically Aimable Sealed Beam
Units—August 1963. . . . . SAE J602a
FMVSS-PART 581 Lighting Inspection Code—July 1970 . . . . . SAE J599b
FMVSS-PART 581 Surface Texture Control—June 1963. . . . . . SAE J449a

**OCCUPATIONAL SAFETY AND HEALTH
ADMINISTRATION**

OSHA No. 29 CFR 1910 Slow Moving Vehicle Emblem . . . . . . SAE J943a

OSHA No. 29 CRF 1926.1001 Minimum Performance
Criteria for Roll-Over
Protective Structures
(ROPS) for Designated
Scrapers, Loaders,
Dozers, Graders and
Crawler Tractors . . . . SAE J1040b
OSHA No. 29 CFR 1928.51 Agricultural Tractor ROPS . . . . . . SAE J1194
OSHA No. 29 CFR 1928.57 Safety of Agricultural Equipment . . SAE J208b

RELATED TECHNICAL REPORTS

RELATED TECHNICAL REPORTS

The publications listed here are standards, recommended practices, information reports, and other material not included in the Handbook. Copies may be ordered by contacting the Publications Division, SAE, 400 Commonwealth Drive, Warrendale, PA 15096.

HS 3—SURFACE ROLLING AND OTHER METHODS FOR MECHANICAL PRESTRESSING OF METALS—This book provides a detailed guide to enhancing the properties of metals through surface rolling and other methods. Calculations for fatigue improvement through surface rolling, tooling for surface rolling, control and inspection, and effects other than fatigue improvement are presented.

$8.00 Mem. $10.00 List

HS 19—SAE DOCUMENTS REFERENCED IN FEDERAL MOTOR VEHICLE SAFETY STANDARDS—Includes SAE reports specifically referenced in FMVSS, and reports that have been revised or new reports issued since the SS were last revised. Reports generated by other organizations are also listed for the convenience of the user.

$8.00 Mem. $10.00 List

HS 40—MAINTENANCE OF AUTOMOTIVE ENGINE COOLING SYSTEMS—This comprehensive guide to servicing modern truck and passenger-car cooling systems clearly defines limitations of coolants in regard to leakage, evaporation, overheating, and loss of capacity. Interrelations between cooling, fuel, lubrication, and exhaust systems are examined. An excellent maintenance guide.

$5.00 Mem. $6.00 List

HS 63—MANUAL ON DESIGN AND MANUFACTURE OF CONED DISK SPRINGS OR BELLEVILLE SPRINGS—Provides complete information on the design and application of coned disk springs. Includes materials, methods calculation, manufacturing methods, design examples, and tables of formulae.

$5.00 Mem. $6.00 List

HS J73—MULTIPURPOSE PETROLEUM BASE FLUIDS—SAE Information Report. Specifications for multipurpose petroleum base fluids are given to reflect current industry usage of such materials in agricultural, construction, industrial and other special-purpose vehicles. Covered is a wide range of fluid properties and their suitability for use at various ambient temperatures depending on vehicle design.

$6.00 Mem. $7.50 List

HS 82—TRUCK ABILITY PREDICTION PROCEDURE—SAE J688—Provides practical method for predicting truck performance. By following directions, it is possible to select a truck on the basis of readily available specifications, information provided, and a minimum of calculation.

$6.00 Mem. $7.50 List

HS 83—TRUCK ABILITY WORK SHEET PAD—Gives procedure and form for determining grade ability at a given road speed and equivalent acceleration rate. Pad contains 150 work sheets. One copy of HS 83a (which is suitable for reproduction) is supplied with each pad.

$4.00 Mem. $5.50 List

HS 83a—SAE COMMERCIAL VEHICLE ABILITY REPORT FORM—Available as a single sheet for reproduction or may be purchased in quantity.

$1.00 Mem. $2.00 List

HS 84—MANUAL ON SHOT PEENING—SAE J808a—Intended as a practical aid to engineers, designers, and men in the shop. HS 84 points out some of the possibilities and some of the limitations of the process. Chapters are devoted to a description of the process, the effect of shot peening, shot peening machines, peening media, quality control, fatigue properties, and x-ray diffraction.

$6.50 Mem. $8.00 List

HS 124—SAE MANUAL ON BLAST CLEANING—SAE J792a—Instructs engineers, designers, and shop men in blast cleaning know-how. Discusses blasting abrasives, blast cleaning machines, production procedures, and process specifications.

$6.50 Mem. $8.00 List

HS 184—SURFACE VEHICLE SOUND MEASUREMENT PROCEDURES—This publication includes an extensive rationale statement to accompany SAE Recommended Practice J184a—Qualifying a Sound Data Acquisition System. Recognizing that the use of only a sound level meter is often impractical or insufficient, there is need to ensure that other systems meet the performance requirements of a standard meter. J184a recognizes recent advancements in sound measurement instrumentation and provides the means to qualify the newer systems to existing performance criteria. The rationale behind the modification of the qualification procedure is explained in detail. In addition to complete systems, the requirements for individual instruments and circuit components are also discussed. HS 184 also includes all of the standards and recommended practices found in the sound level section of the SAE Handbook.

$10.00 Mem. $12.50 List

HS 210—LABORATORY TESTING MACHINES AND PROCEDURES FOR MEASURING THE STEADY STATE FORCE AND MOMENT PROPERTIES OF PASSENGER CAR TIRES—SAE J1106 and SAE J1107—These reports describe some basic design requirements and operational procedures associated with equipment for laboratory measurement of tire force and moment properties for the full range of automotive tires. These properties must be known to establish the tires' contribution to vehicle dynamic performance. This HS is a guide for equipment design and test operation so that data from different laboratories can be directly compared.

$5.00 Mem. $6.00 List

HS 215—HANDBOOK OF MOTOR VEHICLE, SAFETY AND ENVIRONMENTAL TERMINOLOGY—Includes alphabetical listings of more than 1500 technical terms as defined within the Motor Vehicle, Safety and Environmental areas of the 1976 SAE Handbook. Available for the first time in an easy to use format, these definitions were compiled to fill the critical need for a single-source reference. HS 215 is one of the most useful Handbook Supplements ever published by the SAE.

$10.00 Mem. $12.00 List

HS J390—DUAL DIMENSIONING—With the rapidly growing use of metric measurement throughout the world, the need for both metric and inch dimensions on a single drawing has led to growing use of dual dimensioning of engineering drawings. This report presents several approaches to displaying and identifying the two different values for each dimension, although only one is shown as preferred.

$6.00 Mem. $7.50 List

HS J447 JUN81—PREVENTION OF CORROSION OF METALS—SAE Information Report. A guide to principles of metal corrosion and methods of dealing with its prevention. Materials are described and evaluated. Chemical treatments are covered along with metal coatings, paints, and ceramics.

$12.00 Mem. $15.00 List

HS J670e—VEHICLE DYNAMICS TERMINOLOGY—SAE Recommended Practice. Defines mechanical vibration—qualitative terminology, vibrating systems, components and characteristics of suspension systems, vibrations of vehicle suspension systems, suspension geometry, tires and wheels, and directional control. (1978)

$6.00 Mem. $7.50 List

HS J762a—REINFORCED PLASTICS FOR GROUND VEHICLE APPLICATIONS—This information report established an engineering approach to selection and use of reinforced plastic materials. Also acquaints engineers with varied classes of fibrous reinforced plastic materials available and their general range of properties and applications.

$6.50 Mem. $8.00 List

HS J782b—SEATING MANUAL–MOTOR VEHICLES—Developed by the SAE Seating Committee, this manual is designed to provide a more

uniform system of nomenclature, definition of functional requirements, and test methods for the various materials, components, and manufacturing methods used in automotive seating. The information compiled is for reference for body and trim engineers as well as those who work cooperatively with the engineers.

$7.00 Mem. $9.00 List

HS J784a—RESIDUAL STRESS MEASUREMENTS BY X-RAY DIFFRACTION—This manual brings together the most important aspects of the x-ray techniques. It places emphasis on theoretical aspects but at the same time attempts to show how these theoretical considerations are reduced to a practical technique. Techniques are presented which enable satisfactory measurements of stress even when diffraction lines are diffused. Techniques are based on two-exposure method and use of diffractometers.

$10.00 Mem. $13.00 List

HS J788 APR80—MANUAL ON DESIGN AND APPLICATION OF LEAF SPRINGS—A complete design and application guide for leaf springs, this manual covers space requirements, elastic and geometric properties, proper methods of attachment, and much more.

$15.00 Mem. $18.00 List

HS J795 JUN81—MANUAL ON DESIGN AND APPLICATION OF HELICAL AND SPIRAL SPRINGS—A detailed design manual on all aspects of helical and spiral springs, this book covers fatigue, durability, temperature effects on springs, common causes of spring failure, a detailed listing of spring materials, and more, for a variety of types of helical and spiral springs.

$15.00 Mem. $18.00 List

HS J796 SEP81—MANUAL ON DESIGN AND MANUFACTURE OF TORSION BAR SPRINGS—This design guide provides detailed information on all types of torsion springs, including fatigue life, applications, material and processing, adjustment mechanisms, end fastening design, and much more. It even includes examples of actual applications.

$15.00 Mem. $18.00 List

HS J806 MAY82—OIL FILTER TEST PROCEDURE—The purpose of this lubrication oil filter test code is to provide means for evaluating the performance characteristics of full-flow oil filters on bench test equipment. This data collected from "in service" applications may be used for establishing standards of performance for filters tested in this manner.

$8.00 Mem. $10.00 List

HS J836a—AUTOMOTIVE METALLURGICAL JOINING—This report is an abbreviated summary of metallurgical joining by welding, brazing, and soldering, intended to reflect current usage in the automotive industry.

$6.50 Mem. $8.00 List

HS J885 APR80—HUMAN TOLERANCE TO IMPACT CONDITIONS AS RELATED TO MOTOR VEHICLE DESIGN—SAE Information Report. This excellent information report provides a wide variety of data on human tolerance to impact resulting from tests of human volunteers, cadavers, and animal subjects. Its purpose is to provide a basis for crash test evaluation and motor vehicle accident reporting and it meets these needs well. It should, however, also be valuable to anyone involved in any type of trauma or accident investigation or product safety evaluation. Definitions are provided for medical terminology used.

$6.50 Mem. $8.00 List

HS J905—FUEL FILTER TEST METHOD—SAE Recommended Practice. This recommended practice provides a complete description of the procedures for testing final fuel filters for both diesel and gasoline engines. Test apparatus and testing materials are described in detail. An effort has been made in developing this test to simulate actual operating conditions.

$5.00 Mem. $6.00 List

HS J906—AUTOMOTIVE SAFETY GLAZING MANUAL—SAE Information Report. Provides a basic guide to characteristics of safety glazing materials and information on usage for those unfamiliar with glazing.

$5.00 Mem. $6.00 List

HS J965—ABRASIVE WEAR—SAE Information Report. Covers fundamentals of abrasive wear phenomena, testing for abrasive wear resistance, and solutions to abrasive wear problems.

$5.00 Mem. $6.00 List

HS J1066—RECOMMENDED GUIDELINES FOR COMPANY METRICATION PROGRAMS IN THE METALWORKING INDUSTRY—This 40 page booklet is divided into four sections: Drawing Practices; Units, Applications, and Terminology; Education and Training Aids; and Machine and Inspection Tools. Each of these sections recommends practices that will promote effective use of metric units, as well as effective handling of the transition period. Lists are included showing supplier of materials and where to obtain additional information.

$8.00 Mem. $10.00 List

HS J1078—A RECOMMENDED METHOD OF ANALYTICALLY DETERMINING THE COMPETENCE OF HYDRAULIC TELESCOPIC CANTILEVERED CRANE BOOMS

$5.00 Mem. $6.00 List

HS 1086a—SECOND EDITION UNIFIED NUMBERING SYSTEM HANDBOOK FOR METALS AND ALLOYS—The UNS provides a means of correlating many nationally used numbering systems currently administered by various societies, trade organizations, governmental bodies, and individual producers and users of metals and alloys, thereby avoiding confusion caused by the use of more than one identification number for the same material; and by the opposite situation, of having the same number assigned to two or more entirely different materials.

$39.00 Mem. $49.00 List

HS J1093 JUN82—LATTICED CRANE BOOM SYSTEMS—ANALYTICAL PROCEDURE—This SAE Recommended Practice establishes the criteria for analytically evaluating the basic structural competence of wire rope supported latticed crane boom systems. Included is the evaluation of elastic stability for the overall boom system and the individual members of the system.

$6.00 Mem. $5.00 List

HS J1156—STANDARD FOR AUTOMOTIVE RESISTANCE SPOT WELDING ELECTRODES—This Standard outlines the requirements relative to size, specifications and identification for a variety of resistance spot welding electrodes.

$10.00 Mem. $13.00 List

HS J1238—RATING LIFT CRANES ON FIXED PLATFORMS OPERATING IN THE OCEAN ENVIRONMENT—SAE Recommended Practice.

$5.00 Mem. $6.00 List

ANSI B92.1 AND 1a—INVOLUTE SPLINES AND INSPECTION STANDARD—Details all standardized size- and major-diameter fit splines. Side-fit splines are subject of major changes. New table format aids referencing.

$15.00 Mem. $18.00 List

ANSI B92.2M—METRIC INVOLUTE SPLINES AND INSPECTION STANDARD—Provides details of all standardized metric splines including dimensions, tolerances, and fit information.

$18.00 Mem. $21.00 List

SP-407—DRIVER EXPECTANCY AND PERFORMANCE IN LOCATING AUTOMOTIVE CONTROLS—Final report of research on automotive control location conducted for the Vehicle Research Institute of the SAE. This research was undertaken to provide information that can be used to develop recommended practices and convention for the location of certain hand-operated controls in passenger cars, light trucks, and multi-purpose vehicles.

$9.50 Mem. $12.00 List

SP-423—GLOSSARY OF AUTOMOTIVE TERMINOLOGY/FRENCH–ENGLISH–ENGLISH–FRENCH—Developed by the Chrysler Corporation's Engineering Office. Included are approximately 17,000 entries. Accents and annotations for parts of speech, gender, and number appear in the French half. The annotations have been added to all single word entries, and to the first word (key word) of some multi-word entries.

$12.00 Mem. $15.00 List

SP-436—GLOSSARY OF AUTOMOTIVE TERMINOLOGY/SPANISH–ENGLISH—ENGLISH–SPANISH—Developed by the Chrysler Corporation Engineering Office. It contains more than 27,000 entries in each language, complete with accents and annotations indicating verbs. English entries applying only to the U.S. or Great Britain are so noted. Because of its value to the automotive community, it is being published for worldwide distribution by SAE.

$15.00 Mem.　　$18.00 List

SP-450—ANTHROPOMETRY OF INFANTS, CHILDREN, AND YOUTHS TO AGE 18 FOR PRODUCT SAFETY DESIGN—Truly a landmark publication, this book is a must for anyone involved in designing safety systems, restraint systems, controls, or a variety of products or systems to be used by those in infancy through age 18. Range of measurements, average measurements, and scatter frequencies are provided for a long list of physiological dimensions including sitting height, standing height, weight, hand and finger size, hip width, arm length, and much more. Prepared for the U.S. Consumer Product Safety Commission by the Highway Safety Research Institute.

$24.95 Mem. and List

J-REPORTS

Rules, Nomenclature and Guideposts

TECHNICAL COMMITTEE GUIDEPOSTS— SAE J1271 AUG79

SAE Recommended Practice

Report of Publications Advisory Committee approved August 1979.

1. Introduction

1.1 These Guideposts were written to provide information needed by SAE technical committee members. Subject matter covers relations of technical committees to the SAE organization and, in broad terms, committee operating procedures.

1.2 The *Guideposts* are the outgrowth of the principles and policies of the Society, and they reflect the philosophies, traditions, and methodology that have emerged from years of successful operations of SAE technical committees.

1.3 These Guideposts are necessarily brief and presented in an outline form. For additional information refer to the latest issue of the SAE Technical Board Rules and Regulations and appropriate Council Operating Practices.

2. SAE Objective

2.1 The objective of the Society is to promote the Arts, Sciences, Standards, and Engineering Practices connected with the design, construction, and utilization of self-propelled mechanisms, prime movers, components thereof, and related equipment. SAE serves its members and the General Public through meetings and programs developed by its various Engineering Activities and Sections, through its Placement Committee, and through its publications; *it serves industry, government, and the public through the development of technical reports*[1] *including engineering standards and recommended practices, and distributing these documents.*

3. SAE Technical Board

3.1 **Organization**—The Technical Board is the agent of the SAE Board of Directors with authority to direct and supervise all SAE Cooperative Engineering Programs, including standardization, research, and the participation in technical committee activity of other organizations. Fig. 1 shows its position in the Society's structure, the councils, and a few examples of technical committees it administers.

3.2 **Philosophies**

3.2.1 The Technical Board will consider those projects for which industry, government, the public, or other responsible agencies have expressed a need and which lend themselves to cooperative solution. Within their own operations, technical committees frequently generate projects meeting the above-noted criteria.

3.2.2 The Technical Board expects technical committees to set up their own organizations, procedures, and programs within their scopes and the limits of the Technical Board's *Rules and Regulations* and individual council guidelines.

3.3 **Recognition of Achievements**—Annually the Board awards a maximum of 30 *Certificates of Appreciation* to technical committee members and to individuals representing SAE in other organizations. Nominations for awards are submitted through the councils to the Certificates of Appreciation Committee by the various technical committees. Supporting data outlining the basis for nomination is required.

4. Councils of the SAE Technical Board

4.1 The Technical Board delegates to its councils the authority to direct and approve (see paragraph 6.2) SAE Standards, Recommended Practices, and Information Reports (subject to the right of anyone to appeal a decision to the Board). The councils are authorized to establish committees that may be needed to accomplish this assignment.

4.2 **Committee Sponsor**—It is intended that the chairman of each council appoint annually council members to act as sponsors for committees functioning directly under the council. The council chairman may appoint the council technical committee chairmen as members of the council and as sponsors for their committees. The committee sponsor shall represent the committee to the council, and serve as liaison between the committee and the council. During periods when a committee is without a sponsor, the council chairman will perform such functions.

4.2.1 Committee sponsor's responsibilities shall include:

(a) Providing regular communication of significant committee activity to the council and council actions to the technical committees. To facilitate communication, a sponsor report should be included as an agenda item at each technical committee meeting. Each technical committee chairman should prepare an annual status report for submission to the council through his sponsor. (The date for this report to be selected to be convenient to council meetings and national meetings.) Time should be provided on the council agenda for discussion of these reports with the sponsors.

(b) Reviewing and counseling with committee chairman on committee programs and membership and providing council policy guidance.

(c) Providing coordination among sponsor's assigned committees and with other sponsors.

(d) Reviewing technical committee organization and proposing appropriate changes to the council.

5. SAE Technical Committees

5.1 **Objectives**—The objectives of a technical committee are to coordinate and utilize the knowledge, experience, and skill of engineers and other qualified individuals on technical problems within the scope of its activities to:

(a) Conduct necessary investigations and develop technical reports.

(b) Review technical reports periodically, revise as necessary, and maintain content abreast of latest technology.

(c) Advise, consult, and cooperate with industry, government, educational institutions, the public, other standardizing bodies, and other SAE committees and members.

(d) Assist committees of the SAE Engineering Activity Board (see Fig. 1) in the preparation and presentation of papers at national meetings and specialty conferences.

5.2 **Principles**—The end products of the committee's work are offered as the best judgment of a group technically competent to deal with the problems covered and do *not* represent an industry-trade position. Employers of committee members are not committed by an action of an SAE committee. Over many years, the extensive use of SAE technical reports clearly indicates that committee members, working as individuals, do produce results that are practical and useful to industry, government, and the public.

5.3 **Scope**—A technical committee shall be responsible for a field of endeavor, as defined by its scope. In cases where projects overlap areas of interest of another council's committee, the originating committee shall submit the project(s) for review and approval to the other concerned committee and its council prior to issuance. A committee is established when a new major project area is to be undertaken and no existing commitee is available. A committee is discharged when the assigned work is completed and there is no further need for its services. The councils retain responsibility for periodic review of technical reports developed by their disbanded committees.

5.4 **Membership**

5.4.1 QUALIFICATIONS—All participants are appointed to SAE technical

---

[1] The term "technical reports" as used in these Guideposts, stands for the end product of a committee's efforts and may consist of an SAE Standard, Recommended Practice, Information Report, or Aerospace Material Specification.

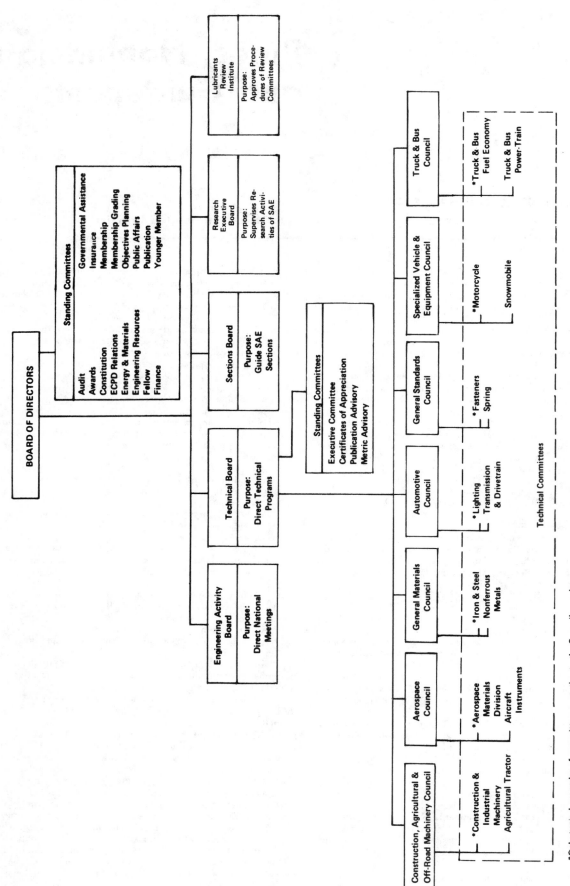

FIG. 1—SAE ORGANIZATION

*Only typical examples of committees reporting to the Councils are shown.

committees by the committee chairman on the basis of their individual qualifications which enable them to contribute to the work of these committees. Overall, committee membership should attain an equitable balance of representation by knowledgeable *parties at interest.* All relevant points of view should be invited to participate. (Ref. paragraph 4.1.1 Technical Board Rules and Regulations.) SAE membership is not a prerequisite for committee membership.

5.4.2 The policy of the Society is that SAE technical committee members act as *individuals* and not as agents or representatives of their employers. Their actions are accepted as personal actions and do not necessarily represent their employers' attitudes or views.

5.4.3 GRADES—In addition to committee officers (see paragraph 5.5.1), committee participants shall be classified as *member, liaison member,* and *consultant member.*

5.4.4 *Liaison and consultant members* are appointed by the chairman on the basis of need for their particular services. *Liaison members* relay information to and from paralleling activities of other committees and organizations. *Consultant members* supply advice on the specific program for which they have been appointed. *Liaison* and *consultant members* are not eligible to vote on committee actions except at the request of the committee chairman.

5.4.5 Governmental agency employees may be appointed as *members, liaison members,* or *consultant members* of the committee with aforementioned responsibilities and privileges.

5.5 Organization—The number of members on a technical committee may vary depending on the specific needs. Typical organization patterns are shown in Figs. 2 and 3.

5.5.1 OFFICERS—The committee shall have a chairman and may have a vice-chairman and/or a secretary.

5.5.1.1 The chairman and vice-chairman of a newly formed committee shall be appointed by the council chairman with advice of council members. Existing committees shall nominate a chairman and vice-chairman annually for council approval. (See paragraph 4.3 of SAE Technical Board Rules and Regulations). The chairman may become a member of a council by appointment by the council chairman.

5.5.1.2 The secretary shall be appointed annually by the committee chairman.

5.5.1.3 Reasonably frequent rotation of committee chairmen, where practical and desirable, is encouraged. However, renominations of chairmen who have served five or more consecutive years shall be reviewed and approved by the council.

5.5.1.4 It is the duty of the chairman to:

(a) Plan and conduct committee meetings.

(b) Establish subcommittees, appoint their chairmen, and supervise their operation.

(c) Establish working panels, including appointment of their chairmen and/or individual member work assignments, and supervise their operation.

(d) Assign projects so as to balance and expedite the committee's work.

(e) Act for the committee between meetings, subject to confirmation at the next meeting.

(f) Supervise and report voting on all committee reports. (See paragraph 5.5.2.1 for responsibilities of SAE staff representative.)

(g) Review the membership annually to maintain an active and balanced committee.

(h) Recommend revisions of committee procedures as needed.

(i) Arrange for the nomination of candidates for the Technical Board Certificate of Appreciation Award. Candidates must be nominated by April 1 (see paragraph 3.3).

(j) Serve as chairman of the steering committee (or executive committee), if applicable.

(k) For additional duties of the chairman, refer to SAE J1159, Preparation of SAE Technical Reports—Surface Vehicles and Machines: Standards, Recommended Practices, Information Reports.

5.5.2 SAE STAFF REPRESENTATIVE—An SAE staff representative will advise the committee officers on procedures and assist the committee in its organization and operation, attend meetings, and assure that meeting minutes are prepared and properly distributed.[2]

5.5.2.1 SAE staff representative performs tally of committee voting and disseminates results of balloting.

5.5.3 EXECUTIVE COMMITTEES (Fig. 2)—When a technical committee has numerous subcommittees, projects, or is so large as to make meetings of the entire group impractical, an executive committee may be established to organize and manage the affairs of the committee. The executive committee shall include all committee officers, and may include all subcommittee chairmen and such additional members as may be desirable to form an efficient working group. The technical committee officers shall be the officers of the executive committee.

5.5.4 SUBCOMMITTEES—Subcommittees are organized to carry out specific continuing technical segments of the committee's scope. The original chairman shall be appointed by the parent technical committee chairman; thereafter, the chairman may be nominated by the subcommittee, subject to review and approval by the parent technical committee chairman. It is desirable that the subcommittee chairman be a member of the parent committee.

5.5.4.1 The original membership will be appointed by either the parent committee chairman or by the subcommittee chairman. Thereafter, membership matters are handled by the subcommittee chairman.

5.5.4.2 Duties of subcommittee officers in relation to their subcommittees are the same as those of the technical committee officers in relation to the technical committee, except for paragraph 5.5.1.4, items b, i, and j.

5.5.5 WORKING TECHNICAL PANELS (Fig. 3)—When a committee or subcommittee wishes to have several of its members work together in preparation of a draft technical report, a temporary working panel may be formed. After completion of its task, responsibility for review and maintenance of resulting technical reports reverts to the committee or subcommittee, and the panel is discharged.

5.6 Committee Relationships with SAE and Non-SAE Groups

5.6.1 INTRA-SAE RELATIONSHIPS—As a primary principle, each SAE technical report should be reasonably self-contained or cross-reference other SAE documents. Development of a draft technical report will often require use of data which falls within the scope of another SAE committee. In these instances, liaison should be established by formation of a joint sub-group, by membership on or from that committee, or through the SAE staff. In any event, comments and/or approval by the consultant committee should be solicited by the committee preparing the draft technical report. Adherence to this principle will avoid duplication of effort and will insure against conflicts and ambiguities. Because of his intimate knowledge of SAE activities, the SAE staff representative can help the technical committee in its relationships with other Society groups. See paragraph 6.6 in SAE J1159.

5.6.2 LIAISON WITH OTHER ORGANIZATIONS—Technical committees should coordinate their efforts with parallel activities in other organizations such as the American National Standards Institute, American Society for Testing and Materials, American Iron and Steel Institute, American Petroleum Institute, and the Aerospace Industries Association. To maintain this liaison, the Technical Board appoints individuals to represent the Society. It is the duty of these representatives to report developments to the appropriate SAE committee, and to present SAE views which are the consensus of the concerned SAE committee(s) to these organizations.

5.6.2.1 Representatives of SAE on American National Standards committees or standards committees of other standards writing organizations shall be appointed by the Chairman of the SAE Technical Board.

5.6.2.2 Representatives of SAE on non-SAE standards committees shall report to a technical committee or, if none exists, to the appropriate council.

5.6.2.3 Representatives of SAE shall, where feasible, develop SAE positions regarding draft technical reports developed by such non-SAE committees through consultation with the appropriate SAE technical committee or council.

5.6.2.4 The representative of SAE shall report activities of the non SAE committee annually and shall advise the technical committee or council of the SAE vote on approval or disapproval of standards or other substantive matters coming before the non-SAE committee. The SAE representative may seek additional SAE support in backing up the SAE position through the appropriate SAE committees and councils.

5.6.2.5 Approval of American National Standards by American National Standards committees for which SAE is sponsor, co-sponsor, or secretariat shall be by the appropriate SAE council on either recommendation of the appropriate SAE committee or the SAE representatives on the American National Standards commitee.

5.6.2.6 Upon approval by SAE of an American National Standard for which SAE is *sponsor, co-sponsor,* or *secretariat,* the subject standard shall be considered an approved SAE Standard. In the event that SAE is not the publisher of the subject standard as an American National Standard, but does provide coverage of the subject matter contained in the standard in the SAE handbook or other SAE publications, such SAE publications will be revised as soon as possible after SAE approval of the American National Standard but not later than one year after such approval. When SAE coverage of the subject matter is approved in advance of a revision to the American National Standard, the Society will immediately initiate a revision of the American National Standard.

5.6.3 JOINT SPONSORSHIP WITH OTHER ORGANIZATIONS—SAE joint sponsorship of committees with outside organizations is discouraged, unless such joint sponsorship is of direct benefit to SAE committees. Where possible, SAE

---

[2]When the chairman or his appointed secretary records the minutes, a copy (or copies, as appropriate) should be forwarded to the SAE office where they will be reviewed and distributed and maintained for at least five years and made available for inspection and for distribution as appropriate.

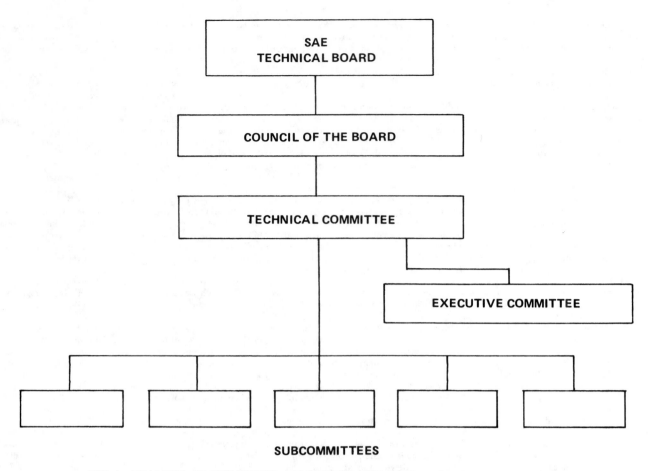

SUBCOMMITTEES

FIG. 2—EXAMPLE OF EXECUTIVE COMMITTEE OF LARGE TECHNICAL COMMITTEE

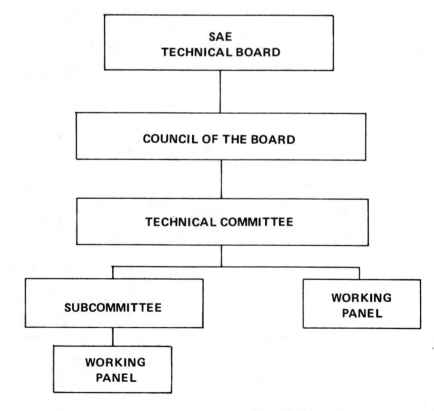

FIG. 3—TECHNICAL COMMITTEE

should perform its standardization and cooperative engineering functions without the establishment of jointly sponsored groups.

5.6.3.1 In cases where SAE technical committee work or technical projects are of major interest outside of SAE (for example, splines and screw threads), cooperation is encouraged in established SAE sponsored organizations such as the American National Standards Institute (ANSI) and the Coordinating Research Council (CRC).

5.6.3.2 Where joint sponsorship of a project with an outside organization is proposed, specific Technical Board approval is required.

5.6.3.3 Any technical reports resulting from such cooperative activity will be subject to normal SAE review and approval procedures. In such technical reports recognition of the participation of outside groups is appropriate.

5.6.4 COOPERATION WITH GOVERNMENT AGENCIES—Technical committee cooperation with government agencies in developing technical reports of mutual interest is encouraged. Such technical reports will be identified by normal SAE numbering systems when published by the SAE, and appropriately cross-referenced when issued in some other manner.

5.6.4.1 Where there is a divergence of technical opinion on a proposed technical report between a committee and interested governmental agency, the committee may offer the government its technical opinion in the form of comments upon a proposed government prepared specification or standard.

5.6.4.2 If the committee so chooses, and with review and approval by the appropriate council, the committee's technical opinion can be published in the form of an SAE technical report.

5.6.5. SAE PARTICIPATION IN INTERNATIONAL STANDARDS

5.6.5.1 SAE may serve as the U. S. technical secretariat for ANSI in International Organization for Standards (ISO) and International Electro-Technical Commission (IEC) technical committees, subcommittees, and working groups only when approved by the Technical Board.

5.6.5.2 In administering such ISO and IEC technical secretariats, SAE shall form a U. S. Technical Advisory Group (TAG) consistent with procedures of the American National Standards Institute. Membership on the TAG shall follow the rules governing membership on SAE technical committees. Appointments to the TAG shall be subject to confirmation by the appropriate SAE council. The TAG will call upon cognizant SAE technical committees and outside activities, if appropriate, to assist in developing U. S. positions on proposed ISO or IEC standards and in the development of draft standards.

5.6.5.3 SAE shall follow the provisions of the ANSI Guidelines for ISO Standards Activities.

6. Technical Committee Technical Reports—The major effort of technical committee activity is the development of technical reports for publication by the SAE.

6.1 Development—The initial work on a draft technical report is usually handled by a task force which presents its work to a parent group, preferably well in advance of a meeting date. Corrections to the proposal are officially recognized at the meeting of the parent group and documented in the minutes. Depending on procedures established for each group, mailing of draft technical reports may be handled directly by the chairman, the SAE staff representative, or by a delegated member.

6.1.1 GUIDES FOR PREPARATION OF TECHNICAL REPORTS—Annually, a large number of documents are developed by the technical committee for publication. It is not practical for the SAE staff to restyle them. Technical committees will use the following SAE publications.

(a) *Preparation of SAE Technical Reports*—Surface Vehicles and Machines: Standards, Recommended Practices, Information Reports—SAE J1159.

(b) *Rules for SAE Use of SI (Metric) Units*—SAE J916—establishes the rules for the use of Système International (SI) units in SAE documents including specifications and standards.

(c) *AMS Editorial Procedure and Form* for the preparation of Aerospace Material Specifications (AMS) and other Aerospace Material Documents.

(d) *Aerospace Council's Organization and Operating Guide for Aerospace Cooperative Engineering Program* for the preparation of Aerospace Standards, Military Standards, Aerospace Recommended Practices, and Aerospace Information Reports.

6.1.2 COMMITTEE CORRESPONDENCE—It is required that all correspondence within and between committees be classified by subject so that it may be readily identified. Copies of committee correspondence should be sent to the chairman and SAE staff representative. Committees shall use technical committee correspondence forms which are available, upon request, from the SAE staff representative. Committees shall not use stationery with a company or business letterhead.

6.2 Approval—Draft technical reports submitted to a council for approval, in general, should have the unanimous approval of the committee making such a submittal. Where unanimous approval cannot be achieved, draft technical reports shall have the approval of at least three-quarters of the responding committee members who have not waived their vote. Dissenting views, including those of liaison and consulting members shall accompany draft technical reports when they are circulated to the council for final review

and approval prior to publication. The committee's reasons for not accepting the dissenting views should be included.

6.2.1 Committee draft technical reports shall normally require confirmation by letter ballot, except when they are submitted for final voice vote approval. In such instances the draft technical reports shall be distributed to the members of the voting group at least two weeks prior to the meeting. Where a single draft technical report is a joint project of two committees reporting to separate councils, it shall be submitted to both councils for review and approval.

6.2.2 The Technical Board retains the authority for final review and approval when dissenting views cannot be reconciled.

6.3 Publication and Timing—After approval by the council, the technical report will be published at the earliest opportunity.

6.3.1 The preparation of technical reports intended for publication in the SAE Handbook should be scheduled so that council approval can be obtained prior to the closing date set by the Publications Advisory Committee. At least three weeks should be allowed for circulating drafts to the councils. Timing on technical reports which are to be released in loose-leaf or pamphlet form is not as critical with respect to publication date. The SAE staff representative should be consulted as required, to determine target dates.

6.4 Distribution and Use—A basic tenet of SAE technical committee operating policy is that technical reports produced by technical committees are advisory in nature. The use of such technical reports by industry, government, or other responsible agencies is entirely voluntary.

6.4.1 Early recognition by the SAE membership of new or revised technical reports is highly desirable. This provides better service for members, government, and the public, and may result in beneficial comment leading to further improvement. For these reasons, information should be submitted by the technical committee chairman to SAE *AUTOMOTIVE ENGINEERING* as a news item, or, if the technical report has wide appeal, it may be given more extensive treatment. With a view to providing increased service, notice of all new and revised technical reports will appear as soon as possible after council approval in *AUTOMOTIVE ENGINEERING* magazine.

6.5 Review—Every technical report shall be reviewed at least every five years. The staff advisor shall initiate such reviews. At such reviews, the technical report may be reaffirmed, revised, or canceled. If reaffirmed, no formal ballot of the affected council is needed, but the council should be informed of the action. Regular balloting of the council is required for a revision or cancellation.

7. Some General Considerations for Technical Reports—SAE technical reports are to be limited to technical and engineering considerations. They are not to include provisions that are of a commercial nature such as prices, warranties, allocation of risk of loss or conditions of acceptance or rejection, nor are such considerations to be a basis for SAE documents.

7.1 Minimum Requirements—SAE technical reports should be written in terms of performance rather than design so as not to exclude any technically adequate equipment, product, design, material, or process. Where technical requirements are established to achieve a stated purpose, such requirements should be the minimum required to achieve such purpose. In terms of standardization or interchangeability of products, only that portion of the product necessary to accomplish such standard or interchangeability should be specified in the document. When a specific product, design, material, or the like is known not to conform to the requirements or conditions of an SAE technical report applicable to the same class of products, designs, materials, or the like, the reasons (in terms of performance characteristics) for such failure are to be set forth in the minutes or files of the appropriate SAE committee together with all data supporting the conclusions of the committee.

7.2 Two Users—An SAE technical report for a particular product, design, material, or process should only be undertaken when there are two or more interested users, unless the only user in the government and the activity is undertaken at the request of an appropriate agency of the government.

7.3 Source of Supply—It is desirable that technical reports not contain a reference to sources of supply of parts or products, or the identity of manufacturers. Where a committee finds it necessary to specify a particular brand of product, such specification is to be accompanied by the statement *or equivalent.*

7.4 Other Society or Association Product Listings—An SAE technical report may reference a list of products that has been developed by other recognized organizations; however, in such case the source of the list is to be clearly identified. A statement is to be made that the listing is included only for the convenience of the user and does not indicate either approval by SAE or the technical committee or its fitness for purposes specified.

7.4.1 An example of a completely referenced technical report is the SAE Information Report, Special Purpose Alloys ("Superalloys")—SAE J467.

7.4.2 An example of a partially referenced technical report is the SAE Standard, Road Vehicle—Hydraulic Brake Hose Assemblies for Use with Non-Petroleum Base Hydraulic Fluids—SAE J1401.

7.5 Test Materials—A particular product or material may be identified by name when it is essential to uniformity in testing. In such cases, an *or*

equivalent statement should be added to the company product or material referenced.

7.6 Patents and Copyrights—The committees in developing a technical report are not to consider whether the subject matter set forth is patented or copyrighted. However, if the committee is aware of any copyrights applicable to published material then such material shall not be used in the technical report. In the event it is known by the committee that following the teachings of a technical report will probably result in the infringement of a patent, the committee is to set forth criteria which will permit the user to conform to the technical report without infringing such patent.

7.6.1 NOTICE ON ALL TECHNICAL REPORTS—Every approved technical report shall carry the following statements: *All technical reports, including standards approved and practices recommended, are advisory only. Their use by anyone engaged in industry or trade or their use by governmental agencies is entirely voluntary. There is no agreement to adhere to any SAE Standard or Recommended Practice, and no commitment to conform to or be guided by any technical report. In formulating and approving technical reports, the Technical Board, its councils, and committees will not investigate or consider patents which may apply to the subject matter. Prospective users of the report are responsible for protecting themselves against liability for infringement of patents, trademarks, and copyrights.*

PREPARATION OF SAE TECHNICAL REPORTS— SURFACE VEHICLES AND MACHINES:
φ STANDARDS, RECOMMENDED PRACTICES, INFORMATION REPORTS—SAE J1159 AUG79

SAE Recommended Practice

Report of Publications Advisory Committee approved July 1976 and completely revised August 1979.

1. Foreword—This SAE Recommended Practice has been developed by the Publications Advisory Committee of the SAE Technical Board. The Publications Advisory Committee was formed as the Publications Policy Committee of the Technical Board in 1956. The objectives of the committee are (1) to guide and promote efficient dissemination of material produced under the Technical Board and (2) to recommend immediate and long-range policies to the Technical Board to assure that Technical Board information will be available to those who need it in a form suitable for their work.

2. Purpose—The purpose of this recommended practice is to establish a uniform practice for technical committees for the preparation of technical reports.

3. Scope—It applies to reports of Surface Vehicles and Machinery Technical Committees only. Aerospace technical reports are covered by editorial practices of the Aerospace Council. Close adherence to this recommended practice by technical committees of SAE will help to assure uniform technical reports. Should questions on format, style, or other matters pertaining to the organization and editorial practices of technical reports be raised within technical committees of the Technical Board, they should be referred to the Chairman of the Publications Advisory Committee for interpretation or for discussion by the full Publications Advisory Committee.

4. Technical Committee Chairman Responsibilities

4.1 A technical committee chairman is responsible for seeing that his committee and all subcommittees or working group members understand their responsibilities relative to publications, particularly:

(a) Accuracy of technical content and references,

(b) Conformance to policies and guidelines outlined in this report, and

(c) Clearance through technical committee chairman of all subcommittee or committee work, whether major or minor (including editorial changes and corrections). It is the chairman's responsibility to see that the following actions are taken relative to technical reports.

4.1.1 CLASSIFICATION—This shall be recommended by the time technical agreement has been reached on the content of the report. See Section 5 of this report.

4.1.2 LEGAL ASPECTS—The report shall be checked against rules prepared by the Society's legal counsel. See Technical Committee Guideposts, SAE J1271, Section 7.

4.1.3 PUBLICATION METHOD—This shall be recommended based on the following methods.

4.1.3.1 *SAE Handbook*—The Handbook is used for technical reports (Standards, Recommended Practices, and Information Reports) of value to a substantial number of SAE members.

4.1.3.2 *Handbook Supplements*—Supplements are used for descriptive or educational material of broad interest to SAE members and other engineers in the automotive and allied industries. They are also used to provide groups of related technical reports from the SAE Handbook.

4.1.3.3 *Separate Reports*—A properly approved technical report may be issued separately in addition to publishing in the Handbook, either because the subject is timely and must not wait for the next Handbook issue, or because of major interest.

4.1.4 ORGANIZATION AND FORMAT—The draft of the report shall be prepared using details given in Section 6 of this report.

4.1.5 METRICATION—The report shall be checked to make sure that metric units have been included or used as the basis for the report. Details of use shall be checked for conformance with Rules for SAE Use of SI (Metric) Units, SAE J916.

4.1.6 KEY INDEX WORDS—Along with the report, the committee shall submit a list of key words to provide a basis for index preparation by staff. A list of 3–10 words is suggested, depending on the nature of the report. Instructions are given in Section 7 of this report.

4.1.7 EXPLANATION OF PROPOSED REPORT—When the report is submitted to a council of the Technical Board, a statement shall be included outlining:

(a) Significance of report,

(b) Background information (rationale),

(c) Reason for choice of classification, and

(d) Recommendation for method of distribution.

The statement will be retained in the committee file by the SAE Technical Division.

4.1.8 CUT-OFF DATE—When beginning the final approval process, the approved committee draft report should be submitted to SAE staff in time to meet the deadline for publication of the Handbook. Time must be allowed for approval by a cognizant council of the Technical Board and submittal of final report draft and transmittal to the Publications Division by June 30 of each year. Staff should be consulted on adequate lead time.[1]

5. Classification and Numbering of Technical Reports[1]

5.1 Classification—Technical reports are approved for publication by the Technical Board, and must be based on sound technology and cooperative engineering work. Before publication, a report must be classified into one of the following three classifications: (See paragraph 4.1.1 of this report.)

5.1.1 SAE STANDARDS—These reports are a documentation of broadly accepted engineering practices or requirements for a material, product, process, procedure, or test method.

5.1.1.1 A product standard may be primarily a descriptive standard covering dimensions, composition, and other details or it may be a functional or performance standard, or both.

5.1.1.2 Performance standards involve requirements or levels against which the functions can be evaluated. This frequently involves the need to define test methods by which these requirements are measured. Preferably, performance standards and test procedure standards should be in separate reports. If this is not practical, they should be in separate sections of the same report. Where performance standards are given, it is desirable to publish the rationale simultaneously as an SAE Information Report in order to provide all users with the basis for selection of performance levels.

5.1.2 SAE RECOMMENDED PRACTICES—These reports are documentation of data that are intended as guides to standard engineering practice. Their content may be of a more general nature, or they may propound data that have not yet gained broad acceptance.

5.1.2.1 A technical committee preparing such a report may add an introductory note stating, "This SAE Recommended Practice is intended as a guide toward standard practice but may be subject to frequent change to keep

---

[1] The Society also approves and issues reports for the aerospace industry. These are called Aerospace Standards (AS), Aerospace Recommended Practice (ARP), Aerospace Information Reports (AIR), and Aerospace Material Specifications (AMS). Their definitions are similar to the above.

pace with experience and technical advances, and this should be kept in mind when considering its use."

5.1.3 SAE Information Reports—These reports are compilations of engineering reference data or educational material useful to the technical community.

5.1.4 Examples

5.1.4.1 *Standard*—Automotive Carburetor Flanges, SAE J623. A product standard based on dimensions.

5.1.4.2 *Recommended Practice*—Surface Texture Control, SAE J449. Description of the techniques of control, including preparation of standards, etc.

5.1.4.3 *Information Report*—Mechanical Properties of Heat Treated Steels, SAE J413. General information giving guidance on the relationship of various properties.

5.2 Numbering—Prior to submission to the appropriate council of the Technical Board, SAE staff will assign a "J" number to all reports.

5.2.1 Suffixes—When a technical report is approved by a council or the Technical Board, the report "J" number will be supplemented by a date suffix (e.g., SAE J1159 AUG79).[2] This date suffix should be shown in all indexes and should be used as appropriate in references. (See paragraph 6.6 of this report.) The date suffix will be advanced for each technical or editorial revision.

5.2.2 Integrity of SAE "J" Numbers—Changes to an SAE Standard or Recommended Practice which alter it sufficiently to affect its interchangeability or interchangeable application shall require a new "J" number identity. The superseded "J" number shall continue to exist unless retired. When an SAE technical report is retired, its "J" number shall continue in the index with its date suffix, classification, a cross reference to any superseding "J" number, and an indication of its last date and method of publication.

6. Guide for Preparation of Technical Reports

6.1 Organization of Report—The following recommendations for items to be included in SAE technical reports are all-inclusive. Accordingly, all items may not be required for every type of report. In addition, the sequence in which they are presented herein may be changed, for good reason, by the responsible technical committee.

6.1.1 Title—Each report shall have a title which does not duplicate an existing title. It should be as short, concise, and descriptive as possible.

6.1.2 Report Classification—See Section 5 of this report.

6.1.3 Approval Note—Includes credit to originating committee, original approval date, and date of last revision or reaffirmation. Latest editorial revision, if any, is included. For example: Report of the Iron and Steel Technical Committee, approved April 1963, last revised June 1975, editorial change March 1979.

6.1.4 Introduction (as applicable)—The introduction shall provide the basis for data or information in the report, background or general description of the report, and a brief explanation of changes from previous version of the report.

6.1.5 Purpose and/or Scope (as applicable)—If both are used, the purpose shall precede the scope. The purpose will explain the objectives or end to be obtained by use of the report. The scope will briefly give the extent of treatment and applicability of the report.

6.1.6 Definitions, Glossary of Terms, Terminology, and Designations—All definitions, glossary, terminology, and designations should be reviewed for consistency with SAE reports; SAE Motor Vehicle and Machinery, Safety and Environmental Terminology, HS215, and Guidelines for Developing and Revising SAE Nomenclature and Definitions, SAE J1115.

6.1.7 Test procedures including:

6.1.7.1 Description of facilities and environment.

6.1.7.2 Listing of instrumentation and equipment. (Where instruments must be identified by brand name, the phrase *or equivalent* must be used.)

6.1.7.3 Details for installation of instrumentation and equipment and preparation required for vehicles or machinery, test samples or components.

6.1.7.4 Forms for data sheets, graphs, and reports.

6.1.8 Dimensional data, including tables and charts.

6.1.9 General specifications which augment dimensional data.

6.1.10 Illustrations, photographs.

6.1.11 Performance requirements (if not included in a separate document)—See paragraph 6.5 of SAE Technical Board Rules and Regulations for reservations on performance requirements.

6.1.12 Component materials and mechanical and physical properties.

6.1.13 Inspection requirements.

6.1.14 Appendices—As applicable, to add supplementary engineering reference data or educational material not an integral part of the basic technical report. They may also be issued as a separate SAE Information Report.

6.1.15 Rationale—The rationale which accompanies a technical report when being sent to upper committees for approval may be included as an Appendix or may be the subject of a separate SAE Information Report. The rationale will provide an expanded explanation of the purpose and scope of the technical report; an explanation of the reasons for decisions, conclusions, and recommendations; and a report on actual tests made which support conclusions and recommendations or which provide the basis for performance criteria.

6.1.16 References—List all SAE technical reports and other standards referenced in the report.

6.1.17 Bibliography (as required)—A list of publications from which authoritative information was gathered for inclusion in the report.

6.2 Preparation of Technical Reports

6.2.1 Paragraph Numbering—A decimal numbering system should be used where practical to aid organization in long or complicated reports. Use decimal point to indicate successive subheadings (Example: 1., 1.1, 1.1.1).

6.2.2 New Reports—Double space drafts of new reports. Mark and date each successive draft legibly.

6.2.3 Revisions to Existing Reports[3]—Revisions may be handled in several ways. The best method depends upon the extent of the revisions. A major revision, for example, would probably best be handled by complete retyping as in paragraph 6.2.2. Other approaches in handling are:

(a) Cut and paste or mark copies of printed report, indicating deletions and insertions clearly.

(b) Double space new copy, describing clearly where it is to be inserted in existing report.

6.3 Artwork—These instructions are based on a 50% reduction for final size. A one-column figure has a final maximum width of 92 mm (3.62 in). Largest maximum final width is 178 mm (7.00 in).

(a) Typewriter lettering and pencil drawings are unacceptable as both fade and drop out in reproduction process. Please use ink.

(b) Clear, sharp glossy prints of specified original artwork are acceptable if originals must be kept in committee's files.

6.3.1 Line Drawings (excluding graphs)

Main lines—Equiv. O Leroy pen (0.3 mm width)

Inside lines
Dimension line leaders } Equiv. 00 Leroy pen (0.2 mm width)
Phantom line, etc.

6.3.2 Graphs—The heaviest line weight used on graphs should be the curves.

Curves—Equiv. 1 Leroy pen (0.4 mm width)
Ordinate and Abscissa—Equiv. 0 Leroy pen (0.3 mm width)
Grid lines } Equiv. 00 Leroy pen (0.2 mm width)
Tic marks }

6.3.3 Lettering (excluding section and reference letters)—All lettering to be capitals unless lower case letters are necessary for a specific term. Lettering shall be vertical except for quantity symbols which shall be in italics. Use only Roman alphabet, except where letters are recognized standard symbols.

6.3.3.1 All lettering should be placed outside visible outline of part. Label, with line and arrowhead to area being identified, should be kept reasonably close to figure.

6.3.3.2 Lettering, including Greek, numbers, fractions: 120 Leroy— Equiv. 00 pen (0.120 in [3.05 mm] letter height).

6.3.4 Section and Reference Letters—All section and reference letters: 140 Leroy—Equiv. 0 pen (0.140 in [3.56 mm] letter height).

6.3.5 Numbers—Align column of numbers on decimal point.

6.3.6 Abbreviations—Do NOT use ″, ′, or ° (angular). Use in, ft, deg.

6.4 Tables—Tables shall be numbered consecutively throughout report, and referred to in the text. Each shall be titled.

(a) Concise descriptions, measurement units, and letter symbols shall be included in column headings.

(b) Be concise in numerical ranges. Do not overlap ranges or leave gaps in ranges. An example of good practice is:

0.75 thru 1.25 mm
Over 1.25 thru 2.00 mm
Over 2.00 thru 3.25 mm

6.5 Decimal Dimensioning—The dimensions in all new and revised SAE technical reports shall be expressed in decimal units. Nominal sizes shall be expressed as decimals or fractions, as determined by their design basis or historic use. Where these considerations are not decisive, decimal nominal sizes will be used.

6.5.1 The number of significant digits used in a dimension should relate to the precision of the quantity stated. This is particularly important in decimalizing dimensions previously expressed as fractions. A dimension of $1\frac{3}{16}$ with an intended precision of about ± 0.01 shall be decimalized as 1.19, not 1.1875.

---

[2] The practice of using date suffixes for SAE technical reports is initiated with the issue of J1159 AUG79. The previous practice of using suffix letters will be phased out as SAE technical reports are revised. (Note: Date suffixes will be phased in in the 1981 SAE Handbook.)

[3] See paragraph 6.9.

A discussion of the precision of a value, and the number of decimals proper to retain, is given in Rules for SAE Use of SI (Metric) Units, SAE J916.

6.5.2 ROUNDING OFF—When it is necessary to reduce the number of decimals by rounding off, the method shown in SAE J916 shall be used.

6.5.3 ZEROS—Where decimal values less than 1 appear, a zero shall be placed to the left of the decimal point.

6.6 Cross-Referencing—As necessary, other SAE reports or reports of other organizations may be referenced.

6.6.1 References shall be made to other standards or technical reports by name of the standards writing organization, number of the standard, and optimally the date of issue (e.g., SAE J804 FEB79; ASTM D1405 JUN78). If date is included, it is assumed that a specific report is being referenced even though it may be obsolete.

6.6.2 Where references are made, the referencing committee shall notify the committee responsible for maintaining the referenced technical report and request that the referencing committee be furnished with drafts of any proposed changes to the referenced report. Such drafts shall be sent to the chairman and SAE staff advisor of the referencing committee.

6.6.3 If the proposed changes are acceptable to the referencing committee, the chairman of the referencing committee should notify the committee responsible for the referenced technical report. The referencing technical report should then be revised to reflect the latest date of the referenced technical report.

6.6.4 If the changes are unacceptable to the referencing committee, the chairman of the referencing committee should notify the committee responsible for the referenced technical report that the proposed changes have affected applicability of the referenced report and a determination should be made between the two committees whether or not a new document number is required.

6.6.5 As an aid to committees and users of SAE Technical Reports, SAE staff shall maintain a listing of cross-referenced technical reports. The listing should give access to both the referenced and referencing technical reports.

6.6.6 If the SAE technical report corresponds to but is not identical to a technical report of another organization, it should be stated in the approval note. Example: This report conforms essentially to American National Standard B18.2.

6.6.7 Joint development of a technical report should be indicated in the approval note. Example: This is a joint report of SAE and ASTM . . .

6.7 Use of Basic Terms

6.7.1 SURFACE VEHICLE OR MACHINE—The term *surface vehicle* or *machine* is preferred to *automotive* for use in identifying technical reports which do not apply to the aerospace industry.

6.7.1.1 *Vehicle*—The term *vehicle* pertains to self-propelled devices for carrying passengers, goods, or equipment . . . a car, bus, truck, or boat.

6.7.1.2 *Machine*—The term *machine* pertains to self-propelled or mobile devices designed to alter or transmit energy and force for the performance of useful work . . . tractor, loader, grader, ditcher, combine.

6.7.2 MECHANICAL PROPERTIES—Mechanical properties are those properties of a material that pertain to its elastic and plastic behavior when force is applied: For example, yield strength, ultimate strength, elongation, hardness, etc.

6.7.3 PHYSICAL PROPERTIES—Physical properties are those properties other than mechanical properties that pertain to the physics of a material: For example, density, electrical conductivity, thermal expansion, etc., often improperly used to express mechanical properties.

6.7.4 USE OF *Shall* OR *Should*—The use of *should* or *shall* has no bearing on the voluntary nature of SAE technical reports. Inclusion of an SAE technical report in a document, standard, or contract by a company or agency is a voluntary act. When a technical report is so cited, the report becomes a requirement within the limitations set forth by the document, standard, or contract. The following shall apply to use of these words:

Shall—*Shall* is to be used wherever the criterion for conformance with the specific recommendation requires that there be no deviation. Its use shall not be avoided on the grounds that compliance with the report is considered voluntary.

Should—*Should* is to be used wherever noncompliance with the specific recommendation is permissible. *Should* shall not be substituted for *shall* on the grounds that compliance with the report is considered voluntary.

6.7.5 USE OF *Safe* AND *Safety*—The words *safe* and *safety* shall be used in SAE technical reports only when they are in whole or in part commonly used engineering terms, such as: fail-safe, factor of safety, safety glass. To preclude any misinterpretation of the words *safe* and *safety*, more definite descriptive words shall be used, such as:

"lock wiring" <u>rather</u> <u>than</u> "safety wiring" . . .

"lock nut" <u>rather</u> <u>than</u> "safety nut" . . .

"relief valve" <u>rather</u> <u>than</u> "safety valve" . . .

"the integrity of the painted surface" <u>rather</u> <u>than</u> "the safety of the painted surface" . . .

"to provide protection against shock" <u>rather</u> <u>than</u> "to provide safety against shock" . . .

"will provide for reliable transportation of the component" <u>rather</u> <u>than</u> "will provide for safe transportation of the component."

If circumstances arise which strongly indicate a need for the use of the words *safe* or *safety*, the Publications Advisory Committee shall be consulted.

6.8 Measurement Unit Symbols and Abbreviations—These may be found in Rules for SAE Use of SI (Metric) Units, SAE J916.

6.9 Indicating Revisions to SAE Standards, Recommended Practices, and Information Reports

6.9.1 INDICATIONS OF TECHNICAL REVISIONS—In drafts of revisions to existing "J" reports, the symbol ϕ shall be used to indicate technical changes.[4] A technical change requires a change in the date suffix, that is, JXXX JUN75 to JXXX JUN79. This indication of change shall be put on the draft revision at the earliest circulation.

6.9.1.1 The ϕ symbol is always placed in the left margin for single column copy and in the left- or right-hand margin, respectively, for double column copy. It is used to indicate change in text, tables, or figures. In the case of text, a separate symbol is used for each paragraph. In the case of tables or figures, the symbol is used once for each table or figure. In no case should it be located where it might be confused with the international symbol for *diameter*, which has a similar appearance.

6.9.1.2 Should the revision be so extensive that most of the report is changed, the symbol is put next to the title of the report, and the history note under the title shall read "completely revised (date)".

6.9.1.3 The ϕ symbol will be carried on the published document. If the document is again revised, the old symbols are deleted and new ones appropriate to the new technical revision are added.

6.9.1.4 The SAE Handbook and any separately published "J" reports will carry the following explanatory note: "The ϕ symbol is for the convenience of the user in locating the areas where technical revisions have been made to the previous issue of the report. If the symbol is next to the report title, it indicates a complete revision of the report."

6.9.2 EDITORIAL REVISIONS—Editorial revisions shall be indicated in both draft and published technical reports by the symbol *ed*. The history note under the report title will also call out editorial revisions by the following: "Editorial change (date)". The ϕ symbol indicating last technical revisions shall be retained.

7. Indexing Information—Following are instructions to assist in providing key words for use by SAE staff in preparing SAE Handbook index.

7.1 Selection—Terms chosen should be taken directly or derived from the material being indexed on the basis of their relative significance and effectiveness in later retrieval of needed information. Terms should be used consistently. Terms should be as specific as the nature of the material and user's requirements allow.

7.2 Clarity—Subject terms should be nouns. Avoid terms that will not be recognized, coined terms, jargon, and slang. Generally the plural form should be used. Terms should be clarified if they have more than one accepted meaning, or must show distinction from other subject terms. This may be done by compound terms such as metal tubing, plastic tubing, or a parenthetical qualifying expression appended to distinguish the homographs as Tolerances (Mechanics) and Tolerances (Physiology).

7.3 Word Order—Terms consisting of two or more words should be listed in their natural word order, that is: Lighting equipment not Equipment, Lighting. When two or more candidate terms are true synonyms, one should be selected as the preferred index term, the other(s) entered as a see reference, that is, air cleaners use air filters, cloth use fabrics.

7.4 Punctuation—Punctuation marks should be used in index terms only when essential.

7.5 Abbreviation—Abbreviated word forms, including acronyms, should be used only when meanings are well established or when significant convenience results.

7.6 Inversions—For committee consideration, inverted entries, that is Engines, Aircraft, or Engines, Passenger Car, etc., make it possible to find most members of a related class together for ease of retrieval. The terms to be inverted must be carefully selected and care taken that another useful grouping is not scattered by inversion.

8. References—Available from the Society of Automotive Engineers, Inc., 400 Commonwealth Drive, Warrendale, Pennsylvania 15096:

Technical Committee Guideposts, SAE J1271 AUG79.

SAE Handbook.

Rules for SAE Use of SI (Metric) Units, SAE J916.

Standard—Automotive Carburetor Flanges, SAE J623.

Recommended Practice—Surface Texture Control, SAE J449.

Information Report—Mechanical Properties of Heat Treated Steels, SAE J413.

---

[4] Symbol made on a typewriter by a combination of a zero and a slash.

SAE Motor Vehicle, Safety and Environmental Terminology, HS 215.

Guidelines for Developing and Revising SAE Nomenclature and Definitions, SAE J1115.

SAE Technical Board Rules and Regulations.

SAE J804.

Available from the American Society for Testing and Materials, 1916 Race Street, Philadelphia, Pennsylvania 19103:

ASTM D 1405—Estimation of Net Heat of Combustion of Aviation Fuels.

Available from the American National Standards Institute, 1430 Broadway, New York, New York 10018:

American National Standard B18.2.

RULES FOR SAE USE OF SI (METRIC) UNITS— SAE J916 JUN82

SAE Recommended Practice

Report of the Publication Policy Committee, approved June 1965, fifth revision prepared by the Metric Advisory Committee June 1982.

1. Introduction—In the spring of 1969 the SAE Board of Directors issued a statement that "SAE will include SI[1] units in SAE Standards and other technical reports." Much investigation has attended the determination of units of measure for use, since measurement practice all over the world is to some degree in a state of transition. Engineering use of measurement units in nearly every metric country of the world, and in all of those nations adopting metric units, is confronted with the struggle between the noncoherent technical metric units, such as kilogram-force and calorie, and the SI units, such as newton and joule.

This document establishes the rules for the use of SI units in SAE reports, including specifications and standards. It must be remembered that a technical committee may produce its reports in any units it feels are proper for the users—U. S. inch-pound, SI, or other metric. However, if the units used do not conform to the Units Approved for SAE Use φ (see paragraph 2), they must be followed by approved SI units in parentheses.

Throughout this document, SI is intended to include recognized SI units as established by the international General Conference on Weights and Measures,[2] (CGPM) and a limited number of other units that are not formal SI units.

These other units are all included in the American National Standard Z210.1, "Standard for Metric Practice" in "The Metric System of Measurement" issued by the Secretary of Commerce in the 10–26–77 Federal Register, and in ISO 1000, the worldwide document for use by all ISO[3] committees.

By careful contact with other countries, the General Conference, and ISO, this document will be updated as often as necessary to keep the use of SI units in SAE reports as nearly as possible in harmony with the units that will be adopted for United States and world use.

2. Units Approved for SAE Use—All SAE documents produced under the Board of Directors' directive to "include SI units" must utilize as applicable:

2.1 Base Units of SI

Quantity	Unit (symbol)
length	—meter[4] (m)
mass	—kilogram (kg)
time	—second (s)
electric current	—ampere (A)
thermodynamic temperature	—kelvin (K)
amount of substance	—mole (mol)
luminous intensity	—candela (cd)

2.2 Supplementary Units of SI

Quantity	Unit (symbol)
plane angle	—radian (rad)
spherical angle	—steradian (sr)

2.3 Recognized Derived Units of SI with Special Names

Quantity	Unit (symbol)	Formula
absorbed dose	—gray (Gy)	J/kg
activity (of a radionuclide)	—becquerel (Bq)	$1/s$, s^{-1}
Celsius temperature	—degree Celsius (°C)	[5]
dose equivalent	—sievert[6] (Sv)	J/kg
electric capacitance	—farad (F)	C/V
electric conductance	—siemens (S)	A/V
electric inductance	—henry (H)	Wb/A
electric potential diff.	—volt (V)	W/A
electric resistance	—ohm (Ω)	V/A
energy, work	—joule (J)	N · m
force	—newton (N)	$kg \cdot m/s^2$
frequency	—hertz (Hz)	$1/s$, s^{-1}
illuminance	—lux (lx)	lm/m^2
luminous flux	—lumen (lm)	cd · sr
magnetic flux	—weber (Wb)	V · s
magnetic flux density	—tesla (T)	Wb/m^2
power	—watt (W)	J/s
pressure or stress	—pascal (Pa)	N/m^2
quantity of electricity	—coulomb (C)	A · s

See Z210.1 paragraph 2, for more complete description.

2.4 Other Units that May be Used with SI

Quantity	Unit (symbol)
plane angle	—degree (°) (decimal divisions preferred)
time	—minute (min), hour (h), day (d), week, and year
mass	—metric ton (t)
area	—hectare (ha)
sound pressure level	—decibel (dB)
volume	—liter[4] (L)[7]
navigation velocity	—knot (kn)[8]
distance	—nautical mile (nmi)[8]

When these units are used, they need not be followed by SI units unless it suits the purpose of the document.

The liter which the General Conference established as a special name for the cubic decimeter, is approved for SAE use, and the only prefixed φ use allowed is mL.

In the case of time, committees are urged to use the second and its multiples, but the units given above are permitted.

The unit metric ton (exactly 1 Mg) is in wide use but should be limited to commercial description of vehicle mass, or freight mass, and no prefix is permitted.

The unit hectare (exactly $1 hm^2$) is restricted to land and water area measurement.

---

[1] SI—The International System of Units (Système International) officially abbreviated "SI" in all languages—the modern metric system.

[2] CGPM Resolutions and Recommendations are published in NBS Special Publication 330, "The International System of Units (SI)."

[3] The International Organization for Standardization.

[4] Spelling with "re" is also used.

[5] In 1976 the CIPM decided that "degree Celsius" is a special name to be used φ instead of "kelvin" to express Celsius temperature. For formula see paragraph 8.

[6] Approved by CGPM in 1979.

[7] In 1979 the CGPM approved the symbol "L" for liter and it is recommended for North American use. The alternative symbol "l" will also be used during a transition period.

[8] Abbreviation, not a symbol.

2.5 Other derived units that are formed from those units and derived units indicated above are also acceptable. For example, the SI unit designation for electric field strength is V/m; however, it is also expressed in terms of base units as kg · m/(s³ · A) or kg · m · s⁻³ · A⁻¹. Likewise, torque and bending moment (N · m) may also be expressed as kg · m²/s² or kg · m² · s⁻².

3. Units Not Approved for Use as SI—Gravimetric force units, such as kilogram-force, or kilogram-force per square millimeter, which have been common in some countries, must not be used in SAE reports. Similarly, calorie, bar, angstrom, and dyne are not SI units and are not to be used. However, as stated in Section 1, this restriction does not preclude use of these units where a committee considers them to be the proper units for the users of the report, and provided they are followed with approved SI units in parentheses.

4. Multiplying Prefixes—Table 1 lists the prefixes to be used with SI units, observing the rules given in Section 5.

5. Rules for Use of Units

5.1 Requirements of this document establish the use of SI units in one of the following manners:

5.1.1 As regular units followed by other units in parentheses.

5.1.2 In parentheses following other units.

φ **5.1.3** As regular units.

5.1.4 Under special circumstances it is permissible to deviate from these rules. See Appendix B.

5.2 SI units must be those shown in Appendix A or their decimal multiples, except as covered in paragraph 6.2. In case of need for other units the Metric Advisory Committee of the SAE Technical Board should be consulted. If units for quantities not included in Appendix A and not clearly covered by paragraph 6.2 are required, the above committee should be contacted for guidance.

An apparent anomaly exists in the use of the joule for work (J = N · m) and the use of N · m for torque or bending moment. These are, however, entirely different units. In the former, the unit of work results from unit force moving through unit distance. In the latter, there is no implication of movement, and unit force acts at right angles to the lever arm of unit length. This would be readily seen if vectors were incorporated in the unit symbols. For these reasons, it is important to φ express work or energy in joules. Moment of force, torque and bending φ moment are expressed in newton meters, not joules.

5.3 Use of Prefixes

φ **5.3.1** Use of prefixes representing 10 raised to a power that is a multiple φ of 3 is recommended. In the case of prefixed units that carry exponents, such as units of area and volume, this may not be practical, however, and any listed prefix may be used.

5.3.2 Compound prefixes, such as milli-micro, are never used.

5.3.3 In general, prefixes in the denominator of a compound unit should be avoided except for established usage. (Since the kilogram is a base unit of SI, use of kg in the denominator is not contrary to this guidance.)

5.3.4 When expressing a quantity by a numerical value and a unit, prefixes should preferably be chosen so that the numerical value lies between 0.1 and 1000. This is, of course, not true where certain multiples and units have been agreed to for particular use, such as kPa for pressure, or where tabular use requires the same unit in a series, even though this means exceeding the preferred range of 0.1–1000.

5.3.5 The prefix becomes a part of the symbol or name with no separation (meganewton, MN).

5.3.6 Errors in *calculations* can be minimized if all quantities are expressed in SI units, and prefixes are replaced by powers of 10.

5.3.7 With SI units of higher order, such as m² or m³, the prefix is also raised to the same order; for example, 1 mm³ is (10⁻³ m)³ or 10⁻⁹ m³.

5.4 Symbols and Abbreviations

5.4.1 DISTINCTION—The distinction between unit symbols and unit abbreviations is not always recognized, particularly with certain U. S. inch-pound units of measurement. The symbols for some U. S. units are also abbreviations (ft, in, yd). In many cases the unit symbol and the abbreviation are not the same (such as unit symbol ft³/min and abbreviation cfm; unit symbol A and abbreviation amp; unit symbol in³ and abbreviation cu in). A positive distinction exists between unit symbols and unit abbrevi- φ ations: the SI unit symbol designation is the same in all languages whereas φ abbreviations are conventional representations of words or names in a particular language; they may be different in different languages.

5.4.2 UNIT SYMBOL COMPOSITION—Unit symbols are letters or groups of letters predominantly from the English alphabet representing the units in which physical quantities are measured (m for meter, W · h for watt-hour). Non-English alphabet unit symbols are (Ω) for ohm, (°) for the plane angle degree or used with the Celsius (°C) temperature scale, and (µ) for the prefix micro. All unit symbols are printed in roman (upright) φ type.

5.4.3 UNIT SYMBOL STYLE⁹—Unit symbols are, in general, shown as lower case letters. If, however, the symbol is derived from a proper name, it or the first letter (where more than one) is an upper case letter (Hz, Wb, Pa). An exception to the above permits the upper case (L) to represent the unit liter because of the confusion that can occur between the lower case unit symbol (l) and the number one (1).

The letter style must be followed for SI unit symbols and prefixes even in applications where all other lettering is upper case (such as technical drawings). The only exception allowed is for computer and machine displays with limited character sets. For symbols for use in systems with limited character sets, refer to ANSI X3.50 or ISO 2955. The symbols for limited character sets must never be used when the available character set permits the use of the proper symbols as given herein.

5.4.4 QUANTITY SYMBOLS—Quantity symbols must not be confused with φ unit symbols. Quantity symbols are single letters representing the magnitude of physical quantities (*I* for electric current, *e* for charge of an electron). The established symbol must always be maintained (*f*—frequency, φ *F*—force, *m*—mass, *M*—moment of force).

Quantity symbols are single letters of the English or Greek alphabet, and are printed in italic (slanting) type.

5.4.5 ABBREVIATIONS—Abbreviations are shortened forms of words or phrases formed in various ways that have been accepted and established (ANSI Y1.1). They are generally letters from the word being abbreviated, except where the abbreviation is taken from another language (no for number, lb for pound). Abbreviations are never to be used when a mathematical operation sign is involved, unless the abbreviation is also the symbol.

5.4.6 SYMBOLIZED COMPOUND (DERIVED) UNITS⁹—Compound (derived) units constitute a mathematical expression. Where compound units include the solidus (/), it must not be repeated in the same expression. In complicated cases, negative powers or parentheses should be used. For example, write: m/s² or m · s⁻² but not m/s/s; or write kg · m/ (s³ · A) or kg · m · s⁻³ · A⁻¹ but not kg · m/s³/A.

5.4.7 PLURAL—The form of symbols and abbreviations is the same for singular or plural (1 in, 10 in, 1 s, 27 s).

5.4.8 Periods are not used after symbols or abbreviations. The same abbreviation is used for related noun, verb, adverb, etc. (inclusion, include, inclusive are all abbreviated incl). When these rules would cause confusion, spell out the word. Words of four letters or less are not abbreviated.

5.4.9 When writing a quantity, a space should be left between the numerical value and a unit symbol—for example, write 35 mm, not 35mm. An exception occurs when the symbols for degree of plane angle or degree Celsius are used, in which case the space is omitted (25°C).

5.5 Miscellaneous

5.5.1 With nominal sizes that are not measurements but are names for items, no conversion should be made: for example, 1/4–20 UNC thread, 1 in pipe, 2 x 4 lumber.

5.5.2 The decimal marker used by SAE is the dot on the line (.) for quantities in either U. S. customary or SI units.

To facilitate the reading of numbers having five or more digits, the

---

⁹ Handling of Unit Names—Names of units are never capitalized except at the beginning of sentences or in titles. (Modifiers used in unit names are capitalized if proper names; for example, degree Fahrenheit.) Compound unit names are formed with a space for product and the word "per" for quotient. Prefixes become part of the world: ampere (A), milliampere (mA), ampere second (A · s), meter per second (m/s).

TABLE 1—SI UNIT PREFIXES

Multiples and Submultiples	Prefixes	Symbols	Pronunciations
10¹⁸	exa	E	ex′a
10¹⁵	peta	P	pet′a
10¹²	tera	T	ter′a
10⁹	giga	G	ji′ga
10⁶	mega	M	meg′a
10³	kilo	k	kil′o
10²	hecto	h	hek′to
10	deka	da	dek′a
10⁻¹	deci	d	des′i
10⁻²	centi	c	sen′ti
10⁻³	milli	m	mil′i
10⁻⁶	micro	µ	mi′kra
10⁻⁹	nano	n	nan′o
10⁻¹²	pico	p	pe′co
10⁻¹⁵	femto	f	fem′to
10⁻¹⁸	atto	a	at′to

TABLE 2—ABBREVIATIONS AND SYMBOLS FOR UNITS OTHER THAN SI

Unit Name	Symbol	Abbreviation	Unit Name	Symbol	Abbreviation
brake horsepower		bhp	inch pound—force	in · lbf	
Brinell hardness number		Bhn	kilocycle	kc	
British thermal unit	Btu		kilogram—force	kgf	
calorie	cal		mile	mi	
candlepower		cp	mile per hour	mi/h	mph
cubic foot per minute	ft³/min	cfm	minute (angle)		min
cubic foot per second	ft³/s	cfs	ounce	oz	
cycle per minute	c/min	cpm	ounce—force	ozf	
cycle per second	c/s	cps	part per gallon		ppg
cycle	c		pint	pt	
degree Fahrenheit	°F		pound	lb	
degree Rankine	°R		poundal	pdl	
dram	dr		pound—force	lbf	
foot	ft		pound—force per		
footcandle	fc		square inch	lbf/in²	psi
foot per minute	ft/min		pound—force per		
foot per second	ft/s		square inch absolute		psia
foot pound—force	ft · lbf		pound—force per		
friction horsepower		fhp	square inch gage		psig
gallon	gal		quart	qt	
gallon per minute	gal/min	gpm	revolution per minute	r/min	rpm
gallon per second	gal/s	gps	revolution per second	r/s	rps
horsepower	hp		Saybolt universal second		SUS
inch	in				
inch of mercury	in Hg		second (angle)	″	sec
inch of water	in H₂O		yard	yd	

digits should be placed in groups of three separated by a space instead of a comma, counting both to the left and to the right of the decimal point. In the case of four digits, the spacing is optional. This style also avoids confusion caused by the use elsewhere of the comma to express the decimal marker.

For example, use:

> 1 532 or 1532 instead of 1,532
> 132 541 816 instead of 132,541,816
> 983 769.788 16 instead of 983,769.78816

5.5.3 Surface roughness expressed in microinches should be converted
φ to micrometers (μm); the term "micron" shall not be used.
φ 5.5.4 Linear dimensions on engineering drawings related to SAE committee documentation will customarily be given in millimeters regardless of length.

6. General
φ **6.1 Mass, Force, and Weight**
φ 6.1.1 The principal departure of SI from the gravimetric system of metric engineering units is the use of explicitly distinct units for mass and force. In SI, the name kilogram is restricted to the unit of mass, and the kilogram-force (from which the suffix *force* was in practice often erroneously dropped) should not be used. In its place the SI unit of force, the newton (N) is used. Likewise, the newton rather than the kilogram-force is used to form derived units which include force, for example, pressure or stress (N/m^2 = Pa), energy (N · m = J), and power (N · m/s = W).

6.1.2 Considerable confusion exists in the use of the term *weight* as a quantity to mean either *force* or *mass*. In commercial and everyday use, the term *weight* nearly always means mass; thus, when one speaks of a person's weight, the quantity referred to is mass. This nontechnical use of the term weight in everyday life will probably persist. In science and technology, the term *weight of a body* has usually meant the force that, if applied to the body, would give it an acceleration equal to the local acceleration of free fall. The adjective "local" in the phrase "local acceleration of free fall" has usually meant a location on the surface of the earth; in this context the "local acceleration of free fall" has the symbol g (commonly referred to as "acceleration of gravity"). Values of g differing by over 0.5% at various points on the earth's surface have been observed.[10] The use of *force of gravity* (mass times acceleration of gravity) instead of *weight* with this meaning is recommended. Because of the dual use of the term weight, care should be taken to assure that the intended meaning is clear.

6.2 Many units for rates are not shown in Appendix A, but should be derived from approved units. For example, the proper unit for mass per unit time is kg/s.

6.3 Expressions that can be stated as a ratio of the same unit, such as 0.006 inch per inch, should be changed to a designation of a ratio such as 0.006:1. Where an expression might be shown in two different units one of which is a multiple of the other, reduce the expression to a common unit and show it as a ratio. Example: 1.50 in per ft = 0.125 ft per ft. Express as a ratio 0.125:1.

6.4 It has been internationally recommended that pressure units themselves should not be modified to indicate whether the pressure is *absolute* (that is, above zero) or *gage* (that is, above atmospheric pressure). If, therefore, the context leaves any doubt as to which is meant, the word *pressure* must be qualified appropriately.

For example:

> ". . . at a gage of 200 kPa" or
> ". . . at an absolute pressure of 95 kPa" or
> ". . . reached an absolute pressure of 95 kPa," etc.

7. Conversion Techniques—Conversion of quantities between systems of units involves careful determination of the number of significant digits to be retained. To convert "1 quart of oil" to "0.9463529 liter of oil" is, of course, nonsense because the intended accuracy of the value does not warrant expressing the conversion in this fashion.

This section provides information to be used as a guide in the conversion of quantities specified in SAE Standards. In certain circumstances, reasons may exist for using other guidance. For example, in the case of interchangeable dimensions on engineering drawings, a more specific approach is outlined in SAE J390, Dual Dimensioning, although the methods given here will usually produce the same results.

All conversions, to be logically established, *must* depend upon an intended precision of the original quantity—either implied by a specific tolerance, or by the nature of the quantity. The first step in conversion is to establish this precision.

7.1 Precision of a Value—It is absolutely necessary to determine the intended precision of a value before converting.

The intended precision of a value *should* relate to the number of significant digits shown. The implied precision is plus or minus one-half unit of the last significant digit in which the value is stated. This is true because it may be assumed to have been rounded from a greater number of digits, and one-half unit of the last significant digit retained is the limit of error resulting from rounding. For example, the number 2.14 may have been rounded from any number between 2.135 and 2.145. Whether rounded or not, a quantity should always be expressed with this implication of precision in mind. For instance, 2.14 in implies a precision of ±0.005 in, since the last significant digit is in units of 0.01 in.

Two problems interfere with this, however:

(a) Quantities *may* be expressed in digits which are not intended to be significant. The dimension 1.1875 in may be a very precise one in which the digit in the fourth place is significant, or it may in some cases be an exact decimalization of a rough dimension 1¾₁₆ in, in which case the dimension is given with too many decimal places relative to its intended precision.

(b) Quantities may be expressed omitting significant zeros. The dimension 2 in may mean "about 2 in," or it may, in fact, mean a very precise expression which should be written 2.0000 in. In the latter case, while the added zeros are not significant in establishing the value, they are very significant in expressing the proper intended precision.

---

[10] The value of g = 9.806 650 m/s² was confirmed in 1913 by the CGPM. This value will be used on earth whenever it is determined that the local differing value may be disregarded.

Therefore, it is necessary to determine an approximate implied precision before converting. This can usually be done by using knowledge of the circumstances or information on the accuracy of measuring equipment.

If accuracy of measurement is known, this will provide a convenient lower limit to the precision of the dimension, and in some cases may be the only basis for establishing it. The implied precision should never be smaller than the accuracy of measurement.

A tolerance on a dimension will give a good indication of the intended precision, although the precision will, of course, be much smaller than the tolerance. A dimension of 1.635 ± 0.003 in obviously is intended to be quite precise, and the precision implied by the number of significant digits is correct (± 0.0005, total 0.001 in). A dimension of 4.625 ± 0.125 in is obviously a different matter. The use of thousandths of an inch to express a tolerance of 0.25 in is probably the result of decimalization of fractions, and the expression is probably better written 4.62 ± 0.12, with an implied precision of ± 0.005 (total implied precision 0.01 in). The circumstances, however, should be examined and judgment applied.

A rule of thumb often helpful for determining implied precision of a toleranced value is to assume it is one-tenth of the tolerance. Since the implied precision of the converted value should be no greater than that of the original, the total tolerance should be divided by 10, converted, and the proper significant digits retained in both the converted value and converted tolerance such that total implied precision is not reduced—that is, such that the last significant digit retained is in units no larger than one-tenth the converted total tolerance.

EXAMPLE: 200 ± 15 psi. Tolerance is 30 psi, divided by 10 is 3 psi, converted is about 20.7 kPa. The value (200 psi) converted is $1\,378.9514 \pm 103.421\,355$ kPa which should be rounded to units of 10 kPa, since 10 kPa is the largest unit smaller than one-tenth the converted tolerance. The conversion should be 1380 ± 100 kPa.

EXAMPLE: 25 ± 0.1 oz of alcohol. Tolerance is 0.2 oz, one-tenth of tolerance is 0.02 oz, converted is about 0.6 cm³. The converted value (739.34 ± 2.957 cm³) should be rounded to units of 0.1 cm³ and becomes 739.3 ± 3.0 cm³.

7.2 Conversion Procedure—In the sections that follow, the "total implied precision" discussed in paragraph 7.1 is referred to as "TIP."

7.2.1 First determine TIP.

7.2.2 Convert the dimension, TIP, and the tolerance if any, by the accurate conversion factor given in this document or ANSI Z210.1.

7.2.3 Choose the smallest number of decimals to retain, such that the last digit retained is in units equal to or smaller than the converted TIP.

7.2.4 Round off to this number of decimals by the following rules:

7.2.4.1 Where the digit next beyond the last digit to be retained is less than 5, the last digit retained should not be changed. Example: 4.46325 if rounded to three places would be 4.463.

7.2.4.2 Where the digits beyond the last digit to be retained amount to more than 5 followed by zeros, the last digit retained should be increased by one. Example: 8.37652 if rounded to three places would be 8.377.

7.2.4.3 Where the digit next beyond the last digit to be retained is exactly 5, the last digit retained, if even, is unchanged; but if odd, the last digit is increased by one. Example: 4.36500 becomes 4.36 when rounded to two places. 4.35500 also becomes 4.36 when rounded.

7.2.5 EXAMPLES

7.2.5.1 Test pressure 200 ± 15 psi

TIP not evident in this case

Total tolerance 30 psi, divided by 10 is 3 psi converted equals 20.68 kPa, for TIP use 10 kPA

Units to use, 10 kPa

200 ± 15 psi equals $1\,378.9514 \pm 103.421\,355$ kPa, round to 1380 ± 100 kPa

7.2.5.2 A stirring rod 6 in long

Estimate of TIP. Assume intended precision $\pm\frac{1}{16}$ in, TIP = $\frac{1}{8}$ in

Converted TIP $\frac{1}{8} \times 25.4 = 3.17$ mm

Units to use, 1 mm

6 in equals 152.4 mm, round to 152 mm

7.2.5.3 50 000 psi tensile strength

Estimate of TIP 400 psi from nature of use and precision of measuring equipment

Converted TIP 2.8 MPa

Units to use, 1 MPa

50 000 psi equals 344.737 85 MPa, round to 345 MPa

7.2.5.4 5.163 in length

Estimate of TIP 0.001 in (significant digits judged correct)

Converted TIP 0.0254 mm

Units to use, 0.01 mm

5.163 in equals 131.1402 mm, round to 131.14 mm

7.2.5.5 12.125 in length

Estimate of TIP 0.06 in from nature of use

Converted TIP 1.524 mm

Units to use 1 mm

12.125 in equals 307.975 mm, round to 308 mm

7.2.6 In dealing with toleranced quantities or quantities that establish limits, the rounding may be required in one direction only. When *maximum* or *minimum* are specified and judgment shows that these terms are mandatory, a maximum quantity must be rounded downward and a minimum rounded upward. The following illustrations show rounding of a dimension to two decimal places under different circumstances.

Dimension converted to 131.7625 mm
Round to two decimal places

(a) Normal dimension, untoleranced
   Round to 131.76 mm (closest to original)

(b) Dimension stated as *minimum*
   Round to 131.77 mm (rounded *up*)

(c) Dimension stated as *maximum*
   Round to 131.76 mm (rounded *down*)

Similarly, a toleranced quantity may be rounded as in item (a). However, if critical it may be first converted to limits and each limit rounded in the appropriate fashion depending on the nature of the individual limit. For absolute maintenance of the original limits, the upper limit should be rounded down and the lower limit rounded up. (This is method B described in ANSI Z210.1.)

8. Temperature Conversion—The SI unit for thermodynamic temperature is the kelvin. The SI unit "degree Celsius"[11] will be used for commonly expressed temperatures.

The Celsius scale is related to the kelvin scale as follows:
One degree Celsius equals one kelvin exactly. Celsius temperature (t_C) is related to kelvin temperature (T_K) as follows:

$$T_K = 273.15 + t_C$$

The Celsius scale is related to the Fahrenheit scale as follows:
One degree Celsius equals $\frac{9}{5}$ of a degree Fahrenheit, exactly. Celsius temperature (t_C) is related to Fahrenheit temperature (t_F) as follows:

$$t_C = \frac{5}{9}(t_F - 32)$$

General guidance for converting tolerances from degrees Fahrenheit to kelvins or degrees Celsius is given below:

Conversion of Temperature Tolerance Requirements

Tolerance, °F	Tolerance, K or °C
± 1	± 0.5
± 2	± 1
± 5	± 3
± 10	± 5.5
± 15	± 8.5
± 20	± 11
± 25	± 14

Normally, temperatures expressed in a whole number of degrees Fahrenheit should be converted to the nearest 0.5 kelvin (or degree Celsius). As with other quantities, the number of significant digits to retain will depend upon implied accuracy of the original dimension, for example:

100 ± 5°F: implied accuracy estimated to be 2°F.
37.7777 ± 2.7777°C rounds to 38 ± 3°C.
1000 ± 50°F: implied accuracy estimated to be 20°F.
537.7777 ± 27.7777°C rounds to 540 ± 30°C.

9. Bibliography

American Society for Testing and Materials, 1916 Race St., Philadelphia, PA 19103.

American National Standards Institute (ANSI), 1430 Broadway, New York, NY 10018.

Standard for Metric Practice (ANSI Z210.1 and ASTM E380).

American National Standards Institute.

ANSI X3.50, Representations for U. S. Customary, SI, and Other Units to be Used in Systems with Limited Character Sets.

---

[11] The term "Celsius" officially replaced "Centigrade" to eliminate confusion with French metric decimalized angular measurement (a "grad" or "grade" is 1% of a right angle, and a "centigrad" or "centigrade" is 1% of a "grad").

International Organization for Standardization,[12] Geneva, Switzerland:

ISO 1000, SI Units and Recommendations for the Use of their Multiples and of Certain Other Units.

ISO 2955, Information Processing—Representations of SI and Other Units for Use in Systems with Limited Character Sets.

Superintendent of Documents, U. S. Government Printing Office, Washington, DC 20402.

National Bureau of Standards, NBS Special Publication 330, The International System of Units (SI).

National Bureau of Standards, Washington, DC 20234.

Federal Register Notice of 10–26–77, NBS Letter Circular LC1078 The Metric System of Measurement as issued by the Secretary of Commerce.

APPENDIX A
Application of SI Units
(including conversion factors)

The following table illustrates recommended SI use for applications in the industries served by SAE. The particular recommendations are not mandatory, but should be followed in all SAE effort unless other use conforming to SAE J916 is strongly preferred.

1. Arrangement—The unit applications are arranged in alphabetical order of quantities, by principal nouns. Thus to find SI use for Surface Tension look under Tension, Surface, and for Specific Energy look under Energy, Specific.

2. Rates and Other Derived Quantities—It is of course not practical to list all possible applications but others such as rates can be readily derived. For example, if guidance is desired for Heat Energy per Unit Volume,

looking up Energy and Volume will show the recommendation kJ/m^3 (or other prefix, depending on factors discussed in paragraph 5.3).

3. Conversion Factors—Conversion factors are shown from Old Units to Metric Units to seven significant digits, unless the precision with which the factor is known does not warrant seven digits.

Exact conversion factors are indicated by *.

For conversion from Metric Units to Old Units, divide rather than multiply by the factor. For example, to convert 16.3 lb/yd^3 to kg/m^3 multiply by 0.593 276 3. The answer is 9.670 403 6 kg/m^3 which should be rounded properly according to the precision of the 16.3 lb/yd^3, probably to 9.7 kg/m^3. To convert 9.7 kg/m^3 to lb/yd^3 divide by 0.593 276 3. The answer is 16.349 886 lb/yd^3 which also should be rounded, probably to 16.3 lb/yd^3.

[12] Available in U. S. from American National Standards Institute.

TABLE A.1

Quantity	Typical Application	From Old Units	To Metric Units	Multiply by
Acceleration, angular	General	rad/s²	rad/s²	1*
Acceleration, linear	Vehicle General (includes acceleration of gravity)†	(mile/h)/s ft/s²	(km/h)/s m/s²	1.609 344* 0.304 8*
Angle, plane	Rotational calculations	r (revolution) rad	r (revolution) rad	1* 1*
	Geometric and general	° (deg) ′ (min) ″ (sec)	° ° (decimalized) ° (decimalized)	1* 1/60* 1/3600*
Angle, solid	Illumination calculations	sr	sr	1*
Area	Cargo platforms, frontal areas, fabrics, roof and floor areas, general	in² ft²	m² m²	0.000 645 16* 0.092 903 04*
	Pipe, conduit	in² ft²	cm² m²	6.451 6* 0.092 903 04*
	Small areas, orifices	in²	mm²	645.16*
	Brake & clutch contact area, glass, radiators, agricultural	in²	cm²	6.451 6*
	Land and water areas　　　　(Small)	ft²	m²	0.092 903 04*
	(Large)	acre	ha	0.404 687 3[c]
	(Very Large)	mile²	km²	2.589 998[c]
Area per time	Field operations (agricultural)	acre/h	ha/h	0.404 687 3[c]
	Auger sweeps, silo unloader	ft²/s	m²/s	0.092 903 04*
Bending moment	(See Moment of force)			
Capacitance, electric	Capacitors	μF	μF	1*
Capacity, electric	Battery rating	A · h	A · h	1*
Capacity, heat	General	Btu/°F[a]	kJ/K[b]	1.899 101
Capacity, heat, specific	General	Btu/(lb · °F)[a]	kJ/(kg · K)[b]	4.186 8*
Capacity, volume	(See volume)			
Coefficient of heat transfer	General	Btu/(h · ft² · °F)[a]	W/(m² · K)[b]	5.678 263
Coefficient of linear expansion	Shrink fit, general	°F⁻¹, (1/°F)	K⁻¹, (1/K)[b]	1.8*
Conductance, electric	General	mho	S	1*
Conductance, thermal	(See Coefficient of heat transfer)			
Conductivity, electric	Material property	mho/ft	S/m	3.280 840
Conductivity, thermal	General	Btu · ft/(h · ft² · °F)[a]	W/(m · K)[b]	1.730 735
Consumption, fuel	(See Efficiency, fuel)			
Consumption, oil	Vehicle performance testing	qt/1000 miles	L/1000 km	0.588 036 4
Consumption, specific, fuel	(See Efficiency, fuel)			
Consumption, specific, oil	Engine testing	lb/(hp · h) lb/(hp · h)	g/(kW · h) g/MJ	608.277 4 168.965 9
Current, electric	General	A	A	1*
Damping coefficient		lbf · s/ft	N · s/m	14.593 90
Density, current	General	A/in² A/ft²	kA/m² A/m²	1.550 003 10.763 91

For footnotes see end of Table.
　† Standard acceleration of gravity 9.806 650 m/s² exactly.

(Table continued on next page)

TABLE A.1 (CONTINUED)

Quantity	Typical Application	From Old Units	To Metric Units	Multiply by
Density, magnetic flux	General	kilogauss	T	0.1*
Density, (mass)	Solid	lb/yd³ lb/in³ lb/ft³ ton (short)/yd³ ton (long)/yd³	kg/m³ kg/m³ kg/m³ kg/m³ kg/m³	0.593 276 3 27 679.90 16.018 46 1 186.553 1 328.939
	Liquid	lb/gal	kg/L	0.119 826 4
	Gas	lb/ft³	kg/m³	16.018 46
Density of heat flow rate	Irradiance, general	Btu/(h · ft²)[a]	W/m²	3.154 591
Diffusivity, thermal	Heat transfer	ft²/h	m²/h	0.092 903 04*
Drag	(See Force)			
Economy, fuel	(See Efficiency, fuel)			

Efficiency, fuel	Highway vehicles
	  economy
	  consumption
	  specific fuel consumption
		mile/gal
		—
		lb/(hp · h)
			km/L
			L/100 km
			g/MJ
				0.425 143 7
				**
				168.965 9

	Off-highway equipment
	  economy
	  consumption
	  specific fuel consumption
	  specific fuel consumption
		hp · h/gal
		gal/h
		lb/(hp · h)
		lb/(hp · h)
			kW · h/L
			L/h
			g/(kW · h)
			g/MJ
				0.196 993 1
				3.785 412
				608.277 4
				168.965 9

	Aircraft gas turbine engines
	  Thrust specific fuel consumption (Turbo-jet)
	  Shaft specific fuel consumption (Turbo-shaft)
		lb/(lbf · h)
		lb/(hp · h)
			kg/(kN · h)
			kg/(kW · h)
				101.971 6
				0.608 277 4

Energy, work, enthalpy, quantity of heat	Impact strength	ft · lbf	J	1.355 818
	Heat[a]	Btu kcal	kJ kJ	1.055 056 4.186 8*
	Electrical	kW · h kW · h	kW · h MJ	1* 3.6*
	Mechanical, hydraulic, general	ft · lbf ft · pdl hp · h	J J MJ	1.355 818 0.042 140 11 2.684 520
Energy per area	Solar radiation	Btu/ft²[a]	MJ/m²	0.011 356 53
Energy, specific	General[a]	cal/g[d] Btu/lb	J/g kJ/kg	4.186 8* 2.326*
Enthalpy	(See Energy)			
Entropy	(See Capacity, heat)			
Entropy, specific	(See Capacity, heat specific)			
Floor loading	(See Mass per area)			
Flow, heat, rate	(See Power)			
Flow, mass, rate	General	lb/min lb/s	kg/min kg/s	0.453 592 4 0.453 592 4
	Dust flow	g/min	g/min	1*
Flow, volume	Air, gas, general	ft³/s ft³/s	m³/s m³/min	0.028 316 85 1.699 011
	Liquid flow, pump capacity	gal/s gal/s gal/min	L/s m³/s L/min	3.785 412 0.003 785 412 3.785 412
	Seal and packing leakage, sprayer flow	oz/s oz/min	mL/s mL/min	29.573 53 29.573 53

For footnotes see end of Table.
** Convenient conversion: 235.215 ÷ (mile/gal) = L/100 km

(Table continued on next page)

Quantity	Typical Application	From Old Units	To Metric Units	Multiply by
Flux, luminous	Light bulbs	lm	lm	1*
Flux, magnetic	Coil rating	maxwell	Wb	0.000 000 01*
Force, thrust, drag	Pedal, spring, belt, hand lever, general	lbf ozf	N N	4.448 222 0.278 013 9
	Drawbar, breakout, rim pull, winch line pull, general[e]	lbf lbf	N kN	4.448 222 0.004 448 222
	General	pdl kgf dyne	N N N	0.138 255 0 9.806 650 0.000 01*
Force per length	Beam loading (See also Spring rate)	lbf/ft	N/m	14.593 90
Frequency	System, sound and electrical	Mc/s kc/s Hz, c/s	MHz kHz Hz	1* 1* 1*
	Mechanical events, rotational (See Velocity, rotational)			
Hardness	Conventional hardness numbers, BHN, R, etc., not affected by change to SI			
Heat	(See Energy)			
Heat capacity	(See Capacity, heat)			
Heat capacity, specific	(See Capacity, heat specific)			
Heat flow rate	(See Power)			
Heat flow-density of	(See Density of heat flow)			
Heat, specific	General[a]	cal/g[d] Btu/lb	kJ/kg kJ/kg	4.186 8* 2.326
Heat transfer coefficient	(See Coefficient of heat transfer)			
Illuminance, illumination	General	fc	lx	10.763 91
Impact strength	(See Strength, impact)			
Impedance, mechanical	(See Damping coefficient)			
Inductance, electric	Filters and chokes, permeance	H	H	1*
Intensity, luminous	Light bulbs	candlepower	cd	1*
Intensity, radiant	General	W/sr	W/sr	1*
Leakage	(See Flow, volume)			
Length	Land distances, maps, odometers	mile	km	1.609 344*[c]
	Field size, turning circle, braking distance, cargo platforms, water depth, land levelling (cut and fill)	rod yd ft	m m m	5.029 210[c] 0.914 4* 0.304 8*
	Engineering drawings, engineering part specifications, motor vehicle dimensions, general	in	mm	25.4*
	Field drainage (runoff), evaporation, irrigation depth, rain and snowfall	in	cm	2.54*
	Coating thickness, filter rating	mil μin micron	μm μm μm	25.4* 0.025 4* 1*

	Surface texture
	  Roughness, average
	  Roughness sampling length, waviness height and spacing
		μin
		in
			μm
			mm
				0.025 4*
				25.4*

	Radiation wavelengths, optical measurements, (interference)	μin	nm	25.4*

For footnotes see end of Table.

(Table continued on next page)

TABLE A.1 (CONTINUED)

Quantity	Typical Application	From Old Units	To Metric Units	Multiply by
Load	(See Mass)			
Luminance	Brightness	footlambert	cd/m²	3.426 259
Magnetization	Coil field strength	A/in	A/m	39.370 08
Mass	Vehicle mass (weight), axle rating, rated load, tire load, lifting capacity, tipping load, load, general	ton (long)	Mg, t	1.016 047
		ton (short)	Mg, t	0.907 184 7
		lb	kg	0.453 592 4
		slug	kg	14.593 90
	Small mass	oz	g	28.349 52
Mass per area	Fabric, surface coatings	oz/yd²	g/m²	33.905 75
		lb/ft²	kg/m²	4.822 428
		oz/ft²	g/m²	305.151 7
	Floor loading	lb/ft²	kg/m²	4.882 428
	Application rate, fertilizer, pesticide	lb/acre	kg/ha	1.120 851[c]
	Crop yield, soil erosion	ton (short)/acre	t/ha	2.241 702[c]
Mass per length	General	lb/ft	kg/m	1.488 164
		lb/yd	kg/m	0.496 054 7
Mass per time	Machine work capacity, harvesting, materials handling	ton (short)/h	t/h, Mg/h	0.907 184 7
Modulus, bulk	(See Pressure)			
Modulus of elasticity	General	lbf/in²	MPa	0.006 894 757
Modulus of rigidity	(See Modulus of elasticity)			
Modulus, section	General	in³	mm³	16 387.06
		in³	cm³	16.387 06
Moment, bending	(See Moment of force)			
Moment of area, second	General	in⁴	mm⁴	416 231.4
		in⁴	cm⁴	41.623 14
Moment of force, torque, bending moment	General, engine torque, fasteners	lbf · in	N · m	0.112 984 8
		lbf · ft	N · m	1.355 818
		kgf · cm	N · m	0.098 066 5*
	Locks, light torque	ozf · in	mN · m	7.061 552
Moment of inertia	Flywheel, general	lb · ft²	kg · m²	0.042 140 11
Moment of mass	Unbalance	oz · in	kg · mm	0.720 077 8
Moment of momentum	(See Momentum, angular)			
Moment of section	(See Moment of area, second)			
Momentum	General	lb · ft/s	kg · m/s	0.138 255 0
Momentum, angular	Torsional vibration	lb · ft²/s	kg · m²/s	0.042 140 11
Permeability	Magnetic core properties	H/ft	H/m	3.280 840
Permeance	(See Inductance)			
Potential, electric	General	V	V	1*
Power	General, light bulbs	W	W	1*
	Air conditioning, heating	Btu/min[a]	W	17.584 27
		Btu/h[a]	W	0.293 071 1
	Engine, alternator, drawbar, power take-off, general	hp (550 ft · lbf/s)	kW	0.745 699 9
Power per area	Solar radiation	Btu/(ft² · h)[a]	W/m²	3.154 591

For footnotes see end of Table.

(Table continued on next page)

TABLE A.1   (CONTINUED)

Quantity	Typical Application	From Old Units	To Metric Units	Multiply by
Pressure	All pressure and bulk modulus	lbf/in²	kPa	6.894 757
		lbf/in² (absolute)	kPaᶠ	6.894 757
		lbf/ft²	kPa	0.047 880 26
		in Hg (60°F)	kPa	3.376 85
		in H₂O (60°F)	kPa	0.248 84
		ft H₂O (60°F)	kPa	2.986 08
		mm Hg (0°C)	kPa	0.133 322
		kgf/cm²	kPa	98.066 5*
		bar	kPa	100*
		atm (standard = 760 torr)	kPa	101.325*
Pressure, sound, level	Acoustical measurements[g]	dB	dB	1*
Quantity of electricity	General	C	C	1*
Radiant intensity	(See Intensity, radiant)			
Resistance, electric	General	Ω	Ω	1*
Resistivity, electric	General	Ω · ft	Ω · m	0.304 8*
		Ω · ft	Ω · cm	30.48*
Sound pressure level	(See Pressure, sound level)			
Speed	(See Velocity)			
Spring rate, linear	General spring properties	lbf/in	N/mm	0.175 126 8
Spring rate, torsional	General	lbf · ft/deg	N · m/deg	1.355 818
Strength, field, electric	General	V/ft	V/m	3.280 840
Strength, field, magnetic	General	oersted	A/m	79.577 47
Strength, impact	Materials testing	ft · lbf	J	1.355 818
Stress	General	lbf/in²	MPa	0.006 894 757
Surface tension	(See Tension, surface)			
Temperature	General use	°F	°C	$t_C = (t_F - 32)/1.8$*
	Absolute temperature, thermodynamics, gas cycles	°R	K	$T_K = T_R/1.8$*
Temperature interval	General use	°F	K[b]	1 K = 1°C = 1.8°F*
Tension, surface	General	lbf/in	mN/m	175 126.8
		dyne/cm	mN/m	1*
Thrust	(See Force)			
Time	General	s	s	1*
		h	h	1*
		min	min	1*
Torque	(See Moment of Force)			
Toughness, fracture	Metal properties	ksi $\sqrt{in}$	MPa · m¹ᐟ²	1.098 843
Vacuum	(See Pressure)			
Velocity, angular	(See Velocity, rotational)			
Velocity, linear	Vehicle	mile/h	km/h	1.609 344*
		knot (international)	km/h	1.851 999 8
	General	ft/s	m/s	0.304 8*
		ft/min	m/min	0.304 8*
		in/s	mm/s	25.4*
Velocity, rotational	Mechanical events (rotational) and general	rad/s	rad/s	1*
		r/s	r/s, r · s⁻¹	1*
		r/min	r/min, r · min⁻¹	1*
Viscosity, dynamic	General liquids	centipoise	mPa · s	1*

For footnotes see end of Table.

(Table continued on next page)

TABLE A.1 (CONTINUED)

Quantity	Typical Application	From Old Units	To Metric Units	Multiply by
Viscosity, kinematic	General liquids	centistokes	mm²/s	1*
Volume	Truck body, shipping or freight, bucket capacity, grain bins and tanks, general	yd³	m³	0.764 554 9
		ft³	m³	0.028 316 85
		bushel	m³	0.035 239 07
	Automobile luggage capacity	ft³	L	28.316 85
	Gas pump displacement, air compressor, small gaseous, air reservoir	in³	cm³	16.387 06
	Engine displacement			
	large engines	in³	L	0.016 387 06
	small engines	in³	cm³	16.387 06
	Liquid—fuel, lubricant, etc.	gal	L	3.785 412
		qt	L	0.946 352 9
		pt	L	0.473 176 5
	Small liquid	oz	mL	29.573 53
	Irrigation, reservoir	acre · ft	m³	1 233.489(c)
			dam³	1.233 489(c)
Volume per area	Application rate, pesticide	gal/acre	L/ha	9.353 958(c)
Weight	May mean either mass or force—see paragraph 6.1			
Work	(See Energy)			
Young's modulus	(See Modulus of elasticity)			

[a] Conversions of Btu and calorie are based on the International Table Btu and calorie.

[b] In these expressions K indicates temperature interval. Therefore K may be replaced with °C if desired without changing the value or affecting the conversion factor, for example: kJ/(kg · K) = kJ/(kg · °C).

[c] Official use in surveys and cartography involves the U. S. statute mile based on the U. S. survey foot, which is longer than the international foot by two parts per million. The factors used in this standard for acre, acre foot, U. S. statute mile, and rod are based on the U. S. survey foot. Factors for all other old length related units are based on the international foot. For detail, see ASTM E 380.

[d] Not to be confused with kcal/g. The kcal is often called "calorie" in the nutritional field.

[e] Lift capacity ratings for cranes, hoists, and related components such as rope, cables, chains, etc. should be rated in mass units. Those items such as winches, which can be used for pulling as well as lifting, shall be rated in both force and mass units.

[f] Refer to paragraph 6.4 for treatment of absolute pressure.

[g] When weighting is specified, show weighting level in parentheses following the symbol, for example: dB (A).

APPENDIX B

As covered in paragraph 5.1, SI units are required in SAE reports. To assist committees in carrying out this requirement in special circumstances, some qualifying rules are covered here.

B1. In standards that have alternative or optional procedures based on apparatus calibrated in either U. S. inch-pound or SI units, converted values need not be included. If optional procedures or dimensions produce equally acceptable results, the options may be shown by using the word *or* rather than parentheses: for example, in a 2-in gage length metal tension test specimen, the gage length may be shown as "2 in or 50 mm."

B2. A specific equivalent, for example 1.00 in (25.4 mm), need be inserted only the first time it occurs in each paragraph.

B3. Special instructions cover the use of tabular material.

Case 1. Limited Tabular Material—Provide SI equivalents in tables in parentheses or in separate columns.

ϕ STRAIGHT WHEEL GRINDERS

H	in	mm	R
3/8-24 UNF-2A	1-1/8	28.58	
1/2-13 UNC-2A	1-3/4	44.45	
5/8-11 UNC-2A	2-1/8	53.98	Governed by thickness of wheel used
5/8-11 UNC-2A	3-1/8	79.38	
3/4-10 UNC-2A	3-1/4	82.55	

Case 2. One or Two Large Tables—When the size of a table and limitations of space (on the printed page) make it impractical to expand the table to include SI equivalents, the table should be duplicated in U. S. inch-pound units and in SI units.

ϕ DIMENSIONS IN U. S. INCH-POUND UNITS

Chain No.	H60	H74	H75	H78	H82	H124
P (in)	2.308	2.609	2.609	2.609	3.075	4.000
A (in)	0.312	0.375	0.312	0.500	0.562	0.750
F (in)	0.73	1.00	0.75	1.12	1.25	1.56
H (in)	0.75	0.88	0.72	0.88	1.19	1.44
Proof test load (lbf)						
Class M	2 800	4 000	2 800	6 400	8 000	12 000
Class P	3 500	5 000	3 500	8 000	10 000	15 000
No. of pitches per nominal 120 in strand	52	46	46	46	39	30
Theoretical length of nominal 120 in strand	120.02	120.01	120.01	120.01	119.92	120.00
Measuring load (lbf)	190	270	190	130	510	810

ϕ DIMENSIONS IN SI UNITS

Chain No.	H60	H74	H75	H78	H82	H124
P (mm)	58.62	66.27	66.27	66.27	78.10	101.60
A (mm)	7.92	9.52	7.92	12.70	11.27	19.05
F (mm)	18.5	25.4	19.0	28.4	31.75	39.62
H (mm)	18.5	22.3	18.3	22.3	30.2	36.6
Proof test load (kN)						
Class M	12.50	17.80	12.50	28.50	35.60	53.40
Class P	15.60	22.20	15.60	35.60	44.50	66.80
No. of pitches per nominal 3048 mm strand	52	46	46	46	39	30
Theoretical length of nominal 3048 mm strand	3048.5	3048.2	3048.2	3048.2	3046.0	3048.0
Measuring load (N)	850	1200	850	580	2270	3600

If the above Cases 1 and 2 would still result in major increase in the size of the standard, consideration must be given to other methods. SAE

staff should first be consulted on techniques of arranging column spacing, etc., to accomplish addition of SI as shown in Cases 1 and 2.

Cases 3 and 4 are two approaches to reduce the number of pages involved in adding SI to reports with extensive tabular data. They should be used only in extreme cases since they do not accomplish the intent of SAE policy. Also, these approaches should not be considered when the users of the report are judged to need SI units for its use.

Case 3. Extensive Tabular Material—When the tabulated data is extensive and the above procedures would require an impractical addition to the standard, a summary appendix may be prepared listing all of the values appearing in the tables, along with the conversion of each, as follows:

TABLE B.1—SI EQUIVALENTS

Inches to Millimeters

in	mm	in	mm	in	mm
0.015	0.38	0.350	8.89	0.987	25.07
0.020	0.51	0.375	9.52	1.000	25.40
0.028	0.71	0.383	9.73	1.128	28.65
0.038	0.97	0.431	10.95	1.178	29.92
0.044	1.12	0.437	11.10	1.270	32.26
0.050	1.27	0.487	12.37	1.410	35.81
0.056	1.42	0.500	12.70	1.571	39.90
0.064	1.63	0.540	13.72	1.963	49.86
0.071	1.80	0.612	15.55	2.356	59.84
0.143	3.63	0.625	15.88	2.749	69.82
0.191	4.85	0.700	17.78	3.142	79.81
0.239	6.07	0.750	19.05	3.544	90.02
0.262	6.65	0.790	20.07	3.990	101.35
0.286	7.26	0.875	22.22	4.430	112.52
0.334	8.48	0.889	22.58		

Square Inches to Square Centimeters

in²	cm²	in²	cm²	in²	cm²
0.11	0.71	0.44	2.84	1.00	6.45
0.20	1.29	0.60	3.87	1.27	8.19
0.31	2.00	0.79	5.10	1.56	10.06

Pounds per Foot to Kilograms per Meter

lb/ft	kg/m	lb/ft	kg/m	lb/ft	kg/m
0.376	0.560	1.502	2.235	3.33	4.96
0.668	0.994	2.044	3.042	4.303	6.403
1.043	1.552	2.670	3.973	5.313	7.906

Pounds per Square Inch to Megapascals

psi	MPa	psi	MPa
50 000	345	80 000	550
60 000	415	90 000	620

Case 4.—In extreme cases when all the above approaches do not apply because of the size and number of tables, conversion factors may be placed in a footnote under each table, as in the following example.

TABLE B.2

Nominal Size, in	Outside Diameter, in[a]	Wall Thickness, in[a]	Nominal Mass per ft, Plain End, lb/ft[b]	Weight Class	Schedule No.	Test Pressure,[c] psi		
						Butt-Welded	Grade A	Grade B
20	20.000	0.250	52.73	—	10	—	450	500
		0.281	59.18	—	—	—	500	600
		0.312	65.60	—	—	—	550	650
		0.344	72.21	—	—	—	600	700
		0.375	78.60	STD	20	—	700	800
		0.406	84.96	—	—	—	750	850
		0.438	91.51	—	—	—	800	900
		0.469	97.83	—	—	—	850	950
		0.500	104.13	XS	30	—	900	1000
		0.594	123.11	—	40	—	1100	1200
		0.812	166.40	—	60	—	1500	1700
		1.031	208.87	—	80	—	1900	2200
		1.281	256.10	—	100	—	2300	2700
		1.500	296.37	—	120	—	2700	2800
		1.750	341.10	—	140	—	2800	2800
		1.969	379.17	—	160	—	2800	2800
24	24.000	0.250	63.41	—	10	—	400	450
		0.281	71.18	—	—	—	400	500
		0.312	78.93	—	—	—	450	550
		0.344	86.91	—	—	—	500	600
		0.375	94.62	STD	20	—	550	650
		0.406	102.31	—	—	—	600	700
		0.438	110.22	—	—	—	650	750
		0.469	117.86	—	—	—	700	825
		0.500	125.49	XS	—	—	750	900
		0.562	140.68	—	30	—	850	1000
		0.688	171.29	—	40	—	1000	1200
		0.938	231.03	—	—	—	1400	1600
		0.969	238.85	—	60	—	1500	1700
		1.219	296.58	—	90	—	1800	2100
		1.531	367.39	—	100	—	2300	2700
		1.812	429.39	—	120	—	2700	2800
		2.062	483.12	—	140	—	2800	2800
		2.344	542.14	—	160	—	2800	2800
26	26.000	0.250	68.75	—	—	—	350	400
		0.281	77.18	—	—	—	390	450
		0.312	85.60	—	10	—	430	500
		0.344	94.26	—	—	—	480	560
		0.375	102.63	STD	—	—	520	610
		0.406	110.98	—	—	—	560	660
		0.438	119.57	—	—	—	610	710
		0.469	127.88	—	—	—	650	760
		0.500	136.17	XS	20	—	690	810
		0.562	152.68	—	—	—	780	910

[a] 1 in = 25.4 mm
[b] 1 lb/ft = 1.49 kg/m
[c] 1 psi = 6.9 kPa

B4. Graphs and charts may be handled in several ways depending on the circumstances. In adding SI units to a graphic presentation of data, the practice of specific addition of metric conversions to existing ordinate or abscissa values should be avoided.

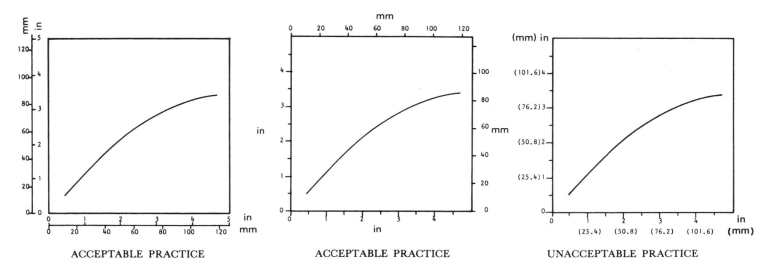

ACCEPTABLE PRACTICE   ACCEPTABLE PRACTICE   UNACCEPTABLE PRACTICE

GUIDELINES FOR DEVELOPING AND REVISING SAE NOMENCLATURE AND DEFINITIONS—SAE J1115

SAE Information Report

Report of Nomenclature Advisory Committee of SAE Automotive Council approved June 1975. Editorial change February 1976.

Introduction—Historically SAE has been concerned with nomenclature as an integral part of the standards development process. Guidelines for automotive nomenclature were written in 1916, were last revised in 1941, and were included in the SAE Handbook until 1962. The present diversity of groups working on nomenclature in the various ground vehicle committees led to the organization of the Nomenclature Advisory Committee under SAE Automotive Council.

Objective—The objective of the Committee is to promote understandable and precise communication relating to the engineering aspects of on-highway vehicles, their components, their design, and their evaluation. In order to reach this objective, the Committee is primarily concerned with the definition or redefinition of needed terms considering (a) current usage, (b) changing needs, and (c) the interactive use of a particular term by various SAE committees, government agencies, and other national and international organizations. In order to facilitate and encourage the use of generally accepted terminology by SAE committees and other organizations, the Nomenclature Advisory Committee plans to prepare and maintain a glossary of terms appearing in SAE technical reports.

Guidelines—Since the basic approach of the Committee is one of advice and coordination, the following guidelines for developing and revising SAE nomenclature and definitions are recommended:

1. Before developing and revising nomenclature, check for similar terms already defined in existing SAE Standards, Recommended Practices, and Information Reports and in Federal motor vehicle standards, in order to minimize duplication, to avoid conflict, and to achieve uniformity of format. In addition to the SAE Handbook, consult the following SAE and DOT reports:

Vehicle Dynamics Terminology, SAE J670d
Seating Manual, SAE J782a
Motor Vehicle Dimensions, SAE J1100a
Recommendations for Writing SAE Technical Reports
49 CFR 571.3 and appropriate FMVSS

2. If dictionary definitions of common generic terms can be used, they need not be included in nomenclature listings; for example, "Acceleration."
3. Develop general definitions for general terms; for example, define

"Fully Latched" generically and not specifically as applied to doors, hoods or trunk lids. General definitions must be valid for all possible situations or contingencies, not just for the situation under immediate consideration.

4. Specific concepts or components should be identified by correspondingly specific terms when defined in a document, so that these terms can stand alone when extracted from that document and integrated with other terms in a glossary. For example, use "Tire Valve Core" rather than "Core" alone, so that the term will not be confused with another type of core, such as "Radiator Core."

5. The abbreviation for a defined term, when included, should follow it and be placed in parentheses; for example, "Decibel (dB)."

6. Terminology should follow normal word order; for example, use "Lighting Device," not "Device, Lighting," and "Brake Cylinder," not "Cylinder (Brake)." The glossary will index the defined term under each significant word in that term. For example, "Accelerator Heel Point" will appear in the index in the following permuted forms:

Accelerator Heel Point
Heel Point, Accelerator
Point, Accelerator Heel

7. Term definitions should be directed at concise statements of the items being defined, rather than at specifications, performance requirements, or test procedures. As an example, the following description includes both a definition and a test procedure:

Windshield Slope Angle—the angle between the vertical reference line and a chord of the windshield arc running from the lower DLO to the upper DLO at the car centerline, when such chord is no longer than 18.0 in. If the windshield is longer than 18.0 in, the angle to be measured will be formed by a chord 18.0 in long, drawn from the lower DLO to the intersecting point on the windshield.

8. The opposite of a term already defined within a document need not also be defined; for example, the definition of "Asymmetrical Beam" is implied by the definition of "Symmetrical Beam."

9. Nomenclature which refers to a diagram should have .a sufficient written definition to make the term understandable without the diagram.

10. Explanatory or historical notes should be stated separately from and should follow the base definition and be so identified. The following example illustrates this usage:

Static Loaded Tire Radius—the loaded radius of a stationary tire inflated to normal recommended pressure.

Note. In general, the static loaded radius is different from the radius of a slowly rolling tire; and the static radius of a tire rolled into position may be different from that of a tire loaded without being rolled.

11. When two or more terms have the same definition and are used interchangeably, a preferred term should be chosen and defined. Synonymous terms may also be listed but with only a reference to the preferred item term. Example:

Barrel Gasket—the cylindrical sleeve of rubber-like material, etc.
Barrel Seal—use Barrel Gasket.

12. Definitions should be clear and useful to all who use the SAE Handbook as an engineering or technical reference.

UNIVERSAL SYMBOLS FOR OPERATOR CONTROLS—SAE J1500 JUN80

SAE Standard

Report of the Symbols Committee of the SAE Technical Board, approved June 1980.

1. Introduction—There is an increasing use of graphic symbols throughout the world in different technical fields to communicate information and identify operation or function.

Vehicles as compared to equipment which have like functions should have like graphic symbol identification.

2. Purpose—The compilation of symbols in this document are for reference use by all current and future committees responsible for the development of symbols.

3. Scope—This standard is to delineate the symbols used to identify controls, indicators, and tell-tales for automotive vehicles, trucks, off-the-road vehicles, construction equipment, industrial and recreational transportation and is for reference purposes only. The symbol application is to be found within the appropriate standards listed.

	UPPER BEAM	LOWER BEAM	HEADLAMP CLEANER	HEADLAMP LEVELING CONTROL	FRONT FOG LIGHT	REAR FOG LIGHT	PARKING LIGHTS
ISO 2575/3 REFERENCE	⊟◗	⊟◖	⊟◖	⊟◖	⫣◗	◖⫣	P⋜

REGULATORY

	UPPER BEAM	LOWER BEAM	HEADLAMP CLEANER	HEADLAMP LEVELING CONTROL	FRONT FOG LIGHT	REAR FOG LIGHT	PARKING LIGHTS
FMVSS 101/80	⊟◗						
CMVSS 101	⊟◗	⊟◖					
EEC 78/316	⊟◗	⊟◖	⊟◖		⫣◗	◖⫣	P⋜

STANDARDS

	UPPER BEAM	LOWER BEAM	HEADLAMP CLEANER	HEADLAMP LEVELING CONTROL	FRONT FOG LIGHT	REAR FOG LIGHT	PARKING LIGHTS
SAE J1048 AUTOMOTIVE	⊟◗	⊟◖	⊟◖		⫣◗	◖⫣	P⋜
SAE TRUCKS							
SAE J389b AGRICULTURAL	⊟◗	⊟◖					
SAE J298 INDUSTRIAL	⊟◗	⊟◖					⊟Ⓟ
SAE J107 MOTORCYCLES	⊟◗	⊟◖					
SAE MARINE							
SAE SNOWMOBILES							

	MASTER LIGHTING SWITCH	TURN SIGNALS	HAZARD WARNING	SIDE LAMPS	CLEARANCE LAMPS	WINDSHIELD WIPER	WINDSHIELD WASHER
ISO 2575/3 REFERENCE	☀	⇦⇨	△			wiper	washer
FMVSS 101/80	≡D	⇦⇨	△		⇥0D0⇤	wiper	washer
CMVSS 101	≡D ☀	⇦⇨	△		⇥0D0⇤	wiper	washer
EEC 78/316	☀	⇦⇨	△	⇥0D0⇤		wiper	washer
SAE J1048 AUTOMOTIVE	☀	⇦⇨	△			wiper	washer
SAE TRUCKS							
SAE J389b AGRICULTURAL		⇦⇨	⚠			wiper	washer
SAE J298 INDUSTRIAL		↖↗	⚠			wiper	
SAE J107 MOTORCYCLES		⇦⇨	△				
SAE MARINE							
SAE SNOWMOBILES							

REGULATORY

STANDARDS

	WINDSHIELD WASHER & WIPER	WINDSCREEN DEMISTER DEFOGGER	REAR WINDOW WIPER	REAR WINDOW WASHER	REAR WINDOW WIPER & WASHER	REAR WINDOW DEMISTER DEFOGGER	VENTILATING FAN
ISO 2575/3 REFERENCE	 ⬚	 ⬚	 ⬚	 ⬚	 ⬚	 ⬚	 ⬚
FMVSS 101/80	 ⬚	 ⬚				 ⬚	 ⬚
CMVSS 101	⬚						⬚
EEC 78/316	 ⬚	 ⬚				 ⬚	 ⬚
SAE J1048 AUTOMOTIVE	 ⬚	 ⬚				 ⬚	 ⬚
SAE TRUCKS							
SAE J389b AGRICULTURAL	 ⬚	 ⬚					 ⬚
SAE J298 INDUSTRIAL		 ⬚					
SAE J107 MOTORCYCLES							
SAE MARINE							
SAE SNOWMOBILES							

REGULATORY (side label spanning FMVSS, CMVSS, EEC rows)

STANDARDS (side label spanning SAE rows)

		BATTERY CHARGING	ENGINE COOLANT	ENGINE OIL	FUEL	UNLEADED FUEL	CHOKE	HORN
	ISO 2575/3 REFERENCE	(symbol)	(symbol)	(symbol)	(symbol)	(symbol)	(symbol)	(symbol)
REGULATORY	FMVSS 101/80	(symbol)	(symbol)	(symbol)	(symbol)			
REGULATORY	CMVSS 101	(symbol)		(symbol)	(symbol)			
REGULATORY	EEC 78/316	(symbol)	(symbol)	(symbol)	(symbol)		(symbol)	(symbol)
STANDARDS	SAE J1048 AUTOMOTIVE	(symbol)	(symbol)	(symbol)	(symbol)	(symbol)	(symbol)	(symbol)
STANDARDS	SAE TRUCKS							
STANDARDS	SAE J389b AGRICULTURAL	(symbol)	(symbol)	(symbol)	(symbol)		(symbol)	(symbol)
STANDARDS	SAE J298 INDUSTRIAL	(symbol)	(symbol)	(symbol)	(symbol)		(symbol)	(symbol)
STANDARDS	SAE J107 MOTORCYCLES	(symbol)	(symbol)	(symbol)	(symbol)		(symbol)	(symbol)
STANDARDS	SAE MARINE							
STANDARDS	SAE SNOWMOBILES							

		LIGHTER	SEAT BELT	PARKING BRAKE	BRAKE FAILURE	FRONT HOOD (BONNET)	REAR HOOD (BOOT)	TRANSMISSION
	ISO 2575/3 REFERENCE							
REGULATORY	**FMVSS 101/80**							
REGULATORY	**CMVSS 101**							
REGULATORY	**EEC 78/316**							
STANDARDS	**SAE J1048** AUTOMOTIVE							
STANDARDS	**SAE** TRUCKS							
STANDARDS	**SAE J389b** AGRICULTURAL			**P**				
STANDARDS	**SAE J298** INDUSTRIAL							
STANDARDS	**SAE J107** MOTORCYCLES							
STANDARDS	**SAE** MARINE							
STANDARDS	**SAE** SNOWMOBILES							
STANDARDS								

		TRANSMISSION OIL PRESSURE	TRANSMISSION OIL TEMPERATURE	TRANSMISSION OIL FILTER	AIR FILTER	GREASE LUBRICANT	OIL LUBRICANT	OIL LEVEL
REGULATORY	**ISO 2575/3** REFERENCE							
	FMVSS 101/80							
	CMVSS 101							
	EEC 78/316							
STANDARDS	**SAE J1048** AUTOMOTIVE							
	SAE TRUCKS							
	SAE J389b AGRICULTURAL							
	SAE J298 INDUSTRIAL							
	SAE J107 MOTORCYCLES							
	SAE MARINE							
	SAE SNOWMOBILES							

		DIPSTICK	FIRING ORDER	ENGINE R.P.M.	FUEL SHUT-OFF	HAND BRAKE	FORWARD	REVERSE
REGULATORY	**ISO 2575/3** REFERENCE							
	FMVSS 101/80							
	CMVSS 101							
	EEC 78/316							
STANDARDS	**SAE J1048** AUTOMOTIVE							
	SAE TRUCKS							
	SAE J389b AGRICULTURAL		1·3·2·4					R
	SAE J298 INDUSTRIAL		1·3·2·4			Engaged Disengaged		
	SAE J107 MOTORCYCLES							
	SAE MARINE							
	SAE SNOWMOBILES							

		NEUTRAL	UP DOWN	ADD INCREASE	DECREASE	CONTROL LEVER	VOLUME LEVEL	TEMPERATURE
	ISO 2575/3 REFERENCE							
REGULATORY	**FMVSS 101/80**							
	CMVSS 101							
	EEC 78/316							
STANDARDS	**SAE J1048** AUTOMOTIVE							
	SAE J680b TRUCKS							
	SAE J389b AGRICULTURAL	N	↓ / ↑	+	−	↕•	●◗○	🌡🌡
	SAE J298 INDUSTRIAL	(N)	⬆Up ⬇Down	+		↕•	●◗○ Full 1/2 Empty	🌡🌡
	SAE J107 MOTORCYCLES							
	SAE MARINE							
	SAE SNOWMOBILES							

	TEMPERATURE CONTROL	DIFFERENTIAL LOCK	ROCK SHAFT	CONNECTION	AXLE DISCONNECT	TOW	POWER TAKE-OFF
ISO 2575/3 REFERENCE							
FMVSS 101/80							
CMVSS 101							
EEC 78/316							
SAE J1048 AUTOMOTIVE							
SAE TRUCKS							
SAE J389b AGRICULTURAL	↑ / ↓			← →			
SAE J298 INDUSTRIAL			Raised / Lowered	Engage / Disengage	Connect / Disconnect		On / Off
SAE J107 MOTORCYCLES							
SAE MARINE							
SAE SNOWMOBILES							

	REMOTE CYLINDER	HEAVY LIGHT	BACKHOE DIPPERSTICK CONTROL	BACKHOE BOOM CONTROL	BACKHOE SWING CONTROL	BACKHOE BUCKET CONTROL	LOADER LIFT ARM CONTROL
ISO 2575/3 REFERENCE							
FMVSS 101/80							
CMVSS 101							
EEC 78/316							
SAE J1048 AUTOMOTIVE							
SAE TRUCKS							
SAE J389b AGRICULTURAL							
SAE J298 INDUSTRIAL							
SAE J107 MOTORCYCLES							
SAE MARINE							
SAE SNOWMOBILES							

REGULATORY

STANDARDS

	LOADER BOOM CONTROL	LOADER BUCKET CONTROL	STABILIZER CONTROL	UNLOADING AUGER	HEADER	REEL SPEED	REEL HEIGHT
ISO 2575/3 REFERENCE							
FMVSS 101/80							
CMVSS 101							
EEC 78/316							
SAE J1048 AUTOMOTIVE							
SAE TRUCKS							
SAE J389b AGRICULTURAL							
SAE J298 INDUSTRIAL							
SAE J107 MOTORCYCLES							
SAE MARINE							
SAE SNOWMOBILES							

	PLATFORM HEIGHT	CYLINDER SPEED (COMBINE)	CONCAVE CLEARANCE (COMBINE)	GROUND SPEED	SPEED RANGE	ALL MECHANISMS	PRESSURIZED OPEN SLOWLY
ISO 2575/3 REFERENCE							
FMVSS 101/80							
CMVSS 101							
EEC 78/316							
SAE J1048 AUTOMOTIVE							
SAE TRUCKS							
SAE J389b AGRICULTURAL	⬚	⬚	⬚	⬚	CONTINUOUSLY VARIABLE	⬚	⬚
SAE J298 INDUSTRIAL					Fast / Slow		⬚
SAE J107 MOTORCYCLES							
SAE MARINE							
SAE SNOWMOBILES							

REGULATORY / STANDARDS

	BASKET LIFT	HOURS	READ OPERATOR'S MANUAL	REVERSING LAMP	HAND ACCELERATOR THROTTLE	DIESEL ENGINE CUT-OFF	
ISO 2575/3 REFERENCE							
FMVSS 101/80							
CMVSS 101							
EEC 78/316				®⊂	)►(	⊗	
SAE J1048 AUTOMOTIVE							
SAE TRUCKS							
SAE J389b AGRICULTURAL							
SAE J298 INDUSTRIAL							
SAE J107 MOTORCYCLES							
SAE MARINE							
SAE SNOWMOBILES							

THE SOCIETY

SAE OFFICERS—1983

Charles C. Colyer, President

H. L. Brock, Treasurer
Rodger F. Ringham, Assistant Treasurer

N. John Beck, 1982 President
Philip J. Mazziotti, 1981 President

Joseph Gilbert, Executive Vice President and Secretary

SAE TECHNICAL BOARD FOR 1982 AND 1983

J. L. Mason, 1982 Chairman
R. C. Lunn, 1983 Chairman

COMMITTEE AND TERM EXPIRATION DATE (END OF ADMINISTRATIVE YEAR)

1982	1983	1984	1985
B. Ancker-Johnson	A. W. Carey	D. R. Blundell	R. W. Decker
J. B. Colletti	W. D. Compton	B. A. Jarrett	A. M. Fischer
G. E. Grant	V. P. Hendrickson	B. L. Koff	G. E. Grant
E. A. Green	R. W. Hildebrandt	J. Malus	S. D. Jeffe
S. D. Jeffe	J. L. Mason	E. A. Perry	Z. J. Lansky
R. C. Lunn	N. R. Parmet	R. J. Potter	R. E. Lyon, Jr.
J. L. Palmer	T. R. Rooney	W. Shapiro	J. C. Murphy
N. H. Pulling	W. H. Weltyk	D. R. Wolfslayer	
	R. C. Lunn		

(M. E. Rumbaugh Jr., Secretary)

SAE TECHNICAL DIVISION STAFF

A. G. Salem, Manager

D. R. Bentley   D. P. Martus   W. G. Wagner

SAE Headquarters, 400 Commonwealth Drive, Warrendale, PA   15096

P. Couhig   R. T. Northrup

SAE Detroit Branch Office, 3001 West Big Beaver, Troy, MI   48084

CERTIFICATES OF APPRECIATION COMMITTEE

N. H. PULLING (Chairman)
R. W. Hildebrandt

B. L. Koff

(SAE Staff, A. G. Salem)

METRIC ADVISORY COMMITTEE

L. C. KISER (Chairman)
J. N. Bagnall
L. E. Barbrow
J. T. Benedict
H. E. Guetzlaff
S. W. Hile

J. T. Keeley
S. E. Mallen
G. B. Pilkington, II
F. P. Stevens
R. P. Trowbridge

(SAE Staff, P. Couhig)

PUBLICATIONS ADVISORY COMMITTEE

S. G. TILDEN, JR. (Chairman)
D. L. Nordeen
J. M. Prange

J. R. Tishkowski
R. P. Trowbridge
F. C. Walters

(SAE Staff, A. G. Salem)

CONSTRUCTION, AGRICULTURAL & OFF-ROAD MACHINERY COUNCIL

F. C. WALTERS (Chairman)
F. W. RITCHEY (Vice Chairman)
L. D. Bergsten
H. D. Bordeaux
J. B. Codlin
J. H. Douma
D. W. Hadden
R. F. Hughes
G. W. Kahle
C. L. Kepner
P. E. Lockie

G. H. Millar
W. E. Miller
R. F. Moglia
M. R. North
R. D. Reed
R. G. Rumpf
R. L. Schmidt
J. E. Staab
J. D. Wetton
L. L. Williams

(SAE Staff, W. G. Wagner)

GENERAL MATERIALS COUNCIL

F. H. LIEB (Chairman)
G. W. TUFFNELL (Vice Chairman)
F. J. Arabia
N. T. Bartholomaei
S. Dinda
J. R. Eagan
D. R. Galliart
S. A. Gunnarson
A. F. Hegerich
W. A. Hertel
A. S. Kasper
K. A. Kaufmann
J. R. Madden

J. B. McCallum
J. L. Palmer
L. G. Pless
R. C. Rice
F. Richards
E. F. Ryntz, Jr.
N. A. Schilke
W. Swayney
W. E. Waddey
W. H. Weltyk
R. A. Wilde
J. Yadron
R. D. Zipp

(SAE Staff, R. T. Northrup, Jr.)

GENERAL STANDARDS COUNCIL

R. S. PIOTROWSKI (Chairman)
J. R. TISHKOWSKI (Vice Chairman)
A. W. Carey, Jr.
H. R. Chappell, Jr.
V. T. Czebatol

G. W. Folland
W. A. Hertel
R. E. Holmgren
E. J. Streichert
D. W. Vial

(SAE Staff, P. Couhig)

MOTOR VEHICLE COUNCIL

W. G. AGNEW (Chairman)
B. Ancker-Johnson
R. L. Atkin
A. W. Carey, Jr.
W. D. Compton
A. L. Gutherie
R. W. Hildebrandt
B. A. Jarrett
R. W. Johnson
D. E. Martin

D. F. Miller
D. L. Nordeen
W. J. Oakley
H. R. Pickford
N. H. Pulling
R. C. Ronzi
W. Shapiro
J. Versace
M. R. Young

(SAE Staff, D. P. Martus)

SPECIALIZED VEHICLE & EQUIPMENT COUNCIL

D. I. REED (Chairman)
J. C. Abromavage
M. A. Berk
G. W. Eger
G. C. Hardwick
D. R. Hartdegen
L. C. Lake, Jr.
R. H. Lincoln
T. H. Lohr
R. H. Madison

J. W. Mohr
J. A. Orvis
A. G. Salem
M. L. Stoner
A. J. Troyan, Jr.
W. G. Wagner
B. R. Weber
W. H. Weltyk
N. C. Woelffer

(SAE Staff, D. P. Martus)

TRUCK AND BUS COUNCIL

R. W. SACKETT (Chairman)
L. W. STRAWHORN (Vice Chairman)
R. Allrand
W. Cattin
E. Chosy
R. Denes
M. J. Denholm
T. A. Fath
D. D. Forester
G. A. Frederiksen
R. E. Fritts
W. L. Giles
P. Griskivich
R. W. Hildebrandt
R. H. Hinchcliff
J. F. Hofstetter
G. A. Hunt
C. R. Jaynes
S. D. Jeffe
V. H. Kaufman, Jr.

J. W. Kourik
K. R. Lewis
J. MacDougall
J. Malus
J. F. Mueller
L. W. Orr
D. M. Parkinson
B. H. Pauly
I. H. R. Rosen
H. E. Seiff
W. B. Smythe
D. P. Stanley
D. L. Stephens
C. Swinburn
R. J. Uffen
P. K. Varma
F. W. Venezia
J. D. Winsor, IV
W. J. Young

(SAE Staff, R. T. Northrup, Jr.)

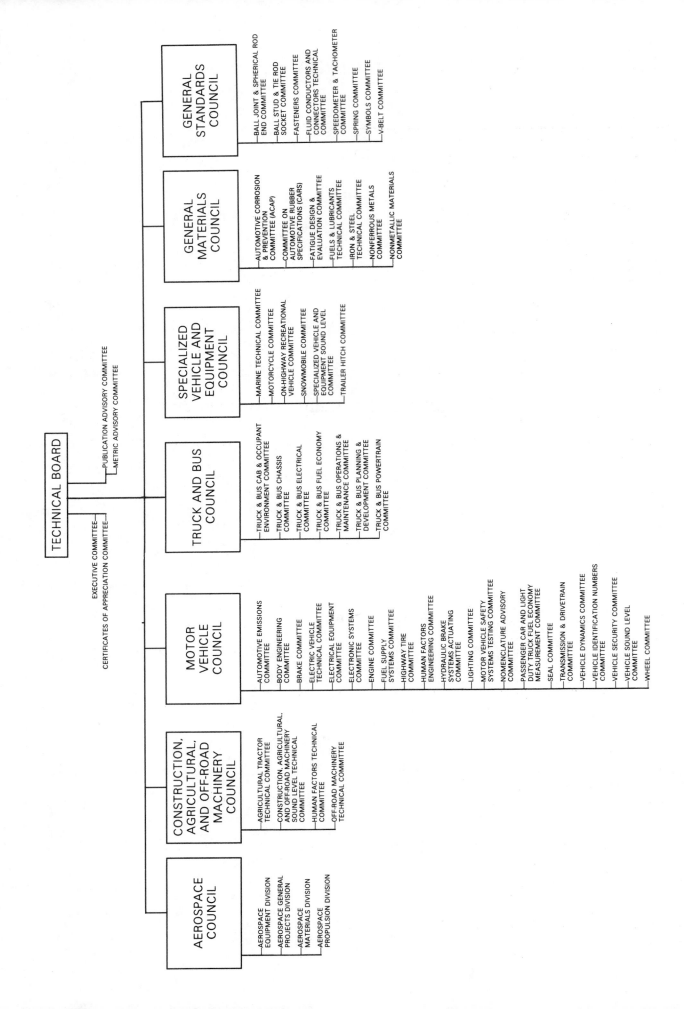

SAE SURFACE VEHICLE TECHNICAL COMMITTEE PERSONNEL

AGRICULTURAL TRACTOR TECHNICAL COMMITTEE

R. D. REED (Chairman)
M. R. NORTH (Vice Chairman)
P. A. Asseff
D. G. Bamford
R. T. Bennett
K. Cheatham
R. Hahn
J. D. Harris

L. I. Leviticus
J. B. Liljedahl
P. E. Lockie
C. E. McKeon
D. V. Post
M. G. Pribyl
W. E. Splinter

L. F. Stikeleather
J. H. Taylor
M. A. Walck
F. C. Walters
J. D. Wetton
E. J. Zeglen
J. H. Zich

(SAE Staff, W. G. Wagner)

AUTOMOTIVE CORROSION & PREVENTION COMMITTEE

G. F. BUSH (Chairman)
L. Allegra
R. Baboian
H. D. Berns
R. L. Chance
A. Cohen
F. Cole
R. H. Fay
J. D. Fobian
C. A. Fordham

H. R. Gilmore
N. S. Hatch
R. A. Hayes
H. R. Jaeckel
G. W. Keller
F. M. Kuhaneck
R. H. Labadie
H. H. Lawson
R. J. Neville
A. Okab

K. H. Park
E. R. Price
L. C. Rowe
V. K. Sharma
W. C. Sievert
A. A. Staklis
E. J. Szabo
G. W. Tuffnell
F. O. Wood
R. W. Zurilla

(SAE Staff, R. T. Northrup, Jr.)

AUTOMOTIVE EMISSIONS COMMITTEE

K. D. MILLS (Chairman)
W. G. AGNEW (Sponsor)
A. W. CAREY, JR. (Sponsor)
J. R. Barr
R. C. Bascom
J. L. Bascunana
W. N. Bazen
F. Bonamassa
W. M. Brehob
P. S. Bush
J. M. DiBella
D. C. Dowdall
J. H. Elwood
W. S. Fagley, Jr.
T. M. Fisher
E. F. Fort

G. L. Goodacre
E. E. Gough
C. M. Heinen
C. R. Hudson
J. E. A. John
J. H. Johnson
G. D. Kittredge
D. R. Liltedahl
M. Lombardo
S. W. Martens
R. D. Matthews
P. V. Mohan
R. G. Murray
A. J. Pahnke
J. M. Perez, Sr.

R. H. Perry, Jr.
C. Pollone
S. S. Quayle
L. Raymond
R. L. Reichlen
P. Ryan
V. Sink
K. J. Springer
J. P. Steiger
D. Stock
L. W. Strawhorn
R. E. Wallace
H. B. Weaver
H. J. Wimette
D. Wood

(SAE Staff, R. T. Northrup, Jr.)

BALL JOINT & SPHERICAL ROD END COMMITTEE

J. G. LANGENSTEIN (Chairman)
D. W. VIAL (Sponsor)
P. A. D'Anza
C. Griffiths
A. Henn

D. M. Johnson
A. Nauta
W. D. Ross
C. F. Schaening

W. C. Stephens
H. Sterkel
J. Weston
J. Whitsett

(SAE Staff, P. Couhig)

BALL STUD & TIE ROD SOCKET COMMITTEE

R. C. KOWALSKE (Chairman)
G. D. SWINNEY (Vice Chairman)
V. T. CZEBATOL (Sponsor)
W. Adkins
R. W. Alexander

D. Campbell
J. W. Creed, Jr.
M. Hassan
R. E. Jayroe
S. Mazur

D. D. Patton
R. D. Perkins
J. J. Turk
H. M. Van Dommelen
G. T. Woerner

(SAE Staff, P. Couhig)

BODY ENGINEERING COMMITTEE

E. G. ZIPP (Chairman)
D. L. NORDEEN (Sponsor)
P. Arbogast
Z. K. Baranowski
R. A. Bergen
J. J. Cantalupo

J. A. Colenso
E. A. Crilley
A. J. Freehan
J. J. Griffin
D. K. Haenchen
D. J. Helder

G. M. Hespeler
H. H. Maruyama
C. J. McLachlan
W. M. Miller
R. L. Morrison
J. Repp

(SAE Staff, P. Couhig)

BRAKE COMMITTEE

S. G. TILDEN, JR. (Chairman)
R. O. TUEGEL (Vice Chairman)
R. W. HILDEBRANDT (Sponsor)
E. T. Andrews
K. Aoki
J. V. Bassett, Sr.
A. G. Beier
V. G. Bloom
R. G. Brown
C. M. Brunhofer
A. J. Burgess
G. F. Butt
G. L. Buyck
W. R. Clawson
R. E. Dix
E. W. Drislane
T. A. Fath

J. E. Fent
A. M. Fischer
R. A. Gallant
P. J. Garthe
J. E. Getz
P. M. C. Hainaut
G. M. Hespeler
F. H. Highley
L. Kiselis
B. W. Klein
H. Klein
R. H. Madison
J. E. Martens
B. G. Mazurek, Jr.
D. W. Morrison
P. A. Myers
A. Negro

N. Nehez
R. E. Nelson
W. J. Oakley
P. Oppenheimer
F. W. Petring
P. H. Raves
J. M. Rowell
B. D. Sibley
C. F. Smith
J. H. Sorsche
R. F. Stelzer
R. K. Super
R. B. Temple
K. R. Thibo
J. A. Urban
C. R. Walker, Sr.

(SAE Staff, D. P. Martus)

COMMITTEE ON AUTOMOTIVE RUBBER SPECIFICATIONS (CARS)

J. R. DUNN (Chairman)
I. A. Abu-Isa
R. D. Allen
F. J. Arabia
F. W. Barlow
L. R. Bradford
J. H. Bramley
R. A. Brullo
A. B. Calhoun
D. Coz
F. N. DeMott
T. J. Dendinger
F. P. DeRosa
J. R. Dillhoeffer
C. Doney
E. Duda
R. C. Edwards
C. E. Erickson
S. K. Flanders
E. P. Francis
E. H. Gibbs
L. T. Gilbert
M. J. Godail

J. R. Hilliard
R. F. Hinderer
T. G. Hutchins
S. H. Itkin
K. A. Kaufmann
R. Koons
D. F. Kruse
J. Laslo
J. J. Leyden
D. F. Lohr, Jr.
M. Lowman
R. W. Malcolmson
L. D. Malone
L. Marenberg
L. G. Marlin
L. R. Mayo
W. J. McCortney, Sr.
D. G. McLeod
A. A. McNeish
S. F. Monthey
M. A. Newberry
W. A. Noll
G. C. Norman

R. E. Ofner
W. W. Paris
R. M. Perzyk
D. Pica
L. S. Porter
J. L. Rees
G. Santoro, Jr.
J. A. Sawicki
S. L. Schafer
E. L. Scheinbart
D. A. Seil
H. D. Shetler
R. J. Slingerlend
R. M. Smith
W. J. Snoddon
L. E. Sollberger
P. F. Stoeck
E. W. Thomas
H. E. Trexler
H. F. Trommer
C. D. Wemmers
B. Wood
A. R. Zander

(SAE Staff, R. T. Northrup, Jr.)

CONSTRUCTION, AGRICULTURAL, AND OFF-ROAD MACHINERY SOUND LEVEL TECHNICAL COMMITTEE

L. D. BERGSTEN (Chairman)
R. Bartholomae
W. Bowlby
L. J. Eriksson
C. W. Farmer
K. Feith
W. H. Flint
C. C. Godsey
G. R. Gray

D. W. Hadden
R. F. Hand
J. D. Harris
D. R. Hartdegen
L. B. Herren
P. D. Hopler
B. J. Lindgren
A. D. Loken

W. E. Miller
R. J. Nelissen
P. D. Schomer
W. E. Splinter
G. A. Stangl
J. B. Walsh
F. C. Walters
J. P. Welsh

(SAE Staff, R. T. Northrup, Jr.)

125

ELECTRICAL EQUIPMENT COMMITTEE

N. S. HATCH (Chairman)
E. J. SZABO (Vice Chairman)
C. E. BATES (Secretary)
R. W. JOHNSON (Sponsor)
A. W. Alexander
G. B. Andrews
F. Bauer
A. J. Burgess
R. J. Craver

J. R. Dawson, Jr.
W. M. Elliott, Jr.
L. W. Ewing
D. A. Fay
J. D. Fobian
E. E. Gough
J. T. Hardin
R. E. Heller

P. Hubbard
R. W. MacKay
J. W. Mueller
L. C. Nyman
R. L. Palen
T. Shewchuck
O. Taraborrelli
F. L. Zeisler

(SAE Staff, P. Couhig)

ELECTRICAL VEHICLE TECHNICAL COMMITTEE

C. C. CHRISTIANSON (Chairman)
W. G. AGNEW (Sponsor)
C. Adler
D. R. Buerschinger
A. J. Burgess
F. T. DeWolf
A. F. Dicker, Jr.
O. Drozd

S. M. Goldsmith
W. H. Koch
L. J. LaDouceur
L. C. Lake, Jr.
J. MacDougall
R. S. McKee
V. Miller
N. A. Richardson

J. T. Salihi
J. Shue
R. L. Strombotne
R. D. Von Seggern
V. Wouk
M. Yew
H. D. Yoder

(SAE Staff, P. Couhig)

ELECTRONIC SYSTEMS COMMITTEE

G. B. ANDREWS (Chairman)
J. F. ZIOMEK (Vice Chairman)
A. L. GUTHERIE (Sponsor)
F. Bauer
A. J. Burgess
M. L. Crawford
W. L. Doelp, Jr.

W. M. Elliott, Jr.
R. G. Fenske
J. D. Fobian
M. E. Hartz
T. O. Jones
J. B. King

M. Kutzin
R. A. Meade
L. L. Nagy
F. F. Oettinger
R. A. Rechul
N. L. Traub

(SAE Staff, P. Couhig)

ENGINE COMMITTEE

C. A. FORDHAM (Chairman)
G. J. DECKER (Vice Chairman)
R. C. RONZI (Sponsor)
L. L. Adams
N. Alvis
M. J. Asensio, Jr.
R. G. Cadwell
A. W. Carey, Jr.
A. J. Caronia
B. C. Clarke
W. B. Clemmens
D. H. Connor
N. A. Cross
A. O. DeHart
J. R. Donald

D. Downs
J. N. Ferguson
R. T. Florine
D. E. France
S. L. Gaal
R. L. Good
E. G. Jacobsen
S. Jakuba
J. E. A. John
V. H. Kaufman, Jr.
W. Lane, Jr.
L. E. Matson
J. T. Mieritz
V. J. Nowak
F. Piech

N. D. Postma
P. T. Reese
C. Reinhardt
L. H. Saylor
W. E. Schwieder
C. D. Shepherd
D. K. Smith
R. W. Stachowicz
J. Stellar
R. H. Syson
D. L. Thorson
K. W. Thurston
M. U. Trenne
C. D. Wink
K. Yamaoka

(SAE Staff, R. T. Northrup, Jr.)

FASTENERS COMMITTEE

H. W. ELLISON (Chairman)
H. R. CHAPPELL, JR. (Sponsor)
A. D. Bancroft
A. G. Baustert

R. B. Belford
A. A. Bien
R. W. Bosse
A. R. Breed

D. Bush
R. M. Byrne
D. B. Carroll
G. L. Cowing

W. J. Derner
W. W. Dodson
T. Doppke
A. W. Gair
D. A. Garrison
D. H. Gill
G. A. Gobb
F. E. Graves
R. W. Hayden
T. P. Hurst
J. Karagozian
R. S. Knecht

F. A. Kocian
J. F. Koenigshof
R. P. Koss
L. M. Lalik
C. S. Larson
S. E. Mallen
H. G. Muenchinger
A. Nauta
J. Passon
R. S. Piotrowski
C. F. Schaening
C. J. Schim

G. A. Schremmer
H. B. Schweppe
L. R. Strang
E. J. Streichert
T. E. Urich
D. W. Vial
D. P. Wagner
R. A. Walker
R. D. Wallace
D. Wampler
C. J. Wilson

(SAE Staff, P. Couhig)

FATIGUE DESIGN & EVALUATION STEERING COMMITTEE

L. E. TUCKER (Chairman)
D. R. GALLIART (Sponsor)
H. D. Berns
S. L. Bussa
B. J. Dabell

N. E. Dowling
H. O. Fuchs
K. A. Kaufmann
R. W. Landgraf

M. R. Mitchell
K. N. Morman, Jr.
M. P. Semenek
R. I. Stephens

(SAE Staff, R. T. Northrup, Jr.)

FLUID CONDUCTORS & CONNECTORS TECHNICAL COMMITTEE

R. J. LOBMEYER (Chairman)
H. D. Berns
H. R. Burns
H. M. Cooke
W. P. Coyne
W. E. Currie
V. T. Czebatol
R. C. Gibson
R. C. Harrison
W. A. Hermann
W. A. Hertel

J. S. Hinske
R. E. Holmgren
N. B. Johnston
J. Jones
B. Keister
D. E. Kimmet
R. B. Koch
O. Linger
R. J. May
H. B. Newman

L. O'Sickey
C. F. Schaening
R. K. Schantz
C. J. Schim
A. M. Schmidt
R. F. Sievert
E. J. Streichert
J. B. Wegmann
R. Wiley
J. Zimmel

(SAE Staff, P. Couhig)

FUEL SUPPLY SYSTEMS COMMITTEE

L. E. ARNETT (Chairman)
G. E. MOORE (Vice Chairman)
D. E. MARTIN (Sponsor)
F. C. Aldrich
A. M. Bower
T. J. Carr
W. D. Confoy
S. D. Curran
T. Detwiler
W. J. Dubsky
J. D. Eckel
A. C. Fink, Jr.
F. S. Flider
R. W. Furrow
R. Gelman
B. Grover
W. B. Hansel

S. Hasko
W. J. Henry
J. C. Hoelle
E. S. Hood
R. W. Jack
W. H. Johnson
R. L. Kirkpatrick
G. D. Kittredge
D. K. Lawrence
S. W. Martens
R. L. May
J. V. Milo
T. Moskovich
E. L. Mosshamer
R. L. Murray
R. R. Perschbacher
R. G. Pochert

G. H. Pope
G. R. Redmer
H. E. Reed
M. Reineman
B. J. Seger
H. J. Silver, Jr.
L. E. Slimak
R. Southers
B. Steinhoff
B. Sutton
C. A. Taylor
H. A. Toulmin, Jr.
C. L. Turner
F. L. Voelz
A. L. Wokas
J. L. Worley

(SAE Staff, W. G. Wagner)

FUELS & LUBRICANTS TECHNICAL COMMITTEE

R. H. KABEL (Chairman)
J. A. MCLAIN (Vice Chairman)

J. L. PALMER (Sponsor)
B. Adinoff

W. R. Alexander
N. T. Bartholomaei

J. L. Bascunana
D. A. Becker
P. A. Bennett
F. J. Blatz
L. O. Bowman
R. A. Carley
K. Cashmore
G. Clark, Jr.
C. C. Colyer
W. F. Connell
B. E. Council
C. M. Cusano
G. J. Decker
H. E. Deen
E. H. DeLong
D. W. Dinsmore
H. V. Doering
H. H. Donaldson, Jr.
R. J. Donaldson
R. E. Elrod
J. D. Fobian
D. H. Garland
A. W. Gilbert
J. M. Gottlieb
D. Gunn
W. Hart
D. P. Haseltine
R. A. Hayes
S. A. Herbert
S. H. Hill
P. D. Hobson

W. C. Hollibaugh
G. E. Holman
G. W. Holmes
H. H. Hopkins
P. S. Hossack
N. A. Hunstad
R. E. Kay
W. H. Keeber
B. D. Keller
N. Kendall
S. Korcek
J. W. Lane
M. E. LePera
R. Q. Little, Jr.
C. F. Long
W. E. MacDonald
G. L. Malone
T. F. McDonnell, Jr.
A. C. McDonough
M. L. McMillan
N. V. Messina
M. I. Michael
H. H. Mullinger
P. S. Myers
J. L. Newcombe
H. T. Niles
L. W. Okon
T. T. Ordiway
A. J. Pahnke
D. P. Pellerito
R. H. Perry, Jr.

L. G. Pless
R. I. Potter
R. L. Riedel
J. C. Root
C. Rubinstein, Sr.
C. H. Ruof
H. G. Russell
A. B. Sarkis
C. F. Schwarz
L. L. Smith
R. K. Smith
R. B. Sneed
S. R. Sprague
R. M. Stewart
R. E. Streets
B. C. Striegler
J. B. Stucker
E. R. Sullivan
S. E. Swedberg
R. E. Teasley, Jr.
P. V. Toffoli, Jr.
W. E. Waddey
J. F. Wagner
T. D. Wagster, Jr.
S. T. Walker
A. B. Weinberg
B. F. White
W. O. Winer
E. Yatsko, Jr.
A. E. Zengel

(SAE Staff, W. G. Wagner)

HIGHWAY TIRE COMMITTEE

R. H. SNYDER (Chairman)
W. J. OAKLEY (Sponsor)
R. H. Attenhofer
J. L. Bascunana
W. Bergman
W. Bergman
R. L. Brown
K. L. Campbell, Jr.
T. J. Carr
A. Casanova
T. Cole
J. W. Davis

T. E. Edson
J. B. Gale
G. Gusakov
W. M. Heath
R. E. Johnson
D. Keane
L. E. Kiselis
D. L. Knight
J. R. Luchini
L. Marick
R. L. Marlowe

L. Nedley
A. Negro
A. Neill
R. A. Pepoy
J. C. Scowcroft
F. D. Smithson
F. E. Timmons
V. L. Vickland
F. C. Walters
D. E. Williams
W. J. Woehrle

(SAE Staff, P. Couhig)

HUMAN FACTORS ENGINEERING COMMITTEE

J. A. STARKEY (Chairman)
J. VERSACE (Sponsor)
J. C. Barton
R. F. Chandler
R. E. DeWald
R. J. Donohue
E. Edge
L. M. Forbes, Jr.
T. G. Gage
M. Glumm

D. E. Gobuty
C. G. Holstein
J. L. Hovey
R. P. Hubbard
C. O. Jones
P. R. Knaff
T. J. Kuechenmeister
M. L. Kunz
M. J. McKale
A. Mital

L. P. Olson
G. S. Popa
D. V. Post
N. H. Pulling
A. Raouf
B. S. Repa
R. G. Snyder
J. F. Stofflet
W. J. Young

(SAE Staff, P. Couhig)

HUMAN FACTORS TECHNICAL COMMITTEE

L. L. WILLIAMS (Chairman)
E. C. WILLIAMS, JR. (Vice Chairman)
W. L. Black
H. D. Bordeaux

G. P. Burton
J. E. Carr
J. W. Carter
K. Conway

D. W. Hadden
E. G. Hanus
R. Hefner
P. P. W. Huang

J. H. Hyler
R. A. Johanningmeier
G. A. Johnson
A. D. Loken
V. M. Pandav

N. H. Pulling
D. A. Raab
R. D. Reed
R. G. Rumpf
J. E. Staab

J. A. Starkey
D. L. Steele
S. A. Tennyson
L. G. Wildey

(SAE Staff, W. G. Wagner)

HYDRAULIC BRAKE SYSTEMS ACTUATING COMMITTEE

R. G. BROWN (Chairman)
D. A. WASMER (Vice Chairman)
R. W. HILDEBRANDT (Sponsor)
R. L. Coffman
J. H. Conley
R. L. Doering
E. P. Francis
C. Harrington
J. L. Harvey

G. M. Hespeler
F. Hussey
C. O. Jones
R. A. C. Ker
H. Klein
J. MacDougall
A. L. Marshall
V. W. Meyer
W. J. Oakley

P. Oppenheimer
J. M. Rowell
R. Salvador
R. W. Shiffler
M. Tamaki, PhD
S. G. Tilden, Jr.
W. Weisbrod, Jr.
A. J. Wilson
K. E. Yost

(SAE Staff, D. P. Martus)

IRON & STEEL TECHNICAL COMMITTEE

B. E. WRIGHT (Chairman)
D. D. DODGE (Vice Chairman)
F. J. Arabia
R. J. Belz
R. D. Bennett
F. P. Bens
E. T. Bittner
H. N. Bogart
F. Borik
R. M. Buck
G. F. Bush
D. P. Buswell
S. R. Callaway
H. R. Chappell, Jr.
E. F. Chojnowski
J. F. Clark
A. G. Cook
W. J. Cormack
H. W. Dailey
D. V. Doane
J. M. Dobos

H. A. Doyle
J. R. Easterday
I. Ekis
A. G. Forrest
M. L. Frey
D. A. Garrison
R. W. Goetz
W. T. Groves
S. A. Gunnarson
J. S. Hanson
D. J. Hayes
L. A. Huebner
K. W. Jerwann
N. O. Kates
J. H. King
C. A. Krubsack
A. S. MacDonald
D. E. McVicker
R. S. Moriarty
W. H. B. Newell
P. K. Patnaik

P. K. Patnaik
W. J. Ptashnik
J. E. Rainey
C. J. Rhodes
G. H. Robinson
D. F. Rundle
E. F. Ryntz, Jr.
S. R. Scales
M. P. Semenek
D. L. Shangle, Jr.
H. T. Sheppard
C. H. Sperry
J. V. Sprong
R. F. Steigerwald
E. J. Streichert
M. E. Suess
J. E. Tripp
L. J. VandeWalle
E. T. Vitcha
R. F. Webster

(SAE Staff, P. Couhig)

LIGHTING COMMITTEE

R. W. OYLER (Chairman)
J. E. BAIR (Vice Chairman)
K. Abramson
A. E. Ackerly, Jr.
R. J. Amorosi
R. L. Austin
J. E. Bennett
V. D. Bhise
A. F. Bleiweiss
G. G. Bonvallet
R. Bosch
J. V. Bough
H. R. Brink, Jr.
A. J. Burgess
A. Cardarelli
S. A. Darby
R. DeCaro
K. Denneler
P. Devaux
C. J. Devonshire
B. Dickinson
R. P. Donley

R. J. Donohue
S. Eguchi
D. Ellenberger
W. M. Elliott, Jr.
C. V. Festenberg
C. F. Finn
B. Francois
C. E. Granfors
W. M. Heath
S. A. Heenan
E. G. Hitzemeyer
K. Honda
M. Iwase
K. L. Johnson
C. O. Jones
S. F. Kimball, III
D. F. King
G. A. Knapp
P. H. Lawrenz
C. L. Lemme
R. M. Levy
A. T. Lewry

G. Lindae
R. J. Love
J. D. Marks
P. W. Maurer
M. V. McConnell
M. J. McKale
W. A. McKinney
G. E. Meese
J. N. Miller
D. V. Missio
H. Miyazawa
J. F. Mizia
R. G. Mortimer
B. C. Muccioli
Y. Nakajima
C. J. Newman
R. A. Nixon, Jr.
R. C. Oliver
P. Olson
K. C. Ploeger
D. V. Post
F. Prevot

N. H. Pulling
J. L. Purpura
P. S. Rust
H. Schmidt-Clausen
P. G. Scully
J. Segsworth
P. R. Smester
J. Speaker
C. W. Spencer
Z. S. Subotich

B. Summers
D. J. Sumple, Sr.
F. Takata
F. Talinucci
T. G. Tallon
R. M. Terry
K. Uding
K. F. VanTill
R. L. Vile

K. Watanabe
P. E. Westlake
J. D. White
J. G. White
R. L. Wilson
G. P. Wright
R. G. Yorks
H. J. T. Young
B. Zinchenko

(SAE Staff, W. G. Wagner)

MARINE TECHNICAL COMMITTEE

A. J. TROYAN, JR. (Chairman)
R. F. KRESS (Vice Chairman)
D. A. Armstrong
B. C. Arnold
D. D. Beach, Jr.
L. C. Bibow
W. M. Crook
J. G. Fleder
E. C. Game, II

L. B. Gray
J. H. Hodge
E. C. Kiekhaefer
J. A. Langley
J. T. Laskey
N. Leeper
G. J. Lippmann
J. M. McClellan
F. L. Miszczak

T. Morgan
D. I. Reed
W. M. Rosenfeld
G. W. Schulz
W. C. Shanks, Jr.
R. L. Sluka
S. Q. Wales
D. H. Wood

(SAE Staff, D. P. Martus)

MOTOR VEHICLE SAFETY SYSTEMS TESTING COMMITTEE

H. G. BRILMYER (Chairman)
R. A. WILSON (Vice Chairman)
J. VERSACE (Sponsor)
L. L. Baker
L. E. Baltz
N. Baracos
J. Brinn

J. J. Cantalupo
R. F. Chandler
R. P. Daniel
R. H. Fredericks
J. E. Hofferberth
H. G. Johannessen
W. W. Koebnick

D. J. McDowell
W. D. Nelson
G. W. Nyquist
N. H. Pulling
J. C. Scowcroft
J. R. Tishkowski
K. Weber

(SAE Staff, D. P. Martus)

MOTORCYCLE COMMITTEE

L. C. LAKE, JR. (Chairman)
R. HAGIE (Vice Chairman)
E. R. Anderson
G. Bonneau
A. J. Burgess
T. J. Carter, III
C. L. Hale
R. T. Harrison
C. H. Hartman
R. R. Huebner
P. Hundemer
A. R. Isley
K. A. Jelinek

P. D. Keller
R. A. Little
W. F. MacKay
A. Meganck
H. Miyazawa
R. G. Mortimer
T. Murphy
R. P. Parker
G. A. Parkison
F. M. Petler
D. V. Post
K. W. Reimers
W. W. Riley

W. J. Ross
S. G. Shadle
M. R. Stahl
I. J. Wagar
J. B. Walsh
K. Watanabe
D. H. Weir
E. C. Wilson
G. L. Winn
H. H. Worthington
H. J. T. Young
M. P. Zimmerman

(SAE Staff, W. G. Wagner)

NOMENCLATURE ADVISORY COMMITTEE

D. A. FAY (Chairman)
K. WEBER (Vice Chairman)
M. J. TAUSCHEK (Sponsor)
L. O. Baker

W. A. Devlin, Jr.
L. C. DeWeese
R. A. Morris

C. F. Thelin
S. G. Tilden, Jr.
V. L. Vickland

(SAE Staff, D. P. Martus)

NONFERROUS METALS COMMITTEE

A. S. KASPER (Chairman)
W. Amber
J. C. Bierlein
Bureau of Ships
R. S. Busk
A. R. Canady
R. G. Cassidy
A. Cohen
A. O. DeHart

H. R. Gilmore
J. G. Harris
W. M. Harris
C. N. Isackson
K. A. Kaufmann
P. J. Kranz
Z. J. Lansky
P. T. Madziar
D. E. McVicker

N. P. Milano
C. J. Rhodes
H. L. Schmedt
C. D. Skrzypek
W. E. Smith
C. R. Straesser
G. W. Tuffnell
W. B. Young

(SAE Staff, R. T. Northrup, Jr.)

NONMETALLIC MATERIALS COMMITTEE

T. J. WALLAG (Chairman)
J. J. MESTDAGH (Vice Chairman)
J. B. MCCALLUM (Sponsor)
R. F. Anderson
H. D. Baker
K. Balliett
A. B. Calhoun
M. Carter, Jr.
G. Christie
J. W. Compton
T. J. Dearlove
F. N. DeMott
J. R. Dunn
M. A. Gale
A. F. Hegerich

J. E. Hinsch
S. H. Itkin
R. J. Kane
Z. J. Lansky
F. H. Lieb
L. D. Malone
R. D. Mayne
W. J. McCortney, Sr.
D. G. McLeod
M. A. Newberry
G. C. Norman
R. E. Ofner
S. Patel
R. L. Pleiness

E. R. Presser
J. L. Purpura
E. R. Rezendes
L. M. Roslinski
J. A. Sawicki
R. D. C. Silver
R. W. Siorek
D. L. Strader
A. E. Williams
W. J. Wilson
G. M. Wolf
F. Woolary
R. L. Wooten
J. F. Ziomek

(SAE Staff, R. T. Northrup, Jr.)

OFF-ROAD MACHINERY TECHNICAL COMMITTEE

R. G. RUMPF (Chairman)
L. E. MILLER (Vice Chairman)
D. C. Ager
L. D. Bergsten
W. L. Black
H. D. Bordeaux
D. R. Buerschinger
J. B. Codlin
L. W. G. Collins
R. E. Dagnall
D. W. Driscol
A. L. Garman
T. O. Goodney
F. A. Green
D. W. Hadden
N. F. Hanson
P. D. Hopler
P. P. W. Huang
A. H. Huebner

L. K. Huffman
R. F. Hughes
S. A. Hyland
J. H. Hyler
D. Juergens
C. L. Kepner
G. L. Klose
D. A. Lockie
W. E. Miller
R. I. Myers
R. J. Nelissen
M. R. North
R. J. Oliver
J. T. Parrett
D. V. Post
P. D. Redenbarger
G. E. Redzinski
H. H. Reeders
F. W. Ritchey

A. J. Rutherford
A. H. Saele
J. R. Salonimer
P. P. Seabase
D. B. Shore
B. J. Smith
T. J. Smith
D. K. Spring
J. E. Staab
C. G. Termont
D. R. Thomas
L. A. Venere
F. C. Walters
L. M. Watts
J. D. Wetton
L. L. Williams
J. L. Woodward
E. J. Zeglen

(SAE Staff, W. G. Wagner)

ON-HIGHWAY RECREATIONAL VEHICLE COMMITTEE

R. H. MADISON (Chairman)
J. C. Abromavage
D. Arnold
W. A. Bartkowiak
L. M. Baulis
J. Boron
J. Crane
R. Curtis
R. C. Frank
J. W. Gechei
P. L. Graney

R. Herzler
W. L. Jacobson
E. Kent
G. Lucas
L. W. Moore
M. Nerem
C. J. Owen
D. V. Post
D. I. Reed
D. Reeker

J. Rockwell
G. Schultz
W. L. Sherry
P. N. Shrake
B. R. Weber
P. White
C. A. Wilhelm
R. E. Wilkinson
J. Wong
A. E. Zollinger

(SAE Staff, D. P. Martus)

PASSENGER CAR & LIGHT TRUCK FUEL ECONOMY MEASUREMENT COMMITTEE

W. S. FREAS (Chairman)
J. B. Baker
J. A. Bert
J. H. Brateman
J. C. Callison
R. J. Dennison
W. S. Fagley, Jr.
D. A. Fay
W. H. Groth
M. L. Halberstadt
E. C. Klaubert

L. J. LaDouceur
S. Luchter
R. A. Marshall
R. D. Matthews
H. E. McGee
W. L. McNulty
W. G. Mears
J. D. Murrell
J. D. Myers
F. Sam
D. J. Schuring

W. E. Schwieder
B. H. Simpson
V. Sink
L. E. Slimak
W. B. Smythe
J. P. Steiger
G. D. Thompson
W. S. Vilda, Jr.
H. B. Weaver
T. Wusz

(SAE Staff, R. T. Northrup, Jr.)

SEAL COMMITTEE

D. L. OTTO (Chairman)
D. A. VAN DEVEN (Vice Chairman)
S. N. SMITH (Secretary)
M. R. YOUNG (Sponsor)
J. W. Abar
D. R. Bainard
D. D. Black
R. V. Brink
J. E. Burk
J. J. Carr
D. A. Cather, Jr.
H. L. Chambers
J. A. Chandler
F. J. Charhut
G. Christie
J. A. Cooper
E. S. Czekansky

R. L. Dega
W. E. Fleetwood
A. H. Ginn
A. L. Gordon
J. M. Gottlieb
J. W. Grant
F. R. Hatch
J. A. Heck
T. S. Hemenway, Jr.
K. L. Hoer
L. A. Horve
A. Jain
M. L. Karcher
R. B. Kerchaert
R. J. Kozerski
R. K. MacLaren

W. W. Maltman
G. E. Manning
L. R. Marcy
L. G. Marlin
K. Martek
A. Matsushima
E. F. McEntee
M. C. Murray
D. E. Perry
J. E. Schaus
J. A. Serio
L. L. Smith
W. J. Snoddon
J. D. Symons
E. D. Taylor
K. Vitrone

(SAE Staff, R. T. Northrup, Jr.)

SNOWMOBILE COMMITTEE

T. H. LOHR (Chairman)
D. Bean
N. O. Berg
M. A. Berk
S. J. Chris
R. R. Cote
R. Fitzsimons

R. T. Harrison
E. Hetteen
L. C. Lake, Jr.
C. P. Leach, Jr.
C. E. Morton, PE
R. W. Muth
D. E. Nelson

R. L. Niemchick
D. V. Post
K. K. Prasad
W. L. Severson
O. E. Strand
H. J. T. Young

(SAE Staff, W. G. Wagner)

SPECIALIZED VEHICLE & EQUIPMENT SOUND LEVEL COMMITTEE

D. R. HARTDEGEN (Chairman)
G. M. Adams
R. S. Bennin
L. D. Bergsten
A. Brenig
L. J. Eriksson
C. C. Godsey

R. Hellweg
R. K. Hillquist
R. A. Lanpheer
R. H. Lincoln
G. C. Michel
J. W. Mohr
J. W. Moore

K. F. Nowak
R. B. Passmore
D. I. Reed
W. E. Roper
W. Snyder
W. G. Wagner
J. B. Walsh

(SAE Staff, R. T. Northrup, Jr.)

SPEEDOMETER & TACHOMETER COMMITTEE

R. D. STRASZHEIM (Chairman)
R. E. HOLMGREN (Sponsor)
R. Abel
W. W. Bischoff
W. C. Ellis
J. J. Haight

J. S. Harley
S. Hasko
R. O. Helgeby
J. H. Jones
M. A. Koler
R. F. Labory

N. H. Pulling
H. B. Rath
W. P. Seniuk
W. C. Subluskey
W. Teska
E. J. Weld

(SAE Staff, P. Couhig)

SPRING COMMITTEE

K. CAMPBELL (Chairman)
G. W. FOLLAND (Sponsor)
T. A. Bank
D. Curtin
W. Frank
J. Gibbs
L. Godfrey
L. A. Habrle
W. J. Jarae

E. H. Judd
J. F. Kelly
W. T. Mayers
G. W. Myrick
E. C. Oldfield
D. J. Perkins
R. F. Pierman
W. Platko
F. T. Rowland

H. L. Schmedt
G. A. Schremmer
K. E. Siler
J. E. Silvis
E. M. Steiner
B. Sterne
F. J. Waksmundzki
W. Wilkie

(SAE Staff, P. Couhig)

SYMBOLS COMMITTEE

D. D. BEACH, JR. (Chairman)
M. Belzer
M. A. Berk
W. L. Black
H. Bream
D. Campbell
J. B. Codlin

T. F. Crusinberry
R. Hagie
L. H. Hodges
L. C. Lake, Jr.
D. Mitchell
V. K. Rajpaul
D. J. Schwarz

S. A. Tennyson
J. R. Tishkowski
C. W. Volland
F. C. Walters
B. R. Weber
B. S. Wood

(SAE Staff, D. P. Martus)

TRAILER HITCH COMMITTEE

J. C. ABROMAVAGE (Chairman)
C. N. FRENCH (Vice Chairman)
S. J. Borden
G. Conradi
S. Davis
B. G. Fandrich
F. R. Fertitta
P. Herdon

E. M. Hermansen
F. J. Huston, Jr.
R. Klein
M. Leonard
R. H. Madison
M. C. Maryonovich
M. Nerem
R. L. Patel

D. I. Reed
A. Roberts
J. Rockwell
W. L. Sherry
J. Smith
D. L. Swanson
B. R. Weber
D. A. Young

(SAE Staff, D. P. Martus)

TRANSMISSION & DRIVETRAIN TECHNICAL COMMITTEE

C. E. COONEY, JR. (Chairman)
M. G. GABRIEL (Vice Chairman)
M. R. YOUNG (Sponsor)
F. H. Abar, Jr.
A. D. Adam
R. E. Annis
M. J. Asensio, Jr.
P. J. Ashburn
W. A. Bartkowiak
J. L. Bascunana
A. H. Berker
A. P. Blomquist
E. S. Bower
C. E. Brady
D. K. Cameron
B. W. Cartwright
E. L. Clary
R. Cleveland
R. G. Colello
R. F. Cornish
R. W. Craig
W. E. Daggett
W. Dundore

E. L. Egbert
R. Emmadi
P. D. Fadow
D. A. Fay
R. B. Gibson
C. W. Greening
R. N. Hazzard
E. T. Hendzel
D. E. Hobson
G. E. Huffaker
D. Hughson
V. J. Jandasek
C. E. Juntunen
V. H. Kaufman, Jr.
K. R. Kaza
J. Koinis
A. C. LaCroix
G. G. Lucas
J. E. Mahoney
E. C. Maki
K. Martek
W. McCall
R. A. Mercure

H. L. Miner
K. Parmee
D. P. Pellerito
S. V. Puidokas
J. A. Repella
C. E. Shellman
P. L. Silbert
E. Y. Sing
D. M. Slaubaugh
J. B. Snoy
R. J. Socin
L. G. Steinl
J. H. Tanzer
E. D. Taylor
G. E. Tozer
R. M. Tuck, Jr.
E. W. Upton
D. A. Van Deven
E. R. Wagner
T. M. Wang
R. W. Wayman
P. J. Weis
F. H. Whitmyer

(SAE Staff, R. T. Northrup, Jr.)

TRUCK & BUS CAB & OCCUPANT ENVIRONMENT COMMITTEE

L. W. STRAWHORN (Chairman)
R. E. HEGLUND (Vice Chairman)
R. A. Batt
T. L. Black
N. A. Bundra
F. M. Callahan
R. M. Clarke
J. H. Culbertson
R. E. Didion
T. E. Dobbs

A. M. Fischer
T. D. Gillespie
D. C. Hammond
J. L. Hearn
T. J. Johnson
C. O. Jones
B. Klingenberg
B. B. Koepke
F. L. Krall

G. Kreaden
S. T. Larsson
J. W. Lawrence
V. E. Pound
W. J. Rheaume
G. W. Rossow
W. E. Whitmer
J. K. Winslow
W. J. Young

(SAE Staff, R. T. Northrup, Jr.)

TRUCK & BUS CHASSIS COMMITTEE

D. L. STEPHENS (Chairman)
R. W. HILDEBRANDT (Vice Chairman)
P. C. Bertelson

R. S. Button
J. E. Fent
R. S. Graham

D. J. Karalash
J. M. Machey
R. W. Morrison, Jr.

(SAE Staff, R. T. Northrup, Jr.)

TRUCK & BUS ELECTRICAL COMMITTEE

E. CHOSY (Chairman)
E. J. SZABO (Vice Chairman)
N. V. FORTE (Secretary)
F. Bauer
T. D. Beaumont
M. B. Brandt
H. R. Brink, Jr.
A. J. Burgess
R. J. Comparet
A. Day

E. H. Debenjak, PE
N. Fortin
C. E. Granfors
N. S. Hatch
M. L. Hutchins
A. C. Lesesky
V. H. Miles, Sr.
C. J. Owen
C. Paullus

D. E. Riley
G. R. Sarkozi
G. H. Schlensker
P. J. Speece
R. C. Speth
J. J. Stephan
J. G. Sutton
R. W. Trexler, Jr.
P. Trummonds

(SAE Staff, R. T. Northrup, Jr.)

TRUCK & BUS FUEL ECONOMY COMMITTEE

W. B. SMYTHE (Chairman)
R. S. JOHNSON (Vice Chairman)
J. E. Allen
R. L. Atkin
M. Balban
L. Batts
R. L. Beckmann
R. Belcer
W. H. Bettes
J. B. Bidwell
T. Boyden
R. G. Cadwell
R. L. Camball
W. H. Close
K. R. Cooper
J. H. Culbertson
T. M. DeJonckheere
R. Ehrlich

C. H. Ek
D. D. Forester
T. Franquist
R. G. Gallivan
T. A. Gelinas
W. J. K. Gibson
M. L. Halberstadt
G. P. Hanley
L. Hieber
R. E. Hoffmeister
R. A. Hunter
D. A. Jesmantas
E. D. Kane
G. S. Kent
J. R. Luchini
E. C. Maki
R. L. Mason
W. R. Minning

T. J. Newell
D. M. Parkinson
J. M. Prange
R. F. Ringham
W. R. Rodger
G. F. Romberg
G. W. Rossow
J. B. Schnell
H. E. Seiff
D. B. Stattenfield
J. G. Stieber
L. W. Strawhorn
P. P. Terrano
C. J. Travis, Jr.
E. W. Upton
J. C. Walter
T. C. Young

(SAE Staff, R. T. Northrup, Jr.)

TRUCK & BUS OPERATIONS & MAINTENANCE COMMITTEE

D. M. PARKINSON (Chairman)

J. M. Mann

T. K. McBride

(SAE Staff, R. T. Northrup, Jr.)

TRUCK & BUS POWERTRAIN COMMITTEE

R. DENES (Chairman)
G. A. FREDERIKSEN (Vice Chairman)
R. M. Clarke
A. Demien
R. V. Gorman
D. W. Holzinger

C. R. Jones
L. L. Langlois
P. J. Mazziotti
H. J. Mellgren
G. J. Montgomery

C. F. Powell
J. L. Rathburn
F. J. Timmins
P. J. Weis
R. W. Wolfe

(SAE Staff, R. T. Northrup, Jr.)

V-BELT COMMITTEE

L. VIRTUE (Chairman)
J. R. TISHKOWSKI (Sponsor)
J. T. Alden
A. E. Beaty
J. C. Blankenship
P. D. Boos
W. H. Buhrmann
V. L. Chuang
D. J. Clifford
H. L. Cox
W. P. Coyne
P. Davison
R. T. Doughty
W. D. Erickson
S. K. Fan
D. Gardner

M. D. Gayer
I. A. Groothuis
D. D. Hall
G. L. Hitchcock
R. D. Hoback
W. Hulse
G. Kettunen
H. May
E. J. McCarthy
L. J. Mehelich
J. C. Minneker, Jr.
C. Mudge
R. J. Nelson
D. Pittman
E. R. Presser

R. S. Putman
L. J. Raver
G. T. Russell
S. Sabharwal
S. W. Schmitt
T. E. Schroer
J. S. Sears
M. Shadday
B. L. Speer
T. A. Sulkowski
R. Wallace
F. C. Walters
C. M. Williams
L. E. Williams
J. J. Zaiss

(SAE Staff, P. Couhig)

VEHICLE DYNAMICS COMMITTEE

R. T. BUNDORF (Chairman)
L. SEGEL (Vice Chairman)
W. Bergman
W. B. Carlson
A. F. Costelli
D. Cox
K. Enke
R. Ervin
D. A. Fay
D. A. Glemming
J. T. Hamilton
G. M. Hespeler
D. H. Iacovoni
C. O. Jones
K. B. Kelly
C. M. Kennedy
J. W. Kent, Jr.
R. H. Klein

W. F. LeFevre
S. A. Lippmann
R. H. Madison
J. M. Mann
J. McHinch
D. T. McRuer
W. F. Milliken, Jr.
A. Negro
W. C. Oswald
D. A. Perrin
N. H. Pulling
B. V. A. Rao
R. E. Rasmussen
H. M. Reigner
B. S. Repa
R. S. Rice
R. A. Rider

P. M. Riede, Jr.
G. F. Romberg
H. K. Sachs
J. Saint Paul
F. K. Schenkel
S. G. Shadle
C. G. Shapley
G. L. Smith
L. M. Sweet
C. F. Thelin
R. W. Topping
V. L. Vickland
B. R. Weber
D. H. Weir
P. G. Willer
F. J. Winsor, Jr.
K. E. Ziwica

(SAE Staff, P. Couhig)

VEHICLE IDENTIFICATION NUMBERS COMMITTEE

M. W. DIXON (Chairman)
N. H. PULLING (Sponsor)
D. D. Bartz
R. F. Campbell
F. C. Corley
D. Costa
J. R. Doto
D. Ellenberger
N. F. Erickson
C. F. Finn
J. E. Forrester
J. E. Forss
D. A. Frisco
F. C. Funk
P. W. Gilliland, Sr.

R. J. Haller
C. Humphrey
R. F. Ingegneri
F. Louis
R. H. Madison
F. W. McClure, Sr.
R. F. Miller
P. Perry
F. M. Petler
B. J. Riley
J. Rockwell
R. J. Salehar
B. Schiff
F. Schwartz
D. M. Schwentker

R. H. Sostkowski
G. O. Stevens
D. W. Taylor
S. G. Tilden, Jr.
J. R. Tishkowski
B. Turner
J. B. Walsh
S. M. Weglian
J. V. Werner
G. R. Williams
R. L. Wilson
D. R. Wolfslayer
R. A. Zebold
A. J. Zerafa

(SAE Staff, D. P. Martus)

VEHICLE SECURITY COMMITTEE

D. R. WOLFSLAYER (Chairman)
D. E. MARTIN (Sponsor)
J. W. Carson
D. Costa
M. W. Dixon
J. R. Doto
D. Ellenberger
N. F. Erickson
D. A. Frisco

P. W. Gilliland, Sr.
J. E. Guido
G. M. Hespeler
C. W. Oliver, Jr.
R. S. Plantan
B. J. Riley
D. M. Schwentker
R. H. Sostkowski
L. W. Spry

S. G. Tilden, Jr.
J. R. Tishkowski
M. F. Von Leer
S. M. Weglian
J. V. Werner
G. R. Williams
R. L. Wilson
A. J. Zerafa

(SAE Staff, D. P. Martus)

VEHICLE SOUND LEVEL COMMITTEE

L. J. ERIKSSON (Chairman)
F. R. KISHLINE (Vice Chairman)
J. M. LEINONEN (Sponsor)
P. F. Allmendinger
T. M. Barry
R. S. Bennin
L. D. Bergsten
R. D. Bruce
A. J. Burgess
J. U. Damian
K. M. Eldred
N. Fabian
R. Hellweg

R. K. Hillquist
L. H. Hodges
T. M. Howell
R. J. Kevala
R. D. Kilmer
R. M. Law
W. A. Leasure, Jr.
K. R. Lewis
S. A. Lippmann
J. T. Lisbon
J. Manuel
W. J. Martin
J. M. Mazzeo

W. E. Miller
C. Mills
J. T. Nadolny
W. H. Page
H. Polz
T. J. Runner
D. G. Thomas
R. W. Van Demark
J. H. Venema
J. B. Walsh
E. G. Willette
K. E. Ziwica
D. M. Zuhse

(SAE Staff, R. T. Northrup, Jr.)

WHEEL COMMITTEE

J. R. AURELIA (Chairman)
M. D. WEBER (Vice Chairman)
H. R. PICKFORD (Sponsor)
I. K. J. Akselsen
R. N. Archer
P. C. Bertelson
T. J. Carr

R. A. DeRegnaucourt
J. Guzek
E. J. Hayes
J. W. Justusson
H. S. Karzun
L. E. Kiselis
D. D. MacIntyre

R. H. Madison
W. C. McIntyre
D. J. Orban
V. L. Vickland
G. D. Williams
N. G. Zorka

(SAE Staff, P. Couhig)

SAE REPRESENTATION IN OTHER TECHNICAL ORGANIZATIONS

COORDINATING RESEARCH COUNCIL, INC.

SAE and the American Petroleum Institute jointly organized the Coordinating Research Council, Inc. in 1942. The object of the CRC is to encourage and promote the arts and sciences by directing scientific cooperative research in developing the best combinations of fuels, lubricants, and equipment powered by internal combustion engines; and to afford means of cooperation with the government on matters of national interest within this field.

In the course of research sponsored by the three technical committees of the Council (the Air Pollution Research Advisory Committee, the Coordinating Fuel and Equipment Research Committee, and the Coordinating Lubricants and Equipment Research Committee), a number of research techniques have been developed. Those considered suitable for standardization have been referred to the American Society for Testing and Materials.

Information on the work of the technical committees may be secured from the Coordinating Research Council, Inc., 219 Perimeter Center Parkway, Atlanta, GA 30346.

TRANSPORTATION RESEARCH COUNCIL

R. S. Shackson (W. M. Spreitzer, Alt.)

U. S. NATIONAL COMMITTEE OF THE INTERNATIONAL COMMISSION ON ILLUMINATION

D. M. Finch, G. E. Meese, P. W. Maurer

U. S. TECHNICAL COMMITTEE TO INTERNATIONAL (CIE) COMMITTEE 4.8, AIRBORNE LIGHTING

(SAE COMMITTEE A-20, AIRCRAFT LIGHTING)
Paul H. Greenlee

COMMITTEE ON COLORS OF SIGNAL LIGHTS
(D. M. Finch, Alt.)

SAE TECHNICAL BOARD RULES AND REGULATIONS

1. SAE TECHNICAL BOARD: The Technical Board (hereinafter called Board) is the agent of the SAE Board of Directors (hereinafter called Directors) with authority to direct and supervise all SAE cooperative engineering programs, including standardization and research, subject only to the right of appeal to the Directors by anyone in disagreement with action of the Board.

The objective of the Board is to make the technical knowledge, experience and skill of engineers effectively useful to the public, industry, government, and educational institutions, through cooperative engineering action; and to enhance the value of Society membership through technical committee activities.

The board will determine engineering relationships with government, industry, other technical societies, educational institutions, or civic organizations. It will authorize all programs to be undertaken for, or in cooperation with, other organizations, as well as SAE participation in their technical committees.

2. EXECUTIVE AND ADMINISTRATIVE COMMITTEES OF THE TECHNICAL BOARD:

2.1 At the Board's first meeting in each administrative year, the Chairman, with the approval of the Board shall appoint an Executive Committee from the membership of the Board to serve for one year. The Chairman of the Board shall be the Chairman of the Executive Committee.

2.2 The Executive Committee shall be the executive and administrative agent of the Board, and, on matters requiring prompt disposition which arise between meetings of the Board, shall exercise all powers of the Board, except the approval of standards, recommended practices and information reports. The Executive Committee shall notify the Board of all actions taken. All actions of the Executive Committee shall be subject to review and confirmation of the Board.

2.3 Committees may make no commitments involving expenditures of Society funds without the approval of the Executive Committee.

2.4 The Executive Committee may approve the payment of necessary and reasonable travel expenses to meetings of the Board or of its committees, of an officer or regular employee of the government, or an instructor of a recognized educational institution, either as a member of such groups or as an invited consultant.

2.5 In intervals between meetings of the Board, the Executive Committee shall place before the Board any question on which a Board member desires the opinion of or action by the entire Board.

2.6 The Board may appoint such administrative committees as are necessary to carry on its work.

3. COUNCILS:

3.1 The Board may organize Councils and delegate to them authority to provide for, promote, direct and supervise the development of SAE standards, recommended practices, information reports and conduct research within defined areas of the Society's interests. The Board retains the authority for final review, approval, rejection or referral of actions taken when dissenting views (of members or nonmembers who were consulted in committee work or the preparation of documents) cannot be substantially reconciled.

Each Council shall organize committees to carry on the various phases of its assignment. Such committees may organize subgroups as they find necessary. These subgroups may be designated as divisions, subcommittees, task forces, or panels (hereinafter these groups are referred to as committees).

3.2 Each Council will determine that a consensus exists of those substantially concerned with the provisions of a proposed standard or recommended practice. The appropriate Council shall verify that the following requirements have been met with respect to each proposed standard or recommended practice:

3.2.1 All substantially concerned parties who are technically competent shall have had an opportunity to participate and their views shall have been given due consideration.

3.2.2 There shall be evidence of use or of potential use of a proposed standard or recommended practice.

3.2.3 Due consideration shall have been given to the existence of other comparable standards having national acceptance in the given field.

3.2.4 There shall be no unfair discrimination inherent in the proposed standard or recommended practice.

3.2.5 There shall be assurance by those concerned of a satisfactory level of technical quality of the proposed standard or recommended practice.

3.3 The Councils may establish operational procedures within their scope and in compliance with these rules and regulations, subject to approval by the Board.

3.4 The Board will appoint the initial membership and chairmen of its Councils. Thereafter, each year each Council shall nominate a chairman for Board approval. The Chairmen of Councils shall be Board members unless otherwise authorized by the Executive Committee. Each new Chairman of the Technical Board will request Board member(s) to serve as sponsoring or liaison member(s) with the various Councils of the Board as may be needed to carry on communications between the Board and its Councils. After the initial membership of each Council has been approved by the Board, the chairman of a Council is authorized to effect changes in non-Board member personnel of the Council.

4. COMMITTEES:

4.1 Selection of participants of SAE technical committees shall be based upon the following:

4.1.1 That a substantial balance of voting members with respect to technical background and experience shall exist within the committee organization. On technical committees dealing with the standardization of parts, products or materials, the organization and operating procedures of the committee, which includes its subcommittees and panels, shall provide an opportunity for qualified individuals from the substantially interested producer, consumer and general interest groups to participate and vote.

4.1.2 That a committee so chosen is competent and authoritative in its field.

4.1.3 Subordinate Committee Structure: Working groups such as task force ad hoc committees, panels or other groups may be organized under operating committees with membership having specific specialized expertise for the purpose of drafting or writing proposed documents. Such groups may or may not be balanced in accordance with the requirements specified in paragraph 4.1.1. Such groups may be specifically organized to develop recommendations for standards for military use or for use by other governmental agencies. The work of all such subordinate committee groups shall be subject to review and approval by parent committee(s) or council(s) wherein balanced structure as noted in paragraph 4.1.1 above is required.

4.2 Committee participants shall be designated as member, liaison member or consultant member. Liaison and consultant members are not eligible to vote on committee actions.

All participants are appointed by the chairmen on the basis of need for their particular services. Liaison members provide coordination with paralleling activities of other committees and organizations. Consultant members supply advice on the specific program for which they have been appointed. Governmental or other agency employees may be appointed as members, liaison members or consultant members of the committee with aforementioned responsibilities and privileges.

4.3 Council chairmen, with the advice of Council members, shall designate chairmen of newly formed committees reporting directly to their Council. Existing committees, reporting directly to the Council, shall nominate a chairman annually for Council approval. Rotation of the chairmen is encouraged where practical. Renominations of chairmen who have served five or more consecutive years shall be subject to review and approval by the Council. Committee chairmen at all levels may appoint chairmen of their subordinate committees.

4.4 A committee may initiate a project within its scope. In cases where such projects overlap areas of activity of another Council's committee, the Board shall be asked for prior review and approval.

4.5 Except as provided in paragraph 7.1, action by committees shall be by vote of the majority of their members.

5. RESPONSIBILITIES AND QUALIFICATIONS OF MEMBERS OF THE BOARD, COUNCILS AND COMMITTEES: In discharging their responsibilities, members of the Board, Councils, and Committees function as individuals and not as agents or representatives of any organization with which they may be associated. Members are appointed to SAE technical committees on the basis of their individual qualifications which enable them to contribute to the work of these committees. Members of the Board shall be members of the Society. SAE membership is not a prerequisite for membership on Councils or technical committees established by the Board or its Councils.

6. STANDARDS, RECOMMENDED PRACTICES, AND INFORMATION REPORTS: Standards, recommended practices and information reports are known collectively as SAE technical reports.

6.1 Reports of committees recommending the approval of a stan-

dard or recommended practice shall represent a consensus of the committee. In standardization practice a consensus is achieved when substantial agreement is reached by concerned interests according to the judgment of the Technical Board and/or one of its Councils.

6.1.1 Consensus implies that all dissenting viewpoints have been considered, and that an objective effort has been made toward their resolution.

6.1.2 Substantial agreement means much more than simple majority, but not necessarily unanimity.

6.2 Standards are documentations of sound, established, broadly accepted engineering practices.

6.3 Recommended Practices are documentations of data that are intended as guides toward standard engineering practice. Their content may be of a more general nature or they may propound data that have not yet gained broad acceptance.

6.3.1 Committees may, at their discretion, add an introductory note to any recommended practice stating that "This SAE Recommended Practice is intended as a guide toward standard practice, but may be subject to frequent change to keep pace with experience and technical advances. Hence, its use where flexibility of revision is impractical, is not recommended."

6.4 Information Reports are compilations of engineering reference data or educational material which are useful to the technical community. Cooperative committee development action is a significant technical feature of such reports.

φ   6.5 SAE committees are encouraged to develop test procedures and may develop and define performance levels[1] where they are appropriate and according to the rules as described in Paragraphs 6.5.1 through 6.5.4.

φ   6.5.1 Performance levels should be separated from test procedures either in separate technical reports or in different sections of the same report. Where they are separated, the two reports shall be cross-referenced. The scopes of reports containing performance levels shall clearly state the applicability and limitations of such levels.

φ   6.5.1.1 Where physical, dimensional or performance characteristics are necessary to identify items and assure compatibility or interchangeability of replaceable components (e.g., material specifications, screw threads, oil grates, hoses and fittings, and flange dimensions), the defining characteristics, dimensions, identifying markings, properties, or performance characteristics may be included in SAE technical reports.

φ   6.5.2 The Councils of the Technical Board are responsible for developing specific policies concerning the advisability of their committees developing performance levels for specific procedures or subject areas. Such policies will direct development of performance values for documents involving dimensional requirements or grade, class or type identification and differentiation. When SAE technical reports concern major systems or complete machines or vehicles, the necessity and desirability of developing performance levels are to be directed to and accepted by the appropriate Council before development work is commenced by a Technical Committee.

φ   6.5.3 Where documents prepared to standardize test procedures and equipment are for the purpose of assuring consistent results between laboratories in the measurement of significant characteristics and properties, such documents should not contain performance levels. In such cases where the performance level is of interest, an information report outlining repeatability or accuracy of methods or data obtained from typical range of tests to show state-of-the-art should be prepared. An alternative is to present such information in a technical paper published through an engineering activities program.

φ   6.5.4 If a Technical Committee concludes that performance levels are appropriate, the rationale used in selecting their applicability and limits must be clearly defined for consideration by and submitted for approval by its Council. The Technical Committee's rationale shall include information giving reason for identified differences between the submitted document and other existing standards or regulations. Values that exceed the state-of-the-art are to be avoided.

φ   6.6 For specific details on preparation of documents, one should refer to guideline preparation documents; i.e., J1159-SAE Recommended Practice for Preparation of SAE Technical Reports—Surface Vehicles: Standards, Recommended Practices, Information Reports; Technical Committee Guideposts—An SAE Technical Committee Guide Recommended by the SAE Technical Board; and the Aerospace Organization and Operating Guide and appendices thereto.

7. PROCEDURE FOR APPROVAL OF STANDARDS, RECOMMENDED PRACTICES AND INFORMATION REPORTS[2]

7.1 Documents submitted to a Council for approval, in general, should have the unanimous approval of the committee making such a submittal. Where unanimous approval cannot be achieved, documents shall have the approval of at least three-quarters of the responding committee members who have not waived their vote. Unresolved dissenting views, including those of liaison and consultant members, as well as non-members, shall accompany the document when submitted to the Council.

7.1.1 Any person (member or non-member of a committee group) submitting an unresolved dissenting view on a document shall have the right to appeal to the Board the approval of the document by a Council. To take his appeal, such person must file with the Council a notice in writing within twenty (20) days after receipt of notification that the document has been approved by the Council, and the notice shall state the person's desire to appeal, shall set forth the reasons for his appeal, identifying all portions of the document to which exception is taken, and shall include supporting information, data and material in support of his position.

7.2 Committee documents shall normally require confirmation by letter ballot except when they are submitted for final voice vote approval. In such instances the documents shall be distributed to the members of the voting group at least two weeks prior to the meeting.

7.3 Every approved document shall carry the following statements: "All technical reports, including standards approved and practices recommended, are advisory only. Their use by anyone engaged in industry φ or trade or their use by governmental agencies is entirely voluntary. There is no agreement to adhere to any SAE standard or recommended practice, and no commitment to conform to or be guided by any technical report. In formulating and approving technical reports, The Technical Board, its Councils and committees will not investigate or consider patents which may apply to the subject matter. Prospective users of the report are responsible for protecting themselves against liability for in- φ fringement of patents, trademarks and copyright."

7.4 Council members will review documents for technical content, for policy implications and for impact of the documents on users and the public in terms of broad technological considerations. Approval by Council will also be based on the committee record of voting and the consensus attained from all participants.

7.5 Councils will strive for unanimous approval and in no case will they approve a document which has not been found acceptable by three-quarters of its responding members. The Chairman of the Board is required to approve all documents. He may declare a document submitted to letter ballot by a Council to have been approved after three weeks from date of circulation of the document, provided ballots have been returned by at least three-quarters of the members, and provided there are no negative ballots. A written negative ballot within three weeks after the circulation of a document will require the proposal to be reconsidered by Council before final action. A Council will approve the document, reject the document, or refer the document with dissenting views to the Board for action. Council will refer to the Board any approved document where a notice of appeal has been filed as provided in paragraph 7.1.1.

7.6 Neither the Council nor the Board will alter the technical content of a document without first referring it back to the responsible Council or committee. All approved documents referred to the Board by a Council where a notice of appeal has been filed shall be handled by either:

7.6.1 Referring the document to the responsible committee with instructions to attempt to resolve the matters appealed and to provide the person appealing an opportunity to present to the committee such evidence as is set forth in his notice of appeal, or

7.6.2 Setting a time at any Board meeting scheduled after the filing of the notice of appeal where the person appealing shall have an opportunity to present to the Board such evidence as is set forth in his notice of appeal. Upon hearing the evidence, the Board shall determine the merits of the appeal and shall approve, reject or refer back to the committee (as in subparagraph (a) above) the document. The Board's decision shall be transmitted to the person appealing within ten (10) days after the decision and it shall briefly set forth the reasons therefor.

Failure of any person appealing to appear at a scheduled Board hearing shall be deemed a waiver or a withdrawal of his appeal.

7.7 The effective date of a document shall be the date it is approved

---

[1] Performance levels are the specified minimum, maximum, mean or average performance requirements.

[2] Hereinafter, Standards, Recommended Practices and Information Reports are referred to as documents.

by the Council or by the Board, unless otherwise stipulated by the Council, the Board or the Board's Chairman.

8. TECHNICAL BOARD MEETINGS:

8.1 Only members of the Board have the right to attend and vote at Board meetings, and to cast letter ballots on matters under consideration by the Board. Others may attend at the discretion of the Board Chairman.

8.2 The Chairman of the Board shall preside at meetings of the Board and, if he is not present, a member of the Executive Committee designated by the Chairman or by that Committee shall preside.

8.3 One-half of the members of the Board shall constitute a quorum.

8.4 Action by the Board shall be a majority vote of those present; provided that any member may call for a letter ballot on action taken, and when a letter ballot is taken, action by the Board shall be by three-quarters vote of the entire Board; documents referred to the Board by the Councils for approval shall require approval by three-quarters of the entire membership of the Board.

8.5 The first order of business shall be an executive session.

8.6 Questions of parliamentary procedure shall be determined by Roberts Rules of Order.

8.7 The last order of business shall be the determination of the time and place of the next meeting of the Board.

9. ELECTION OF ONE DELEGATE AND TWO ALTERNATES TO THE ANNUAL NOMINATING COMMITTEE: At the Technical Board's first meeting of the administrative year, the Executive Committee will submit for the election of the Board, recommendations for one delegate and two alternates to serve on the Society's Annual Nominating Committee. All delegates and alternates shall be voting members of the Society. They need not be members of the Technical Board. These names must be submitted to the Secretary of the Society not later than September 30. (It is the duty of the Annual Nominating Committee, each year, to select nominees for President, Treasurer and four Directors for inclusion in the ballot for election of Officers to be submitted to the voting members.)

10. ELECTION OF TECHNICAL BOARD NOMINATING COMMITTEE: At the Technical Board's first meeting of the administrative year, the Board shall elect, from its membership, seven members to serve as a Nominating Committee to nominate a voting member of the Society to serve as a Director on the Society's Board of Directors. The first member elected to the Nominating Committee shall serve as Temporary Chairman and shall assume the responsibility of calling the first meeting of the Committee. A quorum shall consist of five members. The nomination made by the Committee shall be approved by at least four of these members. It shall be the duty of this Nominating Committee to submit to the Society's Secretary, not later than June 15, each year, the name of a consenting nominee to serve as a Director for a term of three years. This nominee shall be listed on the ballot for election of Officers submitted to the voting members.

11. SECRETARY:

11.1 The Secretary of the Board and his staff assistants shall be designated by the General Manager of the Society.

11.2 The Secretary shall be responsible for the performance of such staff functions as the Board or its Executive Committee may direct, and shall provide for the recording and distribution of minutes of meetings of the Board, Councils and committees, subject to the financial limitations imposed by the Directors for the operations of the Board.

11.3 The Secretary shall have authority to release information and publicity with respect to the work of the Board and its committees, unless the Board specifically directs otherwise.

12. RECORDS: The records of the Board and its committees, shall be maintained for a reasonable time in the offices of the Society where they will be available for inspection by members of the Society except as the Board or the staff security officer (in the case of classified material) directs otherwise.

13. AMENDMENTS: Amendments to these rules and regulations shall be approved by not less than three-quarters of the members of the Board, subject to final approval by the Directors.

Adopted January 10, 1946
Revised January 14, 1972
Revised October 20, 1976
Revised June 8, 1977
Revised May 25, 1978
Under Revision

REFEREE MATERIALS

The materials listed below are available from SAE for use in testing a variety of products for compliance with SAE documents. Where those materials are referenced in a specific document, the number of the document is provided. For information on how to order Referee Materials, contact the Technical Division, SAE, 400 Commonwealth Drive, Warrendale, PA 15096, (412) 776-4841.

SAE Part No.	Description	Reference Document
RM–1	Compatibility Fluid	J1703f
RM–3a	SBR Brake Cups–Wheel Cylinder	J1702f
RM–4a	SBR Brake Cups–Primary Master Cylinder	J1702f
RM–5a	SBR Brake Cups–Secondary Master Cylinder	J1702f
RM–6a	Corrosion Test Strip–Tinned Iron	J1703f
RM–7	Corrosion Test Strip–Steel	J1703f
RM–8	Corrosion Test Strip–Aluminum	J1703f
RM–9	Corrosion Test Strip–Cast Iron	J1703f
RM–10	Corrosion Test Strip–Brass	J1703f
RM–11	Corrosion Test Strip–Copper	J1703f
RM–12	Wheel Cylinder Piston	J1702f
RM–13–01	Brass Master Cylinder Piston	J1702f
RM–13–02	Aluminum Master Cylinder Piston	J1703f
RM–14b	Wheel Cylinder Assembly	J1702f
RM–15b	Master Cylinder Assembly	J1702f
RM–17	Brake Master Cylinder Push Rod Assembly	J1702f
RM–20	Outlet Tube Connection	—
RM–21	Bolt	—
RM–22	Gasket	—
RM–23	Gasket	—
RM–24	Wheel Cylinder Connector	—
RM–25	Copper Gasket	—
RM–26	Inverted Tube Nut	—
RM–27	Tinfoil (Approximately 6 x 6 Inch Sheet)	J1703f
RM–28	Hiding Power Test Chart	J1703f
RM–49	Corrosion Test Jar with RM–63 Lid	J1703f
RM–51	Effect on Rubber Test Jar	J1703f
RM–52a	Tinned Lid–Effect on Rubber Test Jar	J1601
RM–57	Tubing–¼″ O.D.	J1702f
RM–58	Tubing–³⁄₁₆″ O.D.	J1702f
RM–59a	Glass Oil Sample Bottle (4 oz.) with cork	J1703f
RM–60	Storage Corrosion Test Fluid	J1601
RM–61	Screws and Nuts for Corrosion Test	—
RM–62	Screws and Nuts for Resistance to Oxidation Test	—
RM–63	Jar Lids for Humidification Procedures, MVSS116, S6.2	J1703f
RM–66–03	High Boiling Compatibility Fluid DOT 3 HD 50–4 450° Blend	J1703f
RM–68	Neoprene Brake Hose Inter Liner Stock (ASTM D15 Test Slab)	J1401 JAN81
RM–69	EPDM Stock (ASTM D15 Test Slab)	J1601
RM–70	Silicone Base Compatibility Fluid	—
RM–71	Triethylene Glycol Monomethyl Ether	J1703f

ENGINEERING AIDS

SAE is the supplier of drafting templates and machines in its Engineering Aids Program. These drafting templates and machines are referred to in reports prepared by the SAE Human Factors Engineering Committee.

The two-dimensional drafting templates and three-dimensional H-point machine have been certified by SAE for adherence to the SAE standards and for exact repeatability between individual templates and machines.

The reports, templates and machines are as follows:

SAE J826b—DEVICES FOR USE IN DEFINING AND MEASURING VEHICLES SEATING ACCOMMODATION

SAE Part # EA-2—TWO-DIMENSIONAL DRAFTING TEMPLATE—This two-dimensional drafting template is used to aid in displaying data obtained from checks made with the three-dimensional H-point machine. It describes passenger compartment space and seating attitude for comparison and reporting purposes, and describes passenger compartment space and seating attitude during conception, engineering and development stages of any new vehicle. This is a nude male consisting of a 10th, 50th, and 95th percentile measuring 32 x 23 x 2 weighing 7 lbs.

SAE PART # EA-3—THREE DIMENSIONAL H-POINT MACHINE—(Shipped collect from SAE Headquarters, Warrendale, PA.) The three-dimensional H-point machine is used to check vehicle seating compartments for conformance to design specifications; that is, relationship of H-point to body structures, seats, controls, etc. In the absence of design information, the horizontal and vertical H-point location is normally verified graphically using the two-dimensional template, and aids in the design and development of seats and seat materials. SAE also has the H-point machine available for rental purposes. The H-point machine measures 33 x 24 x 37 and weighs 295 lbs.

SAE J94le—MOTOR VEHICLE DRIVER'S EYE RANGE

SAE PART # EA-4—SIX PLAN AND SIX SIDE VIEW EYELLIPSE TEMPLATES (Set of 12)—The 12 templates represent six specific normal driving and riding seat track travel lengths ranging from a minimum of 4.0 inches to a maximum of 6.5 inches in 0.5 inch increments.

The eyellipse template is a design tool from which sight lines can be constructed. These sight lines are used to describe the location of objects in the field of view of a seated driver.

SAE PART # EA-5—EYELLIPSE AND HEAT CONTOUR LOCATOR LINE–ADJUSTABLE SEAT—A drafting tool that describes the position of the eyellipse and the occupant head contour for horizontally adjustable seats with back angles between 5 and 40 degrees.

SAE J1052—MOTOR VEHICLE DRIVING AND PASSENGER HEAD POSITION (Set of 4)

SAE PART # EA-6—FOUR HEAD POSITION CONTOUR TEMPLATES—Two-dimensional shapes that describe the seated vehicle occupant head positions in side and rear view. The driver head position contours with seat travel apply to drivers in horizontally adjustable seats. The heat position contours without seat travel apply to both drivers and passengers in fixed seats.

SAE PART # EA-7—DRAWINGS FOR OBSCURATION CHECKING FIXTURE (Set of 31)

SAE PART # EA-8—DRAWING FOR HYBRID III DUMMY (Set of 246)

SAE PART # EA-9—MIRROR FACING TWO DIMENSIONAL DRAFTING TEMPLATE

SAE PART # EA-10—DRAWINGS FOR ISO 2575–ROAD VEHICLES SYMBOLS FOR CONTROLS, INDICATORS, AND TELL-TALES (Set of 32)

* * * * *

The templates and machine may be ordered by writing to:

SAE
400 Commonwealth Drive
Warrendale, PA 15096

or by telephone at: (412) 776-4841.

HOW TO ORDER
SAE
STANDARDS * RECOMMENDED PRACTICES * INFORMATION REPORTS

SAE publishes technical documents in the following forms:

The SAE Handbook

Four volumes, each available separately, cover ground vehicle standards, recommended practices, and information reports.

Volume 1–Materials
Volume 2–Parts and Components
Volume 3–Engines, Fuels, Lubricants, Emissions, and Noise
Volume 4–On-Highway Vehicles and Off-Highway Machinery
Index Volume (Paperbound)

SAE Ground Vehicle Standards Update Service

The 4-volume 1983 SAE Handbook along with regular update mailings of new and revised standards and an easy-to-use loose-leaf binder.

Reports Not Included in the SAE Handbook

These are SAE ground vehicle documents available individually and not as part of the Handbook. A complete list of these documents is included in this Index.

SAE Aerospace Material Specifications (AMS)

These are standards, information reports, and recommended practices covering aerospace materials, both metals and non-metallic materials. They are available individually, as a complete set, and with a subscription style quarterly update service. A complete index/price list is available . . . also available in microfiche.

SAE Aerospace Standards, Recommended Practices, and Information Reports

These are documents covering a wide variety of aircraft parts, sub-systems, components, and test procedures.
They are available individually, as a complete set, and with a subscription style update service three times each year.
For information or to order any of the above, contact:

Customer Service
SAE
400 Commonwealth Drive
Warrendale, PA 15096
(412)776-4841

**Customers in Western
Europe should order from:**

American Technical Publishers, Ltd.
68A Wilbury Way
Hitchin Herts SG4 0TP England

**Customers in India
should order from:**

Allied Publishers Pvt. Ltd.
751, Mount Road
Madras, India 600 002

**Customers in Brazil
should order from:**

International Library Service
2722 North 650 East
Provo, Utah 84601
(801)374-6214

**Customers in Australia and
New Zealand should order from:**

SAE/Australasia
National Science Centre
191 Royal Parade
Parkville, Victoria 3052, Australia